D1546412

# CENTRAL HEATING & AIR CONDITIONING REPAIR GUIDE
## 2ND EDITION

## BY BILLY & JAMES PRICE

TAB BOOKS Inc.
BLUE RIDGE SUMMIT, PA. 17214

**Also by the Authors from TAB BOOKS INC.**

No. 1176   *The Master Handbook of ALL Home Heating Systems—Tuneup,*
*Repair, Installation & Maintenance*

SECOND EDITION

SECOND PRINTING

Printed in the United States of America

Library of Congress Cataloging in Publication Data

Price, Billy L.
    Central heating and air conditioning repair guide.

    Includes index.
    1. Heating—Equipment and supplies—Maintenance and
repair.   2. Air conditioning—Equipment and supplies—
Maintenance and repair.   I. Price, James Tucker,
1955-      .   II. Title.
TH7345.P74   1983      697'.028'8      82-19362
ISBN 0-8306-0120-1
ISBN 0-8306-1520-2 (pbk.)

# Contents

# Introduction

There have been many changes in home heating and air conditioning since the first edition of this book was written. We have written this edition to bring the homeowner and repairman up to date on what is happening in this rapidly changing field.

One major change has been the important role that energy conservation now plays in home heating and cooling systems. Planning is very important in making a system energy efficient, so we have added discussions on how to plan an energy efficient installation, how to compare systems for energy efficiency, and how to select the lowest cost fuel.

Another change has been the increasing willingness of homeowners to roll up their sleeves and do their own heating and cooling system planning, installation, and repair. For this reason we have expanded many of the "how-to" discussions to give the average do-it-yourself homeowner a more complete step-by-step approach to solving particular problems.

Nevertheless, this book still contains thorough discussions of major heating and cooling system topics, including advanced service and installation techniques that are of benefit to the more experienced repairman working in the field, as well as to the advanced do-it-yourselfer. Such timely topics as wood heat and wood furnace installation, set-back thermostats, and heat pumps are covered. Information on installing and servicing almost all types of central heating and air conditioning equipment is presented. Basic and advanced service techniques, shortcuts, and tips are provided, as well as troubleshooting information to aid in diagnosing problems.

Whether you are a repairman or a do-it-yourself homeowner, this book will save you time, energy, and money.

# Chapter 1

# Tools and Basic
# Servicing Procedures

There are several basic principles a refrigeration and heating serviceman should follow.

- Know how to check and service the equipment.
- Know how to use and care for your tools.
- Be able to select the proper tools for the job.
- Keep tools and replacement parts clean and dry.
- Keep the tools in good repair and in proper working order.

This chapter is designed to acquaint you with the basic service procedures which we will be constantly referring to and give you a basic knowledge of the tools and materials used for these jobs.

## USING TEST EQUIPMENT

Some of the test equipment you will use can be homemade, and other equipment can be purchased at almost any hardware or supply store. Many different brands and types are available, but the important thing is to be familiar with the basic testing devices and how to use them.

### Ammeter

When checking electric motors and circuits, the amperage (current) reading is important. This can tell if the circuit is operating properly. Figure 1-1 shows a clamp-on ammeter. The looped jaws will open to allow a wire carrying current to go inside them. When the jaws are closed so that only one wire is inside the loop, the meter will tell the amperage of the current going through the wire. If two wires are inside the loop of the ammeter, the reading will be incorrect.

The meter has several scales for testing current so that large currents as well as small currents can be checked. If the amperage in the line is not

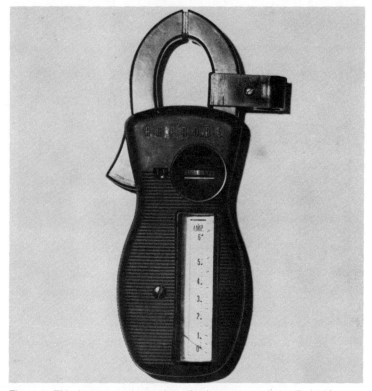

Fig. 1-1. This instrument is used to check amperage but will double as a voltohmmeter. To check amperage, set the scale to AMPS, push the button to open the jaws, and enclose the wire in the jaws. The wire should be surrounded—not grasped—by the jaws. The scale is changed by rotating the dial with the thumbwheel.

known, start checking with the highest scale and go to the smaller scales until a usable reading appears. This will prevent damaging the ammeter by exceeding the current rating of any scale.

This particular unit is used as a voltmeter or ohmmeter as well as an ammeter. Figures 1-2 and 1-3 show how this transformation takes place. To use the instrument as a voltmeter, connect the two leads to the terminals at the bottom of the unit and turn the dial to the voltage scales. A scale of the proper range must be used. Attach the leads to the terminals to be checked and read the meter scale.

As an ohmmeter the unit will check resistance and circuit continuity. To make it serve this purpose, the leads are attached as shown in Fig. 1-3. The scale is turned to the *ohms* scale to take an ohms reading.

### Voltohmmeter

The voltohmmeter (Fig. 1-4) is used to check voltage, continuity, and resistance in electrical circuits. Many of these units are small enough to be hand-held. The top dial on the unit shown is used to select the proper "volts" and "ohms" settings. When the meter is not in use, the dial should be turned to "off."

To check the voltage across two terminals, set the meter to the voltage setting and attach the two instrument leads to the terminals. Now turn on

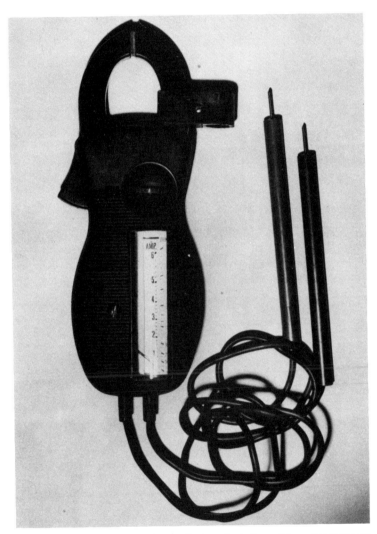

Fig. 1-2. Test probes plug into the terminals on the bottom of the unit to measure voltage. The metal tips of the probes are placed on the terminals to be checked. With the probes attached to the unit as shown, voltage can be checked. Be sure the scale is set for voltage and the correct range is being used.

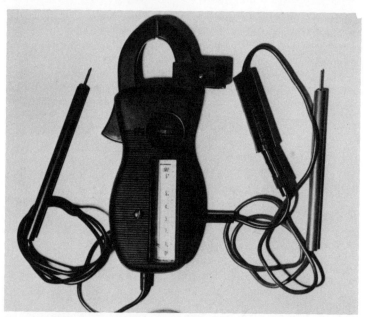

Fig. 1-3. This is the arrangement for connecting the probes to use the unit as an ohmmeter. One probe is attached to the left-hand terminal at the bottom, and special attachment allows the other terminal to plug into the side. The scale should be set for ohms and the resistance is read on the ohms scale.

Fig. 1-4. Voltohmmeter. This meter will check voltage and resistance. The dial top right is used to select the voltage and ohms ranges. The "ohms adjust" control is to adjust the ohmmeter before making a resistance check. Use the "ohms adjust" control to set the pointer to zero with the test leads shorted together.

the power source of the electrical circuit you are checking. The voltage across the terminals will be read on the meter. If the reading on the meter is lower than it should be for the circuit under test, some element of the circuit is defective. The voltage check is most often used to check transformers to be sure that they are putting out the proper voltage.

Never attach the leads of the meter to the circuit terminals with the power on and the meter set on "ohms." It will damage the meter. The voltage check is run with the power on and the meter set on "volts." It is important to be certain that the meter is set on the proper voltage scale before attempting a voltage check.

The meter shown has two scales for alternating current (ac) and two scales for direct current (dc). Be sure to have the meter set correctly for the type of current (ac or dc) that you are checking. Also, be sure not to have the meter set on the 150V scale when checking what might be a 220V; otherwise you may damage the meter. Always start voltage checks on the largest scale and work down to prevent damage to the meter.

The meter also has two resistance (ohms) scales for checking continuity and resistance. There is actually only one scale for the ohms reading, but the dial has two settings: R × 1 and R × 10. If the dial is set to R × 1, read the scale as it appears. If the dial is set to R × 10, multiply the meter reading by 10 to determine the resistance in the circuit (add a zero to the reading).

## BASIC ELECTRICAL TESTS

When performing electrical tests, disconnect all connecting electrical circuits to prevent inaccurate readings. See Fig. 1-5. Some basic ohmmeter continuity tests are shown in Fig. 1-6.

To check for continuity, use the lower resistance setting and attach the probes to the terminals you are checking. If the meter indicates zero (that is, there is little or no resistance), there is a path for electricity to flow. *Always run a continuity check with the power in the circuit off.* Disconnect the power terminals to prevent accidentally applying power to the circuit when running a continuity check.

To check for a short, set the meter for a continuity check and touch one meter lead to one of the terminals and the second lead to a metal part of the unit near the circuit. If the meter reads continuity (zero or little resistance), there is current flowing between the terminal and the metal case. If current is not supposed to be flowing between these parts, there is a short circuit.

With the voltohmmeter on the resistance setting, place one lead on one capacitor terminal and the other lead on the other capacitor terminal. If the capacitor is good, the meter pointer will move immediately to the right (indicating zero resistance) and then slowly drop back to the left as the capacitor becomes charged. Recheck the capacitor by reversing the ohmmeter leads on the capacitor terminals. The same result should occur.

Figure 1-7 shows a makeshift apparatus that can be used to check a capacitor. This uses an electrical plug and cord with a fuse wired into the

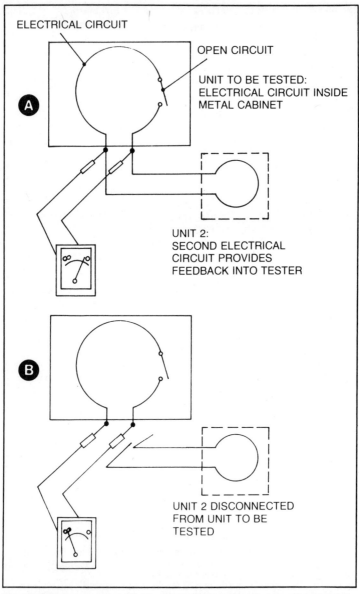

ELECTRICAL CIRCUIT

OPEN CIRCUIT

UNIT TO BE TESTED:
ELECTRICAL CIRCUIT INSIDE
METAL CABINET

**A**

UNIT 2:
SECOND ELECTRICAL
CIRCUIT PROVIDES
FEEDBACK INTO TESTER

**B**

UNIT 2 DISCONNECTED
FROM UNIT TO BE
TESTED

Fig. 1-5. When performing electrical tests it is important that you disconnect the unit you are testing from all other electrical circuits. (A) If the unit being tested is not disconnected, the second unit provides a complete circuit for electricity to travel and gives an inaccurate reading. This is called "feedback." The ohmmeter reading shows the circuit is complete, but the unit intended to be tested has an open circuit. (B) Once the second unit is disconnected, the unit being tested is isolated. A proper reading is obtained.

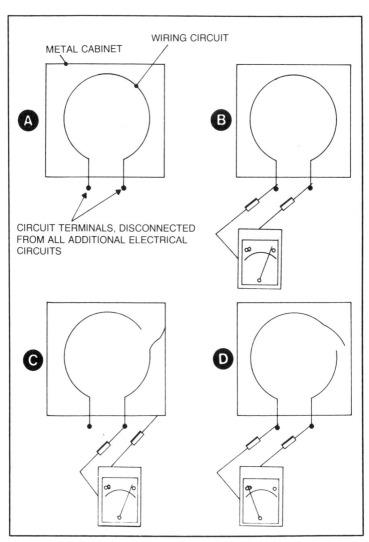

METAL CABINET

WIRING CIRCUIT

A

B

CIRCUIT TERMINALS, DISCONNECTED FROM ALL ADDITIONAL ELECTRICAL CIRCUITS

C

D

Fig. 1-6. This figure diagrams some of the most common tests performed with an ohmmeter. (A) The unit that will be tested here is an electrical circuit housed inside a metal cabinet. This might represent an electrical motor. The first step is to isolate the unit from all other electrical circuits to prevent electrical feedback. (B) An unbroken circuit is shown here. The ohmmeter reading is zero, meaning zero resistance. (C) Here the circuit is broken and touching the metal housing. This creates a short circuit between the circuit and the cabinet. To test for a short circuit, touch one ohmmeter lead to the cabinet and the second lead alternately to each circuit terminal. When there is a short circuit, zero resistance will be shown on the ohmmeter, as indicated in the diagram. (D) This is an open circuit. Because the circuit is broken, there is no complete path for electricity to travel. The ohmmeter reading is "infinity," meaning infinite resistance.

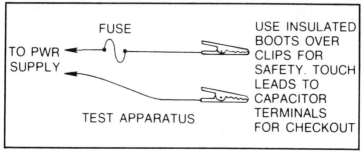

Fig. 1-7. A simple apparatus for checking capacitors.

circuit. To test the capacitor, attach the clips from the cord to the capacitor terminals and plug the cord into an electrical outlet. When the plug is removed from the power supply, the capacitor should be charged. If the fuse blows when the power supply is attached, you know immediately that the capacitor is shorted. If the fuse does not blow and the capacitor charges, shorting across the capacitor terminals with a screwdriver should produce a spark as the capacitor discharges. *Be sure to unplug the cord from wall before shorting the capacitor with the screwdriver.* If the capacitor sparks, it can be assumed to be good. If it doesn't spark, however, you will have to plug the

Fig. 1-8. The capacitor analyzer can be used to check capacitance. Plug the analyzer into an electrical outlet and attach the two leads from the tester to the capacitor terminals. If the capacitor is good, the red light will come on and then go out. The capacitance ($\mu$F or mfd) rating can be read on the meter by pushing a button. If the light doesn't come on, the capacitor is open and should be replaced. If the light stays on, the capacitor is shorted and should be replaced. The meter should be turned to the larger scale if the capacitance rating is not known in order to protect the meter.

cord into the wall again to try to charge the capacitor. You will probably need to try this several times before the capacitor will spark. (This is because alternating current charges and discharges a capacitor at the rate of 60 times a second, and at the instant that you pull the plug from the wall, the capacitor may have discharged.) If you cannot get a spark after numerous attempts, try replacing the capacitor and see if the problems disappear.

A capacitor analyzer like the one in Fig. 1-8 can be used to check a capacitor and its rating in microfarads ($\mu$F). Compare this rating to the rating stamped on the capacitor. A large deviation between the stamped value and the value given by the tester means the capacitor should be changed.

### MOTOR ANALYSIS AND STARTING

If a motor will not start, a motor-starting unit and analyzer (Fig. 1-9) can be attached to get it going. Attach the leads from the analyzer to the proper leads on the motor according to the instructions accompanying the analyzer unit. Some indicator lights indicate current flow, and others indicate short circuits. Observe these lights to determine if the motor windings are defective; if they are, replace the motor.

The analyzer is also used to start the motor running again if it is "frozen" or "stuck." Attach the leads to the motor terminals and press the

Fig. 1-9. This motor analyzer will not only help you diagnose motor problems but will also help get a "frozen" motor running. It has lights to check the windings and "start" and "reverse" switches to get the motor going.

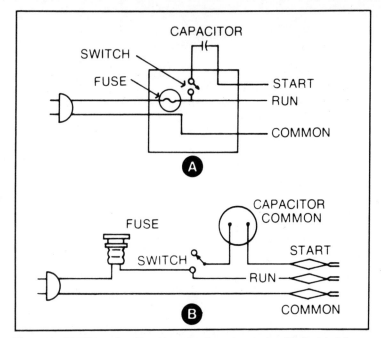

Fig. 1-10. (A) Wiring diagram of homemade motor starter. (B) A pictorial representation to help you make the starter.

starter button. If it doesn't start, set the switch in the "reverse" position and push the button. This will sometimes start a "stuck" motor. Reverse the motor for a few seconds, and it should run.

## HOMEMADE TESTERS

Homemade starting units can be fashioned from only a few spare parts (Fig. 1-10). The start and run leads have to be interchanged to reverse the motor and "unfreeze" it.

Figure 1-11A shows how an ordinary light bulb and pigtail socket can be used to check for voltage. Two light bulbs are wired together to test a 240V circuit (Fig. 1-11B). The bulb (or bulbs) should burn at ordinary brightness if the voltage is correct at the terminals that you are testing.

A simple tester to check continuity can be fashioned using a flashlight battery and bulb. Solder the wires to connect the bulb, battery, and probes as shown in Fig. 1-12. When the probes are touched together, the bulb will light. Likewise, when the probes are attached to two terminals of a circuit, the bulb will light if the circuit is continuous.

A continuity tester using a 120V power source is shown in Fig. 1-13. This tester is usable for testing for continuity in electric motors and other loads on electric circuits. This tester requires more careful use, however, because of the shock hazard with the higher voltage.

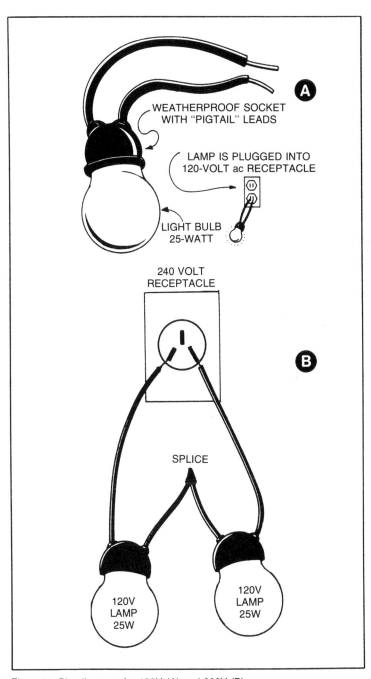

WEATHERPROOF SOCKET
WITH "PIGTAIL" LEADS

LAMP IS PLUGGED INTO
120-VOLT ac RECEPTACLE

LIGHT BULB
25-WATT

240 VOLT
RECEPTACLE

SPLICE

120V
LAMP
25W

120V
LAMP
25W

Fig. 1-11. Pigtail testers for 120V (A) and 220V (B).

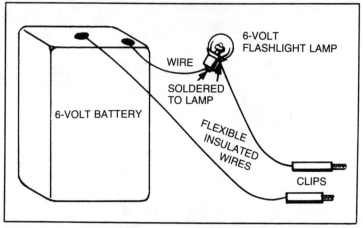

Fig. 1-12. A simple continuity tester you can make. If the bulb lights when the two probes are touched to the terminals of a circuit, the circuit is complete. When checking a coil with this tester, the bulb will barely burn due to the high resistance of the coil.

## TUBING

There are several types of tubing used in refrigeration and air conditioning equipment. The most commonly used are copper, steel, aluminum, and rubber hoses.

**Soft-Drawn Copper Tubing.** There are two kinds of copper tubing: soft- and hard-drawn. Soft-drawn copper tubing comes in coils and can be unrolled as it is used. When a piece is used from the roll, you should pinch the end closed so dirt and moisture will not enter the tubing. Soft copper tubing is most often used in domestic installations, and sometimes as the high-side line in commercial installations. It can be purchased in two wall thicknesses, known as $K$ and $L$. The size of the tubing is determined by the outside diameter, and it can be purchased in sizes ranging upward from 3/16 inch.

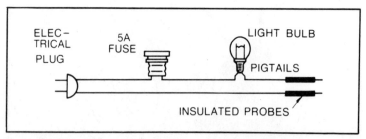

Fig. 1-13. This 120V continuity tester can be used to check for shorts and continuity. The brightness of the bulb will depend on the resistance in the circuit being checked. If this were used to check an electric motor for instance, the bulb would burn at less than full brightness due to the resistance of the motor.

**Hard-Drawn Copper Tubing.** Hard-drawn tubing is purchased in 20-foot lengths with each end sealed. The precaution of sealing the end should be used when cutting off joints of hard-drawn tubing. Hard-drawn tubing can be purchased in a number of different diameters. In installation soft tubing can be bent around corners, but hard-drawn tubing should not be bent. Instead, it is run in straight lines, and fittings are used to make a bend or go around a corner.

**Normal Size Copper.** Normal-size copper, sometimes called *water copper*, is used for plumbing and heating. This tubing, unlike ACR (air conditioning and refrigeration) tubing, has not been cleaned or dehydrated and should not be used for refrigeration or air conditioning installations. It is sized on the inside diameter.

**Aluminum Tubing.** Aluminum tubing is used primarily for evaporator coils and condensing units on car air conditioners. It can be purchased in coils in different sizes. Aluminum tubing is especially susceptible to breaking and kinking, so use care when working with this type of tubing. Also, take care when using it around heat or torches because some types of aluminum melt at fairly low temperatures.

**Rubber Hoses.** Rubber hoses designed for use on refrigeration and air conditioning installations are made to hold high pressure and are constructed with fibers or other material in the rubber. They are quite flexible and are usually found on car air conditioners. Rubber hoses have molded connections, clamps, or fittings to join them together.

### Cutting Tubing

You can cut the tubing using either a hacksaw or a tube cutter. If a hacksaw is used, a sawing tool will be required to insure a straight cut. You will need a blade for the job that has 32 teeth per inch. After the tubing is cut, use a file or reamer to clean the edge of burrs. The filings should be removed from the inside of the tubing.

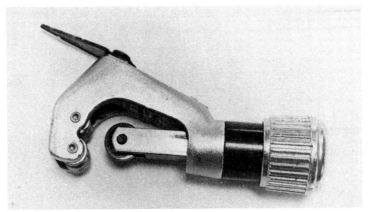

Fig. 1-14. Cutter for copper tubing.

Fig. 1-15. A small tubing cutter is useful for cutting in tight places.

A tubing cutter will generally be easier to use than a saw, and it will not require as much cleaning of the tubing if used properly. Two types of tubing cutters are shown in Figs. 1-14 and 1-15. These have cutting wheels that rotate around the tubing, cutting the tubing as they go. The cutting wheel is tightened against the tubing by turning a knob. When cutting the tubing, be careful not to cut it too quickly. Taking the job a litte slower will leave less of an inside edge to ream out. Tighten the knob a little at a time as the tube cutter is rotated around the tubing.

File the end of the tubing to remove its beveled edge before flaring the tube for the connection (Fig. 1-16). After the end has been filed, use a reamer to remove the burr (Fig. 1-17). If the burr isn't completely removed, it will fold under when the flaring is done. The flare will leak. On the other hand, if the end of the tubing is reamed too much, the tubing walls will be thinned too much, and the flare will split or crack.

Fig. 1-16. The end of the tubing is filed square so the flare will be the proper shape.

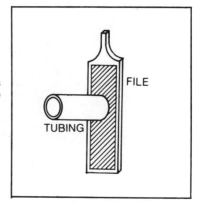

14

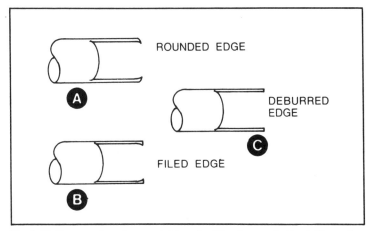

Fig. 1-17. Cross section of copper tubing after it has been cut with a tubing cutter. (A) The rounded edge should be filed so it is square. (B) Here the edge has been filed. (C) The burr has been removed with a reamer.

## Bending Tubing

To bend tubing, there are bending devices such as those shown in Figs. 1-18 and 1-19. Also, many tubing bends can be made by hand.

When bending tubing, care must be taken not to kink or flatten it. This will create restrictions in the line. Sometimes a break will occur as a result of bending. A mechanical bending tool like the one shown in Fig. 1-18 will bend the tubing to the correct degree without kinking or flattening the tubing, when properly used.

The bending spring (Fig. 1-19) is placed over the outside of the tubing if the tubing is fairly small. If the tubing is quite large, the spring will fit inside the tubing. The tubing is bent by hand, and the spring is rolled off the tubing. When the spring is turned in one direction, it will tighten; when it is

Fig. 1-18. Bending tool. The tubing is placed between the die and posts. As the lever is squeezed, the die moves up between the posts, and the tubing is bent. Different dies are used for different bends and for different sizes of tubing.

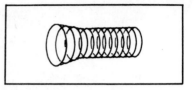

Fig. 1-19. Bending springs (also called inner and outer springs) are used to bend tubing.

turned in the other direction, it will loosen. Bending springs come in different sizes, and the proper size must be used on each size of tubing.

Take care not to put all the stress in one place when bending tubing by hand, since doing so will flatten or kink the tubing and render it useless. To bend it properly, bend it a little, release the tension, and bend it some more. Repeat this until the tubing has the desired bend. Do not place stress on a connection.

The tubing should not, as a general rule, be bent in a smaller radius than 5 to 10 times the diameter of the tubing (Fig. 1-20). If a shorter bend than this is needed, cut the tubing in joints and use a fitting to make the bend.

### Flaring Tubing

Using flare connections, you can join two pieces of tubing that are the same size or different sizes. To make a flare joint, you need two flare nuts the size of the tubing you are connecting. A union is also needed to join the two joints; it will be a reducer union if the two joints are different sizes.

To make the flare, the lines are cut, reamed, and filed as already described. If the burr is left in the tubing, the spinner will press the burr into the flare, and the joint will leak. A flaring block and spinner are used to make the flare connection (Figs. 1-21 and 1-22).

To make the flare, place the flare nut on the tubing and let it slide back about 2 inches from the end of the tubing so it will not be in the way. Place

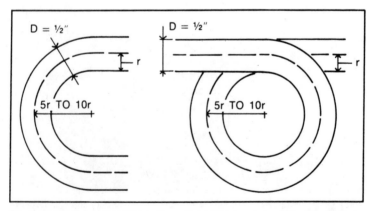

Fig. 1-20. When bending tubing, the radius of the bend should be 5 to 10 times the diameter of the tubing.

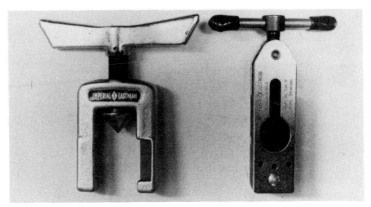

Fig. 1-21. Block and spinner used to flare tubing.

the tubing in the flaring block and tighten the block around the tubing. Tighten it enough that the spinner will not push the tubing out of the block when it starts to form the flare. The tubing should extend above the block about ½ inch. Put the yoke and spinner on the flaring block, and place a drop of refrigerant oil on the spinner. Tighten the spinner handle until the spinner makes contact with the tubing. Be sure it is centered in the tubing and turn the spinner handle ¾ turn, then back off ¼ turn. Repeat this until the flare is formed. Do not flare the tubing too much, because it will split or crack and will not fit the connection properly. After the flare has been formed, remove the spinner and flaring block and check the flare for splits or cracks.

The other line should be flared in the same manner and the union inserted between the two lines. Finally the flare nuts are connected.

A third type of flaring block is shown in Fig. 1-23. For this block stick the tubing into the hole in the block as before. Allow the top of the tubing to extend above the block for a distance equal to one-third of the flare. This will cause the top edge of the flare to come out even with the top edge of the block. The flare will be formed in the beveled sides of the hole.

Sometimes copper will harden if it is old. To soften it so it can be flared, heat the end of the tubing until it is cherry red and let it cool. After cooling, the old copper will be easy to flare. The process is known as *annealing*.

## SWAGING

Copper tubing can also be connected by swaging. The end of the tubing is formed so that a *sweat joint* is created (Fig. 1-24). An unformed end is fit inside the swaged end; then the joint is welded or soldered. Two types of swages are shown in Figs. 1-25 and 1-26. The swages come in different sizes for different sizes of tubing, and the proper size swage must be used for the tubing you are connecting.

Fig. 1-22. Block and spinner. Note the holes in the block for various sizes of tubing.

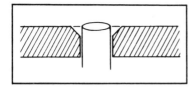

Fig. 1-23. This type of flaring block forms the flare in the block.

After cutting the tubing to the proper length and removing the burr, the tubing is placed in the proper size hole in the swaging block. The swage is driven into the end of the tubing as shown in Fig. 1-27. Then the swage and block are removed. The joint is cleaned before welding.

## Welding

There are several kinds of welding and brazing rods used in connecting refrigerant lines. A brazing rod of 5 percent silver, 88¾ percent copper, and 6¼ percent phosphorus can be used to braze copper tubing without using flux. You may use flux with this rod to ensure the cleanliness of the tubing.

A second type of brazing rod is 15 percent silver, 80 percent copper, and 5 percent phosphorus. The rod can be used with or without flux when brazing copper, but when used with tungsten, silver, or molybdenum, it requires flux. These brazing rods melt at very high temperatures (1200°F to 1500°F). They are recommended for use with high-pressure refrigerant lines. To reach the temperatures required to weld with these rods. you may need an oxyacetylene torch.

The tubing joints should be fitted and reamed before welding. They should also be cleaned of all grease and dirt with a clean cloth and sandpaper to insure a good weld. Once the joint has been cleaned, do not let it come in contact with any grease or dirt. Apply flux around the joint and begin heating

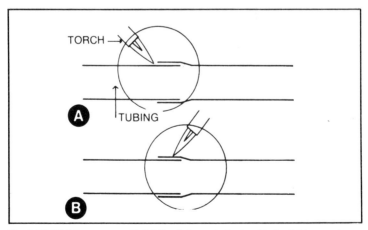

Fig. 1-24. Welding a swaged joint. Begin to apply the heat to the tubing as shown at A. This heats the inside tubing so it will take the brazing. After the joint begins to get hot, move the torch as shown at B. Finish heating and apply the brazing rod.

Fig. 1-25. This type of swage comes in different sizes for different sizes of tubing. The tubing is placed in a flaring block or swaging block extending above the block 1 inch, and the swage is driven inside the tubing. This will expand the joint of tubing so an unformed joint will fit inside it.

it. When the tubing reaches the proper temperature, apply the brazing rod, being sure that the inside tubing is hot enough to take the weld (see Fig. 1-24). If the inside tubing is not hot enough, the brazing rod material will not flow into the pores of the tubing metal properly, and a weak joint will result. If the tubing is not cleaned properly, the joint may come apart or leak.

### Soldering

There are several types of low-temperature solder recommended for refrigerant lines. The melting temperature for such solder is around 400°F to 500°F. Soldering is often used in a situation where the greater heat required for brazing would damage a nearby part. The drawback with soldering is that it is not recommended for lines where the pressure would be more than 150 psi. Solder could be used, however, on the low side and in places where the vibration is slight. Your welding-supply dealer can usually recommend the proper solder for your needs.

The joints should be prepared as before and the proper flux applied. The joint is heated as before. A smaller torch is used because of the reduced heat requirement. Care must be taken not to overheat the joint, because it is possible to fill the inside of the tubing with solder and close the line.

If a joint is not properly fitted and is too tight, the brazing alloy or solder will not flow properly between the joints. This will weaken the joint, and it could break or leak. If the joint fits too loosely, too much brazing alloy or solder will be required to fill the joint, and the joint may leak or break. The joint should fit snugly, but the two pieces should not be forced together. If the joint wobbles, it is too loose and should be refitted.

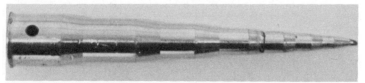

Fig. 1-26. This swaging tool has several different sizes on the same tool. Do not drive the swage too far into the tubing, as this will crack the walls of the tubing or swage the tubing too large.

Fig. 1-27. Swage being driven into tubing.

## TORCHES

There are several types of torches that can be used for refrigeration applications, but we will consider only the basic ones here. A propane torch is shown in Fig. 1-28. This torch is used for welding tubing smaller than ⅜ inch and for soft soldering. It will also produce enough heat to silver-braze a joint. Sometimes if more heat is required, two of these torches are used together. These are widely available.

Another type of torch often used in refrigeration work is the Prest-o-Lite torch. This torch comes with a torch handle and several different tips for different welding applications. The torch handle is connected to a hose running to the tank which holds the fuel. The torch handle and hose make the torch easily maneuvered when welding, and the tank is small enough to be carried from place to place with little trouble.

The tanks for this torch come in different sizes, such as 10 or 40 cubic-foot capacity. Some type of regulator must be used with this torch to control the pressure and adjust the heat for different jobs. These torches are used on 1-inch or smaller tubing. Care should be taken with this torch, and all the parts of the torch must be kept clean.

The tip can be removed and a halide torch installed for checking the refrigerant lines for leaks as described later.

A third type of welding unit is the oxygen-acetylene torch shown in Fig. 1-29. The oxygen-acetylene sets are available with large and small torches and two sizes of tanks. An entire oxygen-acetylene set includes a welding torch, a cutting torch, welding tips, hoses, regulators, and tanks.

Fig. 1-28. This hand-held propane torch can be used on small repair jobs.

Fig. 1-29. Oxygen-acetylene welding set. The larger tank is for oxygen, and the smaller tank is for acetylene. The two gages on each tank at the regulator show the pressure on the tank and torch. The regulator is adjusted for different torch pressures. If more heat is needed, the pressure is turned up.

Usually the tanks are leased from a welding-supply company. Two tanks—an oxygen tank and an acetylene tank—are needed. An oxy-acetylene welding set can be used on small or large tubing and will produce enough heat for almost any refrigeration job.

The pressure is adjusted with the regulators on the tanks so the proper amount of each gas is delivered to the welding tip, and the proper heat is produced. For small jobs start by adjusting the acetylene pressure to 3-5 psi and the oxygen pressure to 5-6 psi. The pressure chart that comes with the welding unit will show how the pressure should be adjusted for heavier jobs.

To light the welding unit, make sure the torch valves are off and turn the oxygen tank valve on. Turn the regulator handle counterclockwise until the pressure on the handle is released. Turn the torch valve on and turn the regulator handle clockwise until the correct reading appears on the gage.

Close the valve on the torch handle and adjust the pressure on the acetylene tank in the same way.

The torch is now ready to light. Turn on the acetylene valve on the torch handle about ¼ turn and light the torch. The flame will burn yellow and produce a lot of soot at this point. Now turn on the oxygen torch valve about ⅛ turn. Adjust the flame as desired by adjusting the acetylene and oxygen on the torch valves.

To turn the torch off, close the oxygen torch valve first, then the acetylene torch valve. Shut off the tanks and regulators to prevent any gases from escaping from the tanks through leaky valves or hoses.

## REFRIGERATION GAGES AND CHARGING

Figure 1-30 shows the gages that are installed in a refrigeration system for checking and charging the system. This gage set is made of a pressure gage and a compound gage. The two gages are both used to measure the pressure in the system, but the pressure gage reads only positive pressure, while the compound gage reads *negative* pressure—that is, vacuums—as well as positive pressure.

To attach the gages, connect the hoses from the manifold (the part of the unit on which the gages are mounted). The hose from the compound gage is connected to the low-side line (the larger line at the top of the unit),

Fig. 1-30. On the left, a compound gage for the low-side line that reads in increments from 30-inch Hg (vacuum) to 250 psi (pressure). On the right, a pressure gage that reads from 0 to 500 psi pressure (high-side gage).

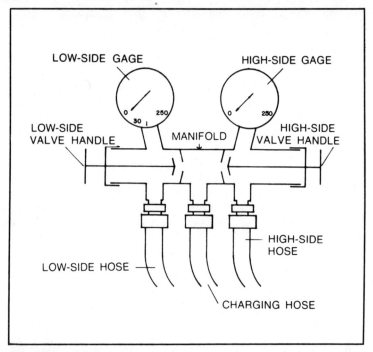

Fig. 1-31. Parts of the gage set. To get a pressure reading on the system without charging; you can connect the high- and low-pressure gages to the service valves and open the service valves. The only time the manifold valve is opened is when the system is being charged, gas is being removed, or the system is being "pulled" on a vacuum.

and the hose from the pressure gage is connected to the high-side line (the smaller line from the bottom of the unit). The center hose will connect to the service cylinder when refrigerant is being added to the system, or to the vacuum pump when the refrigerant lines are being cleared before charging. The diagrams in Fig. 1-31 and 1-32 show the gages and the way they are attached to the cooling unit.

To determine whether the unit is low on refrigerant, one method is to feel the high-side line going to the condenser. If this line is slightly warmer than room temperature, the unit probably is low on refrigerant. A second method is to check the sight glass on the unit, if there is one. Bubbles in the sight glass indicate lack of refrigerant. The sight glass is sometimes located near the condensing unit. When the refrigerant in a system is changed or refrigerant is put into a new system, the lines have to be evacuated to remove the air and moisture and prevent contamination of the refrigerant.

To "pull" the system on a vacuum, connect the vacuum pump to the center manifold hose (Fig. 1-32). Start the vacuum pump and open the low-side manifold valve. The vacuum pump will have to run for several hours to get all the air and moisture out of the system. After the system has been evacuated, close the valves and disconnect the hose from the vacuum pump.

## Charging the Unit

After evacuating the system, refrigerant will have to be charged into the system. Connect the center hose to the service cylinder and open the valve on the cylinder. Bleed the air out of the center hose by loosening the connection at the manifold for a few seconds to allow the air to escape. Tighten the connection and start the air conditioning unit.

Start the compressor and charge the unit through the low side. Open the low-side manifold valve for a few seconds, then close it. Since the system is evacuated, the compound gage attached to the low side should indicate a vacuum, measured in inches of mercury (inches Hg). As the valve is opened and the refrigerant allowed to flow in, the gage should indicate a pressure rise, that is, less vacuum in the lines. It will take several openings and closings of the valves before the system will get to zero pressure. If the system started out reading 25 inches Hg vacuum, after the first charge the system may move up to 20 inches Hg vaccum. As the valve is opened and closed several times, the pressure should increase slowly until positive

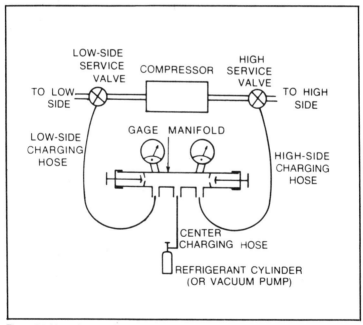

Fig. 1-32. Here the manifold has been connected to the service valves on the air conditioning system. Open the low-side service valve on the unit and at the manifold to charge the system. To pull the system down, remove the service cylinder and connect the vacuum pump to the center charging hose.

pressure is reached. The same manner of charging is continued until the proper pressure for the system is reached.

## Pressure Readings

The pressure readings on the gages will vary from day to day as temperature changes occur. The low-side pressure will vary depending on the air temperature moving across the evaporator. The high-side pressure will vary according to the outside temperature. The normal evaporator temperature is 40°F, and the normal refrigerant pressure at this temperature is 69 psi for R-22 refrigerant. If the evaporator temperature is less than 40°, the evaporator could ice over or freeze up. If the evaporator temperature is higher than 40°, the efficiency of the evaporator will drop.

Low temperature around the evaporator will lower the pressure in the low-side line. In the summer, with the unit cooling the house, there will be cool air circulating. If the serviceman took a pressure reading on the low-side to check for proper refrigerant, he would find low pressure. The fact is, however, that the system is operating properly and the lower pressure is due to the cool air the unit is putting out. Hence the repairman must be careful not to charge more refrigerant into the system on the basis of gage pressure alone. Conversely, warmer air blowing over the coil will raise the pressure in the low-side line.

## Low-Pressure Gage

Figure 1-33 is a diagram showing the different scales of a low-pressure

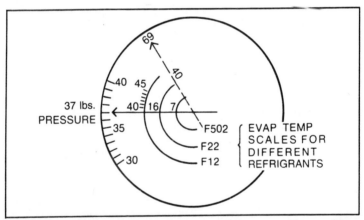

Fig. 1-33. This diagram of a low-pressure gage shows how the different refrigerants are charged according to the evaporator temperature. For air conditioning, the evaporator temperature should be around 40°F. When the 40° temperature is read on the F12 scale, the outer scale shows a pressure reading of 37 psi. For F22 scale at 40° evaporator temperature, the pressure reads around 69 psi. Each system is different, and the temperature of air moving over evaporator coil will be different, so each system will have a little different evaporator temperature reading.

gage. This gage attaches to the low-side line. The low-pressure gage reads from 30 inches Hg vacuum to 250 psi pressure. It should never be attached to the high-side line, because the higher pressure in this line will damage the gage.

The outside scale on the gage is the pressure-vacuum scale. The inside scales are evaporator temperature scales for the different types of refrigerants. If F-12 (sometimes designated R-12 refrigerant is used, you should have 37 psi of pressure in the system. F-22 (R-22) refrigerant should be charged to 69 psi and 502 refrigerant to 80.5 psi. These pressure figures are not absolute, however, because some units become fully charged with more or less than these pressures. When charging the system at different evaporator and outside temperatures, the pressure and temperature combinations can be taken from the gages or from pressure-temperature charts. Once again, these are not absolute.

## LEAK DETECTORS

To check for a leak in the refrigerant tubing there are several preparations, both commercial and household, that can be used. Most commonly used to check for leaks is a simple soap and water solution that is brushed on the area where the leak is suspected. The soap must be the type that will make suds so that when the leak appears, it will show up as a bubble expanding from the tubing.

A halide torch leak detector (Fig. 1-34) can be used to check a Freon refrigerant system for leaks. These torches use a propane fuel. A hose which attaches to the cover around the torch is run along the tubing of the refrigerant system. When the hose comes to a place where Freon is leaking from the tubing, the flame will turn green. A large leak will produce a blue flame.

An electronic leak detector is shown in Fig. 1-35. There are several types of these on the market. They are very useful in finding extremely small leaks, but are also used for finding larger leaks.

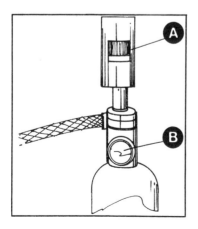

Fig. 1-34. Halide torch used to locate leaks in a Freon system. Valve A is turned on and the burner lit at B. The hose is run along the refrigerant lines. When Freon is detected, the flame will change color.

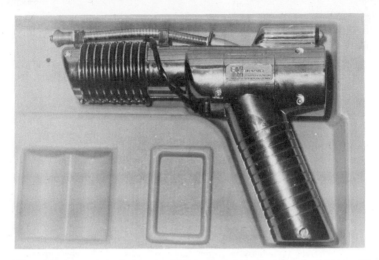

Fig. 1-35. Electronic leak detector. This instrument is run along the tubing, and when a leak is detected a beep will be emitted from the detector.

## THERMOMETERS

Thermometers used in heating and refrigeration servicing use alcohol, bimetal strips, or mercury. The better thermometers have the scales marked on the body of the thermometer instead of on a cardboard back.

## SERVICE VALVES

These valves are located in the refrigerant lines near the condensing unit to provide a way to check the refrigerant. There are several types of service valves, including two-way service valves, line tap valves, and Schraeder valves. Figure 1-36 shows a two-way service valve. These valves have a ¼-inch fitting to permit the manifold charging hose to connect to the valve to pump refrigerant into the system if needed.

Figure 1-37 shows a line tap valve that can be attached to copper tubing. These are also called *saddle* valves because they are clamped around the tubing like a saddle. A piercing screw punches a hole in the line, opening the line to the valve. The charging hose is connected to the ¼-inch fitting to charge the system or take a gage reading.

Another type of service valve is the *Schraeder* or *snifter* valve. This valve is much like the valve used on automobile tires. The same principles apply. The body of the snifter valve is welded or brazed into the refrigerant line, and the valve core is screwed into the valve body. The valve core is operated just like the tire valve core and prevents the refrigerant from escaping. Refrigerant can be added by attaching a charging hose with a stem in the center to the snifter valve. The stem in the charging hose will depress the stem on the snifter and open the valve so refrigerant can be added. A cap goes over the outside of the snifter when the valve is not being used.

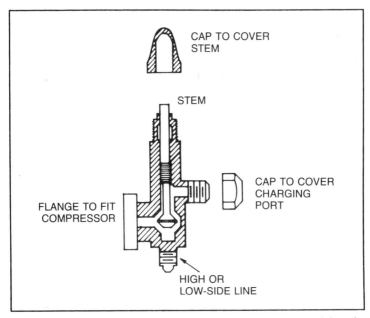

Fig. 1-36. In this two-way service valve, the stem is turned to open and close the valve for gage readings or refrigerant charging. Opening and closing the valve is accomplished by turning the stem only about ¾ turn, but if you want to close off the refrigerant line entirely, you can turn the stem several turns.

## MISCELLANEOUS HANDTOOLS

The amount of refrigeration or heating work you do will determine the number, amount, and variety of handtools that you will want to own. On the other hand, the variety of tools available to you will determine the number and types of jobs you will be able to perform. You should strike a balance between an ample tool supply to take care of the majority of jobs you will

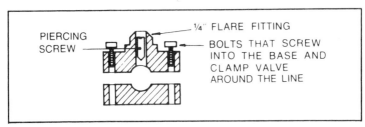

Fig. 1-37. Line tap valve or saddle valve. The two halves of the valve clamp over the line, and the hold-down bolts are tightened. A cap with a plunger is placed in the service fitting on the top of the piercing screw. As cap is tightened down the piercing screw punches a hole in the line. When the cap and plunger are removed, the charging hose is attached to the fitting to take a gage reading. When the hose is removed, the cap is replaced to seal the valve.

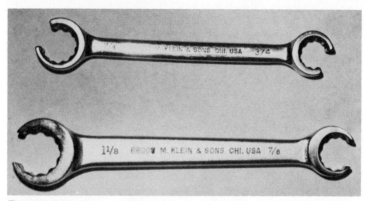

Fig. 1-38. Refrigeration wrenches are used to loosen flare nuts. These wrenches are open on the end so they can be placed over the refrigeration lines and slipped over the flare nuts.

encounter and, on the other hand, drawers full of tools you will never use. You will want to have more than a screwdriver and a Crescent wrench.

Your handtool set should include, for openers, a set of open-end wrenches, a set of box-end wrenches, and some adjustable wrenches. The open-end and box-end wrenches will be used to loosen and tighten cap screws and bolts. The wrenches will also be used to tighten flare fittings. Be sure to use two wrenches when adjusting a flare fitting to keep from twisting the tubing. Sometimes a socket set will come in handy when working in close places.

These wrenches shown in Fig. 1-38 are known as refrigeration wrenches, and their only application is to tighten and loosen fittings on tubing. These wrenches are essentially box-end wrenches with part of the end cut away so the wrench will fit over the tubing to grasp the flare fitting. These wrenches have stronger jaws than other wrenches. You may find a set of these wrenches useful if you plan to do a lot of tubing work, but for do-it-yourself repair you can do without them.

## HANDTOOLS FOR DUCT INSTALLATION

There are different types of tin snips for cutting different weights of metal. Tin snip types include center cut, left-hand cut, and right-hand cut. These terms refer to the way the blades of the tin snips are formed and the way the metal cleans from the snips after it has been cut. For large amount of duct that work you will need all three types of snips to make the job easier.

The right- and left-hand snips cut much like scissors. One side of the metal being cut will roll and clean from the snips. The use of the right or left snips will depend on which side you want to clean and roll from the snips.

When cutting around a duct pipe, you will have to use the center-cut snips. A round pipe will not clean as it is cut; thus the ordinary snips will be unusable for this application. The center-cut tin snips cut a ¼-inch ribbon out of the metal so that a straight line is formed when cutting around the duct. It is possible to cut a round pipe using both the right and left snips at the same time and leaving a 2-inch strip between the snips. This strip will clean and roll from both snips as the cut is made.

## Folders

Folders are used to grasp a straight edge of sheet metal to fold it and make a flange. The folders have marks on the jaws for measurement so the proper size flange can be formed. Besides bending the ducts for making flanges, the folders can be used to make S-clamps or straighten the raw edge of a duct that has just been cut.

## Crimpers

The crimpers fold the edge of the duct in small ripples to reduce the size and allow it to fit into the next joint. Factory duct joints come with one end already crimped, so this will not be needed until you have to cut a section of duct and join it.

To crimp the edge of a duct, place the duct between the jaws of the crimper and press the handles together. Run the crimpers around the entire edge to crimp the entire end. Be careful not to squeeze the handles too hard because this can crimp the edge so much that it will be too small to fit properly.

## Pop-Rivet Gun

The pop-rivet gun is used to attach pieces of sheet metal together. The alternative to the pop-rivet gun is to use screws to hold the pieces. To use the gun, you must first have a hole drilled through the two pieces to be joined. A nail-like pop rivet is placed in the barrel of the gun with the head sticking out. The head is placed in the hole, and the handle of the gun is squeezed. The pop rivet should seal and snap off. Remove the nail part of the rivet from the barrel of the gun.

# Chapter 2

# Heat Loads and Cooling Loads

It is important for the homeowner and serviceman to know the basic techniques of figuring the size of any heating or cooling unit that is required. First we must consider some of the basic physical properties that affect this calculation.

The heating capacity of a furnace is measured in *British thermal units (Btu)*. A British thermal unit is the amount of heat required to raise the temperature of 1 pound of water 1°F. When you figure the heat loss for a house, you get a Btu-per-hour rating. Furnace capacities are rated accordingly, that is, in Btu per hour. When selecting a furnace, it is important to choose one with a capacity to put out at least enough heat per hour to match the heat loss of the area to be heated.

Usually a furnace will have two Btu ratings: the *input* rating and the *output* rating. The output rating tells the actual heat output capacity of the furnace. The difference between the two ratings is the heat loss through the flue. It is important, in buying a furnace, to make sure that you know the output Btu rating, because often a furnace will be advertised (or even sold to an unsuspecting buyer) according to its Btu input rating rather than its output rating. The Btu ratings are usually found on the nameplate of the furnace (Fig. 2-1).

The only type of furnace which will not have two different Btu ratings is an electric furnace. Electric heat has an insignificant heat loss and does not use a flue. There will be only one Btu rating on electric furnaces. When figuring electric heat, 1 watt will be equivalent to about 3.415 Btu. If a portable heat unit were purchased with an element rated at 1500W, the element would put out 5122 Btu per hour (1500 × 3.415 = 5122). This would heat an area about 8 × 6 feet.

Air conditioning and refrigeration units are often rated in *tons of refrigeration*. A ton of refrigeration is the amount of heat required to melt a

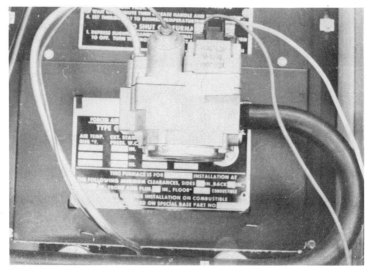

Fig. 2-1. The nameplate on the furnace gives the model, Btu input and output ratings, serial number, and perhaps even instructions on how to light the furnace.

ton of ice in 24 hours, and this is equivalent to 12,000 Btu/hour. One ton of refrigeration is the equivalent of 12,000 Btu. This means that if you wanted a unit to produce 36,000 Btu/hour, you would need to buy a unit rated at 3 tons. Similarly, if you bought a unit rated at 18,000 Btu (Btu/hour is often shortened to Btu), you would have a 1½-ton air conditioner, about enough cooling power for three or four average rooms.

Not all air conditioners have a Btu rating stamped on the nameplate. Some only have the model number, which may have to be decoded. Some have a horsepower rating; 1 horsepower equals ¾ ton, or 8000 Btu.

The *heat load* is the amount of heat loss in a building. It is expressed in Btu per hour, the same as furnace ratings. The key to a successful heating and cooling system is getting a unit the right size for the room or building air volume. This chapter explores heat loads and cooling loads, taking into account the effects of humidity, insulation, room volume, and window area.

## HUMIDITY

The moisture in the air is called humidity, and air will hold a certain maximum amount of moisture at a given temperature. *Relative humidity* is the amount of actual moisture in the air compared to the air's moisture-holding capacity. For example, if the relative humidity is 50 percent, the air is only holding 50 percent as much moisture as it is capable of holding at a certain temperature.

As the temperature of the air is increased, the air's capacity to hold moisture is increased. Therefore, if the amount of moisture in the air remains constant and the temperature is raised, the relative humidity will be decreased. When the relative humidity is lowered, evaporation will increase. We already know that by increasing evaporation we can make an object cooler; lowering the relative humidity will tend to cool the surrounding objects.

You can check the relative humidity of an area with a *psychrometer* (Fig. 2-2). The sling psychrometer consists of two thermometers, a *wet bulb* thermometer and a *dry bulb* thermometer. The wet bulb thermometer has a sleeve over the bulb to keep it wet. The water evaporating from this sleeve as the psychrometer is twirled through the air cools the bulb of the thermometer, which gives the wet bulb temperature. The dry bulb temperature is read on the other thermometer.

## Controlling Humidity

In the winter, when the house is closed up, the humidity inside the house can get as low as 5 percent. By increasing the difference between the moisture in the air and the moisture on the outer skin, evaporation is speeded up and a person may feel cold. A simple solution to the problem is to operate the furnace at a lower temperature, which will save on the gas bill, as well as protect the furnishings and cut down on the lint problems.

The more practical solution is to add moisture to the air in the house. One way is to put a pan of water on the stove and let it boil to release water into the air. Most people prefer a humidifier that will add water without requiring attention. There are several types of humidifiers that can be added to a furnace and a variety of console humidifiers that operate independently of the furnace system.

Humidifiers and their installation are discussed in Chapter 8.

## Evaporation and Cooling

As an air conditioner runs the air is moved over the evaporator and is cooled. Since cool air will hold less moisture than warm air, the air gives up its moisture and deposits it on the evaporator. The removal of the moisture from the air makes the body cooler than it otherwise would be.

A small air conditioner will put more air in contact with the evaporator and remove more moisture than a larger unit. This is due to the fact that the

Fig. 2-2. The sling psychrometer is used to measure relative humidity in a room.

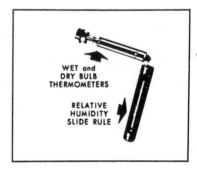

WET and
DRY BULB
THERMOMETERS

RELATIVE
HUMIDITY
SLIDE RULE

smaller unit runs a greater part of the time to cool an area. Since it will remove more moisture from the air, it will keep you cool by operating at a higher thermostat setting than a unit too large for the space. By cooling more effectively at a higher temperature, operating costs will be reduced. The homeowner saves twice because a smaller unit can be purchased initially at a smaller cost.

On the other hand, buying a unit too small for the space to be cooled is not a wise decision. The homeowner must be careful to figure the size of the unit correctly and not buy one too large or too small. Cooling load charts can help you select the correct size unit. These are found later in this chapter.

## LOCATION OF THE BUILDING

The location of the building will affect the heat load. Factors such as the direction the building faces, available shade, and nearby terrain will change the effects of the sun's rays on the heat load.

The sun is by far the greatest source of heat in both winter and summer; in fact, some experimental units are heated entirely by energy from the sun. In the summer it becomes necessary to get rid of the excess heat produced by the sun. The heat from the sun, solar heat, will enter the closed building through the walls, windows, doors, ceilings, and floors. The amount of heat that will enter a given area will depend on the type of structure.

The direction the house faces plays a large part in the heat load of the building. If the length of the house is north and south, the heat gain will be less than if the length is east and west.

Other aspects of the location may have an effect on the load. For instance, if there are trees, tall shrubs, other buildings, or another obstruction such as a hill, the sun's rays will be deflected. Trees and other buildings thus will reduce the heat load several degrees. The average temperature for the climate in which the building is located will also help determine the heat load. Remember, the greater the difference between the inside and outside temperature, the faster the heat will travel through the structure.

## THE IMPORTANCE OF BUILDING MATERIALS

The amount of heat gained or lost is influenced by the location of the structure in relation to the sun, the amount of window space in the building, the kind and amount of insulation used, and the amount of heat produced by people and appliances within the building. When this information has been gathered, it is used with a heat chart to determine exactly the size unit needed for a structure.

The *U-factor* is the base figure for most tables and charts, but to understand its significance we must first look at another element—the k-factor. The k-factor is the amount of heat that can pass through a given material under certain conditions. Table 2-1 shows the k-factors for some common building materials. The k-factor tells you how many Btu will flow through 1 square foot of surface area in one hour for each degree of

**Table 2-1. Conductivities (k-Factors) for Various Materials.**

| Material | Thickness (inches) | k-factor |
|---|---|---|
| Cork board | 1 | 0.27 |
| Glass foam | 1 | 0.40 |
| Glass fiber | 1 | 0.27 |
| Mineral wool | 1 | 0.29 |
| Polystyrene foam | 1 | 0.25 |
| Wood fiber | 1 | 0.33 |
| Cork (Granulated) | 1 | 0.31 |
| Sawdust | 1 | 0.41 |
| Pine | 1 | 0.86 |
| Fir | 1 | 0.67 |
| Brick wall | 8 | 0.50 |
| Brick wall | 12 | 0.30 |
| Brick wall | 12 (½″ plaster) | 0.25 |
| Stone wall | 8 | 0.70 |
| Stone wall | 12 | 0.50 |
| Poured concrete | 8 | 0.70 |
| Poured concrete | 12 | 0.50 |
| Concrete block | 8 (air space) | 0.55 |
| Concrete block | 12 | 0.45 |
| Cinder block | 8 | 0.50 |
| Cinder block | 12 | 0.35 |

temperature difference between the two faces of the material. Using the chart, we see that pine has a k-factor of 0.86. This means that for each degree temperature difference, 0.86 Btu will flow through a 1-inch pine board that is 1 foot square.

Notice that 1 square foot of concrete would need to be 12 inches thick to equal the insulating value of 1 square foot of wood 1 inch thick. This shows the difference in the k-factors of the two building materials. Heat moves through concrete much more easily than through wood.

The U-factor is the heat flow through an actual *wall*, not just a single material. The U-factor is a function of the k-factors of all the materials making up the wall. The U-factor is used in figuring the size of the unit needed for both heating and cooling cycles. If heating is being considered, it is necessary to know how much heat provided by a furnace will escape. If cooling is the main concern, it is necessary to know how much heat is going to come into the enclosed space and how much heat will be generated within the area.

Different kinds of walls have different U-factors, depending on the k-factors of their materials. For example, more heat will escape (or enter, as the case may be) through a 6-inch concrete and plaster wall than through one constructed of wood and brick.

In figuring the heat transfer through a wall, it is also necessary to know the thickness of the various materials used in the construction. Two inches of fiberglass insulation would be figured differently from 4 inches of fiberglass insulation. Table 2-1 gives the k-factors for most materials based on a 1-inch thickness; some materials are given with other thicknesses. The thickness has to be taken into account when figuring the U-factor.

The U-factor for a wall is also related to the difference between the inside and outside temperatures. The U-factor is based on a 1°F temperature difference.

All of these considerations are combined in a formula. To find the U-factor, you will first have to find the k-factors of the materials used. The U-factor is given by

$$\text{U-factor} = \cfrac{1}{\cfrac{\text{thickness of A}}{\text{k-factor of A}} + \cfrac{\text{thickness of B}}{\text{k-factor of B}} + \cfrac{\text{thickness of C}}{\text{k-factor of C}}}$$

where A, B, and C are the different materials in the wall. Remember to relate the thicknesses to those in the k-factor chart. For a 4-inch brick wall, use a thickness figure of 0.5 since the chart gives the k-factor for an 8-inch wall, and 4 inches is one-half of 8 inches. The figure that results from these calculations is the number of Btu flowing through the wall each hour for each degree temperature difference and for each square foot.

For example, assume we want the U-factor for a wall which has a 1-inch pine board on the inside, ½-inch fir on the outside, and 2-inch fiberglass insulation in the middle. The first step is to find the k-factors for the three materials from Table 2-1. Figure 2-3 shows the wall referred to the formula, A is 1-inch pine with a k-factor of 0.86, B is 2-inch fiberglass with a k-factor of 0.27, and C is ½-inch fir with a k-factor of 0.67. Plugging the values into the formula we get

$$\text{U-factor} = \cfrac{1}{\cfrac{1}{0.86} + \cfrac{2}{0.27} + \cfrac{0.5}{0.67}}$$

$$= \cfrac{1}{1.16 + 7.41 + 0.75} = \cfrac{1}{9.31} = 0.107$$

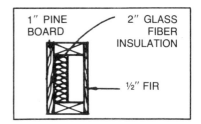

Fig. 2-3. The U-factor for this wall is figured with the help of a chart such as in Table 2-1.

1″ PINE BOARD    2″ GLASS FIBER INSULATION

½″ FIR

The U-factor for this wall is 0.107. This means that for each square foot of wall space and for each degree temperature difference, this wall will allow 0.107 Btu per hour to pass through.

If the wall is 8 × 14 feet and the house is in a region with a 70° temperature difference, the heat load is 0.107 × 112 square feet × 70° temperature difference = 839 Btu per hour. Thus, 839 Btu will escape through this wall each hour. (The temperature difference is the difference between the lowest average winter temperature and the heating temperature of the house. If the house is heated to 70° and the lowest average temperature is 0°, the temperature difference is 70°.) This chapter includes heat gain charts which provide a much easier way to measure the heat load. The reason for this discussion of U-factors and k-factors is to provide a method of figuring the heat load through a wall that may not appear in the heat gain tables.

## INSULATION EFFECTS

One inch of insulation installed in a wall or ceiling reduces the heat loss through the wall by 40 percent to 50 percent, depending on the type of insulation. Two inches will reduce the heat loss by around 60 percent, 3 inches by 70 percent, and 4 inches by 75 percent. Four inches of wall insulation is now the minimum recommended for new home construction in most parts of the country.

### Heat Movement Through the Ceiling

The insulation in the ceiling is more important than that in the walls. Around 75 percent of all the heat lost in the winter is through the ceiling because warmer air rises and escapes through the ceiling and roof. In the summer the attic of a house might reach a temperature of 125°F, which increases the cooling load considerably.

There are several ways to reduce the loss of heat through the roof of the house, but insulating the ceiling is the most important. Four inches of fiberglass insulation will reduce the heat loss by 70 percent to 75 percent. Six to 10 inches of ceiling insulation is the minimum recommended in most parts of the country.

The extremely high summer temperatures in the attic can be lowered by having proper ventilation for this area. Often this is done with louvers at each end of the house.

The type and color of the roofing has an effect on the heat gain or loss, too. Wooden shingles provide more insulation than the asphalt type. Dark shingles have a tendency to absorb sunlight, while lighter ones reflect the sun's rays.

### Heat Movement Through Windows

Figure 2-4 shows that windows have a relatively high heat loss. A single-glass window has a U-factor of 1.14. Adding a second pane of glass in

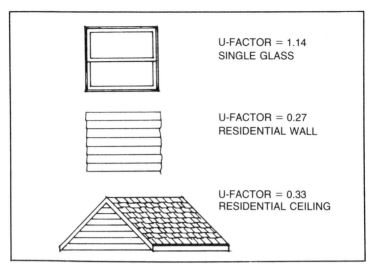

U-FACTOR = 1.14
SINGLE GLASS

U-FACTOR = 0.27
RESIDENTIAL WALL

U-FACTOR = 0.33
RESIDENTIAL CEILING

Fig. 2-4. The heat loss is much greater through single glass than through either walls or ceilings.

the form of a storm window reduces the U-factor to 0.45 or 0.65. This represents a 40 percent to 60 percent reduction in the heat loss through the window.

Storm doors have a similar effect in reducing the heat gain and loss. Caulking storm doors and windows further increases their effectiveness. Awnings over the windows can reduce the summer heat gain through the windows by 15 percent.

### Infiltration

Infiltration is another source of heat gain or loss. Infiltration is air leakage through cracks around floors and windows, as well as other places. Weather-stripping and caulking these cracks and repairing the foundation will limit the amount of infiltration that can enter the building.

Infiltration should not be confused with ventilation. Ventilation is fresh air that is brought in purposely through air ducts.

### Indoor Heat Loads

There are two heat sources found within most buildings that must be considered when figuring the heating and cooling load. The first source of heat is the people who normally occupy the space. To figure the heat produced from this source, you will need to estimate the average number of people normally in the building and the activities which they will be undertaking. A person at rest will produce about 350 Btu per hour. A person doing heavy work will produce 1400 Btu per hour. The normal heat load per person is around 500 Btu per hour. Heat loads for people are listed in Table 2-2.

Table 2-2. Heat Load (People).

| Activities | Total Btu Per Hour |
|---|---|
| Theater or movie | 350 |
| Office work | 450 |
| Medium-to-light work | 650 |
| Dancing | 900 |
| Medium-to-heavy | 1050 |
| Bowling | 1350 |
| Extra-heavy work | 1450 |

A second source of heat is lights and appliances (oven, iron, hair dryers, etc.). Table 2-3 gives the Btu produced by several common appliances.

Counting these extra heat sources is not as important in figuring the heat load as it is in figuring the cooling load. When figuring the cooling load for a house, failure to take these heat sources into consideration may result in undersizing a unit. Since the salesman is eager to make a sale, he may guess at the size of unit needed, failing to consider all the factors entering into the cooling load. When the unit is installed, it may be too small to adequately cool the space.

## HEAT LOAD CHART

There are several ways to estimate the heat load or amount of heat escaping when the furnace is heating. One way is to guess, on the basis of experience or what works for other people, as to the size that will work satisfactorily. Another way is to use the k-factors of each material in the walls, ceiling, and floor and calculate the U-factors. The third method is to use factors from a chart compiled for various types of construction.

Usually the first way will not work out very well. Very few people will be able to "guesstimate" correctly the heat load for a house. There are quick

Table 2-3. Heat From Electric and Gas Appliances.

| Appliance | Heat—Electrical Appliance (Btu per hour) | Heat—Gas Appliance (Btu per hour) |
|---|---|---|
| Coffee brewer, ½ gal. | 1120 | 1700 |
| Light (100W bulb) | 350 | |
| Electric motors (1W hp) | 2900 | |
| Food and plate warmer | 700 | |
| Grill, meat | 4600 | |
| Grill, sandwich | 3400 | |
| Hair dryer (blower) | 2700 | |
| Hair dryer (helmet) | 2200 | |
| Fry pan | | 7200 |
| Stove (electric) | 5500 | |
| Stove (gas) | 6500 | |
| Toaster, pop-up (per slice) | 45 | |
| Waffle iron | 1850 | |
| Irons | 800 | |

methods of finding the heat loads, but in the end the only way to get it right is to do the calculating required, using methods two and three.

The third method, using charts to find the heat load, is the easiest and fastest. Using the k-factors and U-factors takes considerable time and calculation. You will probably only want to use that method when you do not have heat charts available, or when you want to find the heat loss through a type of construction that is not found on the heat chart. Charts in this book were developed by the Air Conditioning and Refrigeration Institute.

One of the first things you need to know when using the heat chart is the design winter and summer temperatures for your area. The winter temperature will be used in reading the heating charts, and the summer temperature in reading the cooling charts. The outdoor design conditions are presented in Appendix A. If your particular town is not in Appendix A, you should be able to locate a city nearby to use for your base.

Table 2-4 is the heat chart. Take the outdoor design temperature for your area from Appendix A and read under the proper column in Table 2-4 to find the proper factors to use for your area. If the design temperature is −10°, locate this column under *Factors* and use the factors in that column for all your calculations.

*Windows:* Windows are the first items on the heat chart. Find the total window area in the entire house in square feet. Break this down into single-pane windows and double-pane windows. Figure window area on the basis of the window opening. Suppose you had 100 square feet of single-pane window area. Multiply the number of square feet by the factor in the chart. For −10° design temperature (from here on, a −10° design temperature will be used in the examples), the factor for single-glass windows is 96. The product of the factor and the area (96 × 100) gives the Btu-per-hour heat loss. The heat loss (or heat load) through the windows in the house is 9600 Btu. (Write this figure down on a piece of paper.)

*Walls:* Find the total outside wall area. If the house is 50 × 30 × 8 feet, the area of the area of the outside walls will be 1280 square feet. You may subtract the total window area from this figure, but it will probably not have much effect. Find the wall description on the chart that most nearly corresponds to your walls. If category 2a-4 in Table 2-4 (more than 2 inches insulation) fits the walls closest, the factor is 7. The heat loss is 8960 Btu (1280 × 7 = 8960 Btu). Write down this figure. A partition wall, such as a wall between the garage and living area, is not counted.

*Ceiling:* If category 3a-4 in Table 2-4 describes the ceiling in the building (more than 4 inches in the ceiling with an attic), the ceiling factor will be 7. The ceiling area is 1500 square feet (30 × 50). The heat load for the ceiling is 1500 × 7 = 10,500 Btu. Put this figure with the other heat loss figures.

*Floors:* Find the floor category that applies to your building. If the floor is category 4a-2 (enclosed crawl space), the factor is 20. The area is 1500 square feet, same as the ceiling. The heat load is 1500 × 20 = 30,000 Btu. Add this figure to the total.

Table 2-4. Residential Heating Load Factors, 75°F (courtesy American Refrigeration Institute).

| ITEMS | \-40F | \-30F | \-20F | \-10F | 0F | 10F | 20F | 30F | 40F |
|---|---|---|---|---|---|---|---|---|---|
| **Outdoor Design Temperature** | | | | | | | | | |
| **1. WINDOWS** | | | | | | | | | |
| a. Single Glass | 130 | 119 | 107 | 96 | 85 | 73 | 62 | 51 | 40 |
| b. Double Glass | 63 | 58 | 52 | 47 | 41 | 36 | 30 | 25 | 19 |
| **2. WALLS AND DOORS** | | | | | | | | | |
| a. Frame and veneer-on-frame | | | | | | | | | |
| (1) No insulation | 31 | 28 | 26 | 23 | 20 | 18 | 15 | 12 | 10 |
| (2) Less than 1 in. insulation, or one reflective air space | 23 | 21 | 19 | 17 | 15 | 13 | 11 | 9 | 7 |
| (3) 1 in. to 2 in. insulation, or two reflective air spaces | 15 | 14 | 12 | 11 | 10 | 9 | 7 | 6 | 5 |
| (4) More than 2 in. insulation, or three reflective air spaces | 9 | 8 | 8 | 7 | 6 | 5 | 4 | 4 | 3 |
| b. Masonry walls, 8 in. block or brick | | | | | | | | | |
| (1) Plastered or plain | 58 | 53 | 48 | 43 | 38 | 33 | 28 | 23 | 18 |
| (2) Furred, no insulation | 36 | 33 | 29 | 26 | 23 | 20 | 17 | 14 | 11 |
| (3) Furred, with less than 1 in. insulation, or one reflective air space | 24 | 22 | 20 | 18 | 16 | 14 | 12 | 9 | 7 |
| (4) Furred, with 1 in. to 2 in. insulation, or two reflective air spaces | 16 | 15 | 13 | 12 | 11 | 9 | 8 | 6 | 5 |
| (5) Furred, with more than 2 in. insulation, or three reflective air spaces | 10 | 9 | 9 | 8 | 7 | 6 | 5 | 4 | 3 |
| (6) Wall below grade | 7 | 6 | 6 | 5 | 4 | 4 | 3 | 3 | 2 |
| *c. Partitions | | | | | | | | | |
| (1) Frame, finished one side only, no insulation | 35 | 32 | 29 | 26 | 23 | 20 | 17 | 14 | 11 |
| (2) Frame, finished both sides, no insulation | 20 | 18 | 16 | 15 | 13 | 11 | 9 | 8 | 6 |
| (3) Frame, finished both sides, more than 1 in. insulation, or two reflective air spaces | 8 | 7 | 7 | 6 | 5 | 5 | 4 | 3 | 3 |

## 3. CEILINGS AND ROOFS / 4. FLOORS / 5. OUTSIDE AIR

| | | | | | | | | |
|---|---|---|---|---|---|---|---|---|
| **(4) Masonry, plastered one side, no insulation** | 20 | 18 | 17 | 15 | 13 | 11 | 10 | 8 | 6 |
| **d. Wood doors†** | 61 | 56 | 50 | 45 | 40 | 34 | 29 | 24 | 19 |
| **3. CEILINGS AND ROOFS** | | | | | | | | | |
| **a. Ceilings under naturally vented attic or vented flat roof** | | | | | | | | | |
| (1) Uninsulated | 70 | 64 | 58 | 52 | 46 | 40 | 34 | 27 | 21 |
| (2) Less than 2 in. insulation, or one reflective air space | 17 | 16 | 14 | 13 | 11 | 10 | 8 | 7 | 5 |
| (3) 2 in. to 4 in. insulation, or two reflective air spaces | 12 | 11 | 10 | 9 | 8 | 7 | 6 | 5 | 4 |
| (4) More than 4 in. insulation, or three or more reflective air spaces | 9 | 8 | 8 | 7 | 6 | 5 | 4 | 4 | 3 |
| **b. Built-up roof, no ceiling** | | | | | | | | | |
| (1) Uninsulated | 55 | 50 | 46 | 41 | 36 | 31 | 26 | 22 | 17 |
| (2) 2 in. roof insulation | 24 | 22 | 20 | 18 | 16 | 14 | 12 | 9 | 7 |
| (3) 3 in. roof insulation | 17 | 16 | 14 | 13 | 11 | 10 | 8 | 7 | 5 |
| **c. Ceilings under unheated rooms** | 14 | 13 | 11 | 10 | 9 | 8 | 7 | 5 | 4 |
| **4. FLOORS** | | | | | | | | | |
| **a. Over:** | | | | | | | | | |
| (1) Basement | 0 | 0 | 0 | 0 | 0 | 0 | 0 | 0 | 0 |
| (2) Enclosed crawl space | 27 | 24 | 22 | 20 | 17 | 15 | 13 | 10 | 8 |
| (3) Open crawl space | 39 | 36 | 32 | 29 | 26 | 22 | 19 | 15 | 12 |
| **\*\*b. On ground with:** | | | | | | | | | |
| (1) No edge insulation | 12 | 11 | 10 | 9 | 8 | 7 | 6 | 5 | 4 |
| (2) 1 in. edge insulation | 10 | 9 | 8 | 7 | 6 | 6 | 5 | 4 | 3 |
| (3) 2 in. edge insulation | 8 | 7 | 7 | 6 | 5 | 4 | 4 | 3 | 2 |
| **c. Basement floors** | 7 | 6 | 6 | 5 | 5 | 4 | 3 | 3 | 2 |
| **5. OUTSIDE AIR** | | | | | | | | | |
| a. Infiltration, Btuh per sq ft of gross exposed wall area | 16 | 14 | 13 | 12 | 10 | 9 | 7 | 6 | 5 |
| b. Mechanical ventilation, Btuh per cfm | 124 | 113 | 103 | 92 | 81 | 70 | 60 | 49 | 38 |

* Partitions are considered to be unheated on one side. Walls between garage and living space are to be treated as outside walls.
† Consider glass area of doors as windows. If storm doors are used, multiply factor by 0.6.
** Btuh per sq ft of gross exposed wall area.

Table 2-5. Residential Cooling Load Factors, 75°F (courtesy American Refrigeration Institute).

HEAT GAIN FACTORS
Btuh per sq ft

| Item | No Shading Devices | Roller Shades Half-Drawn | Draperies or Venetian Blinds | Ventilated Awnings | Outside Shading Screens |
|---|---|---|---|---|---|
| **1a. Windows—Solar cooling load** | | | | | |
| **(1) Regular Single Glass** | | | | | |
| (a) N (or shaded) | 19 | 14 | 11 | 16 | 4 |
| (b) NE and NW | 51 | 37 | 28 | 17 | 12 |
| (c) E and W | 77 | 57 | 43 | 18 | 18 |
| (d) SE and SW | 66 | 48 | 36 | 17 | 9 |
| (e) S | 36 | 26 | 20 | 16 | 5 |
| **(2) Regular Double Glass** | | | | | |
| (a) N (or shaded) | 17 | 13 | 10 | 11 | 3 |
| (b) NE and NW | 45 | 35 | 26 | 12 | 8 |
| (c) E and W | 67 | 53 | 40 | 12 | 12 |
| (d) SE and SW | 57 | 45 | 34 | 12 | 6 |
| (e) S | 31 | 25 | 18 | 11 | 3 |
| **(3) Heat-Absorbing Double Glass** | | | | | |
| (a) N (or shaded) | 10 | 8 | 7 | 8 | 2 |
| (b) NE and NW | 26 | 22 | 18 | 9 | 7 |
| (c) E and W | 40 | 33 | 28 | 10 | 10 |
| (d) SE and SW | 34 | 28 | 23 | 9 | 5 |
| (e) S | 20 | 16 | 13 | 9 | 3 |

**1b. Window—Air-to-air cooling load**

| Outdoor Design Temperature | 90F | 95F | 100F | 105F | 110F |
|---|---|---|---|---|---|
| (1) Single Glass | 8 | 12 | 16 | 20 | 24 |
| (2) Double Glass | 4 | 7 | 9 | 11 | 13 |

## 2. Walls and Doors

| Daily Temperature Range | Low | | Medium | | | | High | | | |
|---|---|---|---|---|---|---|---|---|---|---|
| Outdoor Design Temperature | 90 | 95 | 90 | 95 | 100 | 105 | 95 | 100 | 105 | 110 |
| **a. Frame and veneer on frame walls** | | | | | | | | | | |
| (1) No insulation | 5.9 | 7.2 | 4.8 | 6.1 | 7.4 | 8.7 | 4.8 | 6.1 | 7.4 | 8.7 |
| (2) Less than 1 in. insulation, or one reflective air space | 4.3 | 5.2 | 3.5 | 4.5 | 5.4 | 6.4 | 3.5 | 4.5 | 5.4 | 6.4 |
| (3) 1 in. to 2 in. insulation, or two reflective air spaces | 2.9 | 3.6 | 2.4 | 3.1 | 3.7 | 4.4 | 2.4 | 3.1 | 3.7 | 4.4 |
| (4) More than 2 in. insulation, or three reflective air sp. s | 1.8 | 2.2 | 1.5 | 1.9 | 2.3 | 2.7 | 1.5 | 1.9 | 2.3 | 2.7 |
| **b. Masonry walls, 8 in. block or brick** | | | | | | | | | | |
| (1) Plastered or plain | 7.3 | 9.7 | 5.4 | 7.8 | 10.2 | 12.6 | 5.4 | 7.8 | 10.2 | 12.6 |
| (2) Furred, no insulation | 4.6 | 6.1 | 3.4 | 4.9 | 6.4 | 7.9 | 3.4 | 4.9 | 6.4 | 7.9 |
| (3) Furred, with less than 1 in. insulation, or one reflective air space | 3.1 | 4.1 | 2.3 | 3.3 | 4.3 | 5.3 | 2.3 | 3.3 | 4.3 | 5.3 |
| (4) Furred, with 1 in. to 2 in. insulation, or two reflective air spaces | 2.1 | 2.8 | 1.6 | 2.3 | 3.0 | 3.7 | 1.6 | 2.3 | 3.0 | 3.7 |
| (5) Furred, with more than 2 in. insulation, or three reflective air spaces | 1.4 | 1.8 | 1.0 | 1.5 | 1.9 | 2.4 | 1.0 | 1.5 | 1.9 | 2.4 |
| **c. Partitions** | | | | | | | | | | |
| (1) Frame, finished one side only, no insulation | 8.4 | 11.4 | 6.0 | 9.0 | 12.0 | 15.0 | 6.0 | 9.0 | 12.0 | 15.0 |

**Table 2-5. Residential Cooling Load Factors, 75°F (courtesy American Refrigeration Institute) (continued from page 45.)**

HEAT GAIN FACTORS Btuh per sq ft

| Item | | Low | | Medium | | | | High | | | |
|---|---|---|---|---|---|---|---|---|---|---|---|
| Daily Temperature Range | | Low | | Medium | | | | High | | | |
| Outdoor Design Temperature | | 90 | 95 | 90 | 95 | 100 | 105 | 95 | 100 | 105 | 110 |
| c. Partitions (continued) | | | | | | | | | | | |
| (2) Frame, finished both sides, no insulation | | 4.8 | 6.5 | 3.4 | 5.1 | 6.8 | 8.5 | 3.4 | 5.1 | 6.8 | 8.5 |
| (3) Frame, finished both sides, more than 1 in. insulation, or two reflective air spaces | | 2.0 | 2.7 | 1.4 | 2.1 | 2.8 | 3.5 | 1.4 | 2.1 | 2.8 | 3.5 |
| (4) Masonry, finished one side, no insulation | | 2.6 | 4.4 | 1.2 | 3.0 | 4.7 | 6.5 | 1.2 | 3.0 | 4.7 | 6.5 |
| d. Wood doors* | | 11.3 | 13.8 | 9.3 | 11.8 | 14.3 | 16.8 | 9.3 | 11.8 | 14.3 | 16.8 |
| 3. Ceilings and Roofs | | | | | | | | | | | |
| a. Ceilings under naturally vented attic or vented flat roof | | | | | | | | | | | |
| (1) Uninsulated | dark | 9.9 | 11.0 | 9.0 | 10.1 | 11.3 | 12.4 | 9.0 | 10.1 | 11.3 | 12.4 |
| | light | 8.1 | 9.2 | 7.1 | 8.3 | 9.4 | 10.6 | 7.1 | 8.3 | 9.4 | 10.6 |
| (2) Less than 2 in. insulation, or one reflective air space | dark | 4.3 | 4.8 | 3.9 | 4.4 | 4.9 | 5.4 | 3.9 | 4.4 | 4.9 | 5.4 |
| | light | 3.5 | 4.0 | 3.1 | 3.6 | 4.1 | 4.6 | 3.1 | 3.6 | 4.1 | 4.6 |
| (3) 2 in. to 4 in. insulation, or two reflective air spaces | dark | 2.6 | 2.9 | 2.3 | 2.6 | 2.9 | 3.2 | 2.3 | 2.6 | 2.9 | 3.2 |
| | light | 2.1 | 2.4 | 1.9 | 2.2 | 2.5 | 2.8 | 1.9 | 2.2 | 2.5 | 2.8 |
| (4) More than 4 in. insulation, or three or more reflective air spaces | dark | 1.7 | 1.9 | 1.6 | 1.8 | 2.0 | 2.2 | 1.6 | 1.8 | 2.0 | 2.2 |
| | light | 1.4 | 1.6 | 1.2 | 1.4 | 1.6 | 1.8 | 1.2 | 1.4 | 1.6 | 1.8 |

| Item | | 1 | 2 | 3 | 4 | 5 | 6 | 7 | 8 | 9 | 10 |
|---|---|---|---|---|---|---|---|---|---|---|---|
| **b. Built-up roof, no ceiling** | | | | | | | | | | | |
| (1) Uninsulated | dark | 17.2 | 19.2 | 15.6 | 17.6 | 19.6 | 21.6 | 15.6 | 17.6 | 19.6 | 21.6 |
| | light | 14.0 | 16.0 | 12.4 | 14.4 | 16.4 | 18.4 | 12.4 | 14.4 | 16.4 | 18.4 |
| (2) 2 in. roof insulation | dark | 8.6 | 9.6 | 7.8 | 8.8 | 9.8 | 10.8 | 7.8 | 8.8 | 9.8 | 10.8 |
| | light | 7.0 | 8.0 | 6.2 | 7.2 | 8.2 | 9.2 | 6.2 | 7.2 | 8.2 | 9.2 |
| (3) 3 in. roof insulation | dark | 6.0 | 6.7 | 5.5 | 6.2 | 6.9 | 7.6 | 5.5 | 6.2 | 6.9 | 7.6 |
| | light | 4.9 | 5.6 | 4.3 | 5.0 | 5.7 | 6.4 | 4.3 | 5.0 | 5.7 | 6.4 |
| c. Ceilings under unconditioned rooms | | 2.7 | 3.6 | 1.9 | 2.9 | 3.8 | 4.8 | 1.9 | 2.9 | 3.8 | 4.8 |
| **4. Floors** | | | | | | | | | | | |
| a. Over unconditioned rooms | | 3.4 | 4.6 | 2.4 | 3.6 | 4.8 | 6.0 | 2.4 | 3.6 | 4.8 | 6.0 |
| b. Over basement, enclosed crawl space, or concrete slab on ground | | 0 | 0 | 0 | 0 | 0 | 0 | 0 | 0 | 0 | 0 |
| c. Over open crawl space | | 4.8 | 6.5 | 3.4 | 5.1 | 6.8 | 8.5 | 3.4 | 5.1 | 6.8 | 8.5 |
| **5. Outside Air** | | | | | | | | | | | |
| a. Infiltration, Btuh per sq ft of gross exposed wall area | | 1.1 | 1.5 | 1.1 | 1.5 | 1.9 | 2.2 | 1.6 | 1.9 | 2.2 | 2.6 |
| b. Mech. ventilation, Btuh per cfm | | 16.2 | 21.6 | 16.2 | 21.6 | 27.0 | 32.4 | 21.6 | 27.0 | 32.4 | 37.8 |

| 6. People | No. of occupants x 300 Btuh |
|---|---|
| 7. Kitchen appliance allowance | 1200 Btuh |
| 8. Heat gain to ducts | Subtotal (Items 1 thru 7) x Factor = _____ Btuh |
| 9. Total Estimated Sensible Heat Gain | Total (Items 1 thru 8) _____ Btuh |
| 10. Latent Heat Gain Allowance | Item 9 x 0.3 = _____ Btuh |
| 11. Total Estimated Design Heat Gain | Item 9 + Item 10 = _____ Btuh |

*Consider glass area of doors as windows.

*Outside air:* If air is brought in from the outside, multiply the cfm figure (cubic feet per minute) by the factor to get the Btu loss. Usually the infiltration air will be enough for most houses. So we will take the square feet of the wall area (1280) and multiply this figure by the factor of 12 given on the chart 1280 × 12 = 15,360 Btu per hour. Add this figure to the other heat losses.

Total all the figures for the house to get the total heat load. For our example the total was 74,420 Btu per hour. Since furnaces are rated in Btu per hour, we would normally refer to this heat load as a 74,420 Btu heat load and drop the per hour qualification.

The furnace size should be at least the same in Btu rating as the heat loss for the house. Be sure when buying a furnace to buy one according to its Btu output rating, and not according to its Btu input rating.

## COOLING LOAD CHART

The cooling chart (Table 2-5) furnished by the Air Conditioning and Refrigeration Institute, like the heat chart, does not use U- or k-factors.

*Windows:* The solar cooling load for the windows is figured using the factor that applies to the type of windows in the structure. Since the solar load for cooling is the greatest load, there are two calculations to make for figuring the heat gain through the windows. Notice in Table 2-5 that there are two parts to the window calculation. Under 1-a the window heat gain is figured according to the type and construction of the windows. Under 1-b the air-to-cooling load is figured using the outside design temperature. The results of these two calculations must be added together.

Assume that a house has 20 square feet of storm window area on the north side, 30 square feet on the west, 20 square feet on the south, and 30 square feet on the east. If the windows have a storm sash with the shades half drawn, the factor is 13 for the windows on the north sides. The cooling chart is used much the same as the heating chart.

The north-side window area is multiplied by the table factor to give a Btu heat gain of 260. The gain on the west side is 53 × 30 = 1590 Btu. The gain on the east side is also 53 × 30 = 1590 Btu. For the south-side windows the gain is 20 × 25 = 500 Btu. The total heat gain for all the window area is 3940 Btu. Write this figure down on paper just as you did for the Btu figures for the heating load.

The second part of the window load, the air-to-cooling load, is figured using the design summer temperature of your area taken from Appendix A. If the design temperature is 100°F and we have double-glass storm windows, the factor is 9. Multiplying the factor by the total window area, 910 = 900 Btu. Write this figure down with the first figure.

*Walls:* To figure the walls, you will have to select a temperature range taken from Appendix A. The L, M, and H in the table correspond to low, medium, and high ranges on the cooling chart. If the walls fall under description a-4, the factor is 2.3. The Btu rating is the wall area minus the window area, times the factor: 1280 square feet − 100 square feet = 1180 square feet, 1180 × 2.3 = 2714 Btu.

If all of the house is to be air conditioned, there won't be any partition walls to figure. If one room isn't going to be air conditioned, the wall of that room will have to be figured.

*Ceiling:* With a ceiling in category 3a-4 (more than 4 inches insulation, A-frame ceiling) with light shingles, the factor will be 1.6. The ceiling area is 1500 square feet. The heat gain is 1500 × 1.6 = 2400 Btu.

*Floor:* For a floor over a crawl space the factor is zero. If other types of floors are used, the factors are indicated on the chart.

*Outside air:* Since infiltration air is used for this house, the factor is 1.9 times the wall area, just as for the heat load. The heat gain is 1280 × 1.9 = 2432 Btu.

The cooling load for the people in the house must be figured. If five people will normally be occupying the house, figure 5 times 300 Btu per person (5 × 300 = 1500 Btu). Using the data in Table 2-3, find the cooling load for the appliances. For our example assume an appliance load of 1200 Btu.

Total all the Btu cooling loads. In the example we had 1200 + 1500 + 2432 + 2400 + 2714 + 900 + 3940 = 15,085 Btu. Figure a latent heat gain factor of 0.3. (Latent heat is the heat that will be present from objects in the house, chemical reactions, and other sources.) The latent heat, then, is 15,085 × 0.3 = 4525 Btu. The total cooling load is 15,085 + 4525 + 19,610 Btu. This would require a 2-ton conditioner.

## HEAT LOADS FOR ELECTRIC HEAT

Electric *furnaces* are rated in Btu, but electric heaters such as ceiling cable or baseboard heaters are rated according to wattage. One watt equals 3.415 Btu. Hence 1500W heater will produce 1500 × 3.415 = 5122 Btu.

Conversely, if you had figured the heat load for a room and the heat load was 6000 Btu, you would need to convert this to watts to get a baseboard heater the correct size. One Btu equals 1/3.415W. You would divide the Btu figure by the conversion factor of 3.415 to get the number of watts: 6000/3.415 = 1750W. A 1750W heater would be required to heat the room.

## R-FACTOR

The R-factor is a *resistance* factor. It is the reciprocal of the k-factor, that is, 1.0 divided by the k-factor. For example, a single-glass window has a k-factor of 1.11, the R-factor for this window is 1/1.11 = 0.9.

Conversely, to convert the R-factor rating to a k-factor, simply divide 1.0 by the R-factor. For example, assume you knew the R-factor of a single piece of glass. If the R-factor is 0.9, the k-factor is 1/0.9 = 1.11.

R-factors are used in measuring the insulating values of insulation materials. For example, 6 inches of fiberglass batt insulation has an R-value of R-19. R-factors have the advantage or permitting easy calculation of an entire wall's resistance. Simply add up the R-values of all the wall's materials at a given point.

# Chapter 3

# Selecting and Planning a Heating and Cooling System

In the past few years rising energy prices have drastically changed prevailing concepts about heating and cooling systems. There is no end in sight to these escalating energy costs. The result is that careful planning today is more important than ever in selecting and installing a central heating and cooling system.

Reducing energy costs is a primary concern of all homeowners, and planning the central heating and cooling system should revolve around that objective. Things are being planned into home heating systems today that seldom were considered a little more than a decade ago during the days of cheap energy. For example, wood heat has become an important supplementary—and sometimes primary—heat source. Rooms or sections of homes are closed off and heated with supplementary heat only when they are being used. This can change the central heating and cooling plan for the home. Other factors that must be considered in planning the central heating system include the amount of insulation and weather stripping needed for the home and the role that ventilation, such as a ceiling fan, will play in meeting the home's cooling needs. If you fail to account for these factors, the central heating and cooling system may be improperly sized, or air will be improperly distributed.

## PLANNING OPPORTUNITIES AND PITFALLS

There are a number of choices to be made when selecting a heating system. You can select between three primary types of fuel: gas, oil, and electricity. Recently renewable energy sources such as wood have become popular as supplementary or primary heating fuels. Coal is making a comeback as a heating fuel in many of the same applications as wood. Solar heating is an option as a supplementary and a primary source of heat. Selecting the proper fuel is discussed later in this chapter.

Other basic choices include the size of the heating/cooling unit, the type of heating system, the role supplementary heating and cooling will play in the home's overall needs, and the amount of flexibility that will be built into the system for future expansion or alterations.

## Selecting the Unit Size

The furnace and air conditioner must be large enough to handle the entire load of the house during weather extremes. The discussion in Chapter 2 will help you determine your home's heating and cooling requirements. Recent experiences have shown that when a home is weather-stripped, insulated, and sealed better than average, the heating and cooling loads may be less than indicated by conventional heat load charts. Also, when a home is retrofitted with insulation and weather stripping, homeowners frequently find that their furnaces and air conditioners are suddenly oversized for the new reduced heat load. Oversizing should be avoided because it cuts efficiency.

## Types of Heating Systems

This book concentrates on central air heating and cooling systems, but there are other types. *Hydronic* heating systems use hot water to deliver heat to the rooms where the heat is distributed by radiators. Hydronic systems have much in common with warm air heating systems. Both are central systems, and the unit producing the heat in both types of systems is quite similar. The major difference is the method of delivering heat. Hydronic systems sometimes are set up by zones. Each zone has its own separate thermostat control with such an arrangement. This has the advantage of allowing the homeowner to set different temperature settings throughout the house and to turn up the heat only in the zones that are in use. Although it is possible to use hydronic systems for central cooling, most residences that have hydronic heat use room air conditioners.

This book focuses on the central air heating and cooling system. Warmed or cooled air is taken from the central unit through ducts to the living area. Figure 3-1 shows one type of central air system.

Room heating systems have individual heaters in each room of the home. These commonly use gas or electricity as a fuel. Chapter 15 discusses room heaters and their potential for use as supplementary heating devices.

Room heaters present many planning opportunities. They can be used for remodeling additions. They also are useful for keeping bedrooms warm at night while the heat in the remainder of the house is turned down.

The *heat pump* is another type of heating system. Although it is a central heating and cooling system, its operation during the heating season is entirely different from a traditional warm air furnace. The heat pump saves energy costs over some types of heating systems, but it can be more expensive to operate than some others. This depends on the relative costs of heating fuels in your region and is discussed later in this chapter.

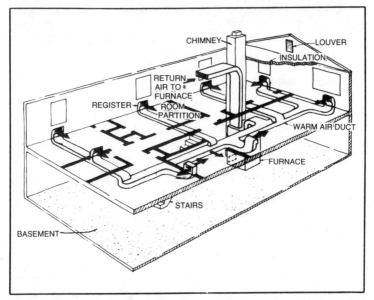

Fig. 3-1. This is a typical central heating and cooling system in a residential application. Warm air or cool air originates at the furnace or air conditioning unit, which is centrally located. Fans deliver the air through the duct system to the rooms of the house. The duct system very often is located under the floor of the home's main living area.

### Wood Heating Options

Heating with wood has become very popular in the last decade. The primary reason is that for many homeowners wood is cheaper than other types of energy. This is not true for all homeowners, and whether wood will save energy costs depends upon the relative costs of wood and other fuels in the region. You can calculate the relative costs by following the formula given later in this chapter.

There are many ways to use wood heat in a home. Some options include fireplaces, room-size wood heaters, circulating wood heaters, central add-on wood furnaces, and dual-fuel furnaces. Except for the central wood furnaces, wood heat is used for supplementary heat for one or a few rooms of a home. The expected use of wood heat in some rooms may affect the size of the central heating system you would want to install in such a home and the duct system layout.

A central wood furnace can be installed into the central heating duct system as an add-on unit working in tandem with the conventional furnace or as a primary heating furnace. This installation of wood furnaces is discussed in Chapter 12. When considering a central wood furnace, be sure to carefully plan its location. Wood furnaces take up much more space than do conventional gas or oil furnaces. You must take this into account when planning such an installation.

Another wood heating option worth considering is a dual-fuel furnace. This furnace burns wood and oil or gas, and it uses the conventional fuel only when there is not enough wood to provide sufficient heat.

Before installing any wood heating system, you must consider the drawbacks of wood heat. Wood is relatively messy, and it takes some space to store. You must have an idea of where you will get your wood and the cost.

## SUPPLEMENTARY HEAT

Supplementary heating simply means placing a separate heater in a particular location in the home that is used the most. Common applications are bedrooms, family rooms, and home additions.

The use of supplementary heat to save money involves careful considerations of the relative energy costs involved. For example, in many areas of the country electricity is considerably more expensive than natural gas per unit of heat.

Electricity is commonly used as a single-room heating fuel. Electric room heaters are available in several styles, including baseboard heaters and wall heaters with fans that distribute warm air throughout the room. These are discussed in detail in Chapter 15.

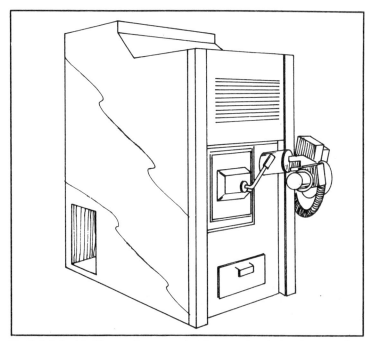

Fig. 3-2. A dual-fuel furnace burns wood and a secondary fuel such as gas or oil. If the wood in the firebox runs low and wood can no longer heat the home, the secondary fuel burner comes on and supplies heat for the house.

Gas room heaters also are available. These generally are wall units with a fan to distribute the warm air. They are connected to a gas line and must have a flue vent to the outside to carry away the carbon monoxide gas produced inside the unit's combustion chamber.

## AIR CONDITIONING AND VENTILATION

The effective use of ventilation can reduce the cooling load of the house during the summer. Adequate attic ventilation reduces the buildup of heat from the sun in the attic. Without ventilation this heat radiates from the attic downward into the living area and increases the home's cooling load. The use of ventilators such as turbines with power fans that turn on automatically at preset temperatures is an effective way to curb this attic heat problem. See Fig. 3-3.

An attic fan or a ceiling fan is another ventilation device that can cut your air conditioning costs (Fig. 3-4). An attic fan draws air in through the house windows, takes it through louvers in the ceiling, and exhausts it through the attic. Many people successfully use attic fans as a substitute for air conditioning on all except the hottest summer nights.

When planning air conditioning, you must think about several other factors. If your home already has a duct system installed for warm air heating, there may be some problems in effectively retrofitting that system to accommodate central air. See Chapter 5.

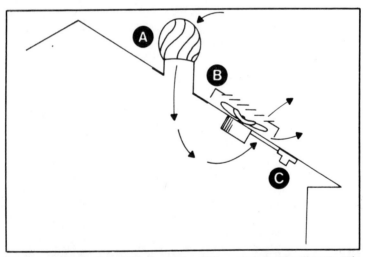

Fig. 3-3. Summer air conditioning costs will be reduced with adequate attic ventilation. Ventilation exhausts the extremely hot air that builds up in the attic and draws in relatively cooler outside air. This prevents built-up heat in the attic from radiating downward into the house and adding to the cooling load. A thermostatically controlled power vent system turns on the attic exhaust automatically when the attic temperature reaches a preset level. (A) The turbine vent. (B) A power exhaust vent. (C) A thermostat that controls the power vent.

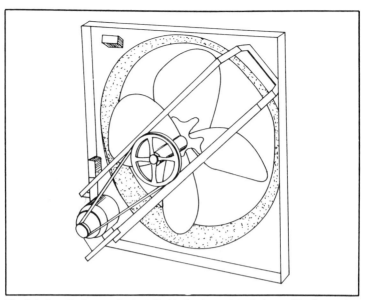
Fig. 3-4. An attic fan can be installed in the home to cut air conditioning costs.

You must decide whether you want central air or room air conditioners. Central air gives you more even cooling through the home, but it may be more expensive to operate in some cases. Sometimes you can use room air conditioners together with central air to save energy. For example, a room air conditioner installed in a much-used living area can keep that space cool while the temperature is permitted to rise elsewhere in the home.

## INSULATION AND WEATHER STRIPPING

The importance of insulation and weather stripping in the overall heating and cooling picture of a home is overlooked all too often. Studies have shown that the most effective way to cut energy costs is to insulate the home and weather-strip around doors and windows. Generally these things can be done at a low cost, and the energy savings can be substantial. Although these subjects are beyond the scope of this book, don't overlook their importance in planning the overall energy system for a home. Effective insulation and weather stripping will reduce the size of the central heating and cooling unit required for a home.

## FUEL COST COMPARISONS

One of the most important elements of selecting a heating system today is cost of operation. Everyone wants and needs a heating system that will reduce utility bills.

The following formula will tell you how much heat per dollar you will obtain from any fuel:

$$C = \frac{F \times E}{P}$$

C = cost of heat in Btu per dollar;
F = Btu value of the fuel per purchasing unit;
E = heating system efficiency;
P = price of fuel in dollars per purchasing unit.

By plugging into the formula the values for different available fuels, you can arrive at a figure of Btu per dollar for each fuel. The fuel that is the best value is the one that gives you the most Btu per dollar.

## Price

The "P" value in the formula is the cost per unit of fuel in dollars. You can obtain the cost of your fuel from your fuel supplier or from a recent bill. Remember that some fuels, particularly electricity, are billed in graduated rates. As your usage increases, the price per unit declines. The figure you are interested in is the price for the last unit purchased each month. Your fuel supplier will be able to help you estimate the fuel unit costs for your home.

To make a good decision about which fuel is best for you in the long run, estimate the expected future increases of various fuels relative to each other. Unfortunately, this is almost an impossible task, but it is one worth thinking about. In establishing a unit price, be sure to include all adjustments and taxes.

## Btu Value

The "F" value in the formula is the Btu value of the fuel per unit purchased. Table 3-1 will tell you what the Btu per unit is for each common fuel. For example, heating oil is purchased by the gallon. A gallon of No. 1 fuel oil has 136,000 Btu of heat energy. To determine the precise Btu content for LPG gas, which may be propane, butane, or a mixture of the two, contact your supplier.

## Btu Values and Wood Heat

If you are considering using wood heat as a primary or secondary heat source and you want to know whether this will save you money, you can use the formula. You must make some adjustments in dealing with the Btu value variable.

The nature of wood makes estimation of its Btu per unit an inexact process. While all woods have about the same number of Btu per pound—8600—wood is not commonly sold by the pound. Wood usually is sold by the cord—a volume measurement. Softwoods weigh less per cord than hardwoods, so softwoods have fewer Btu per cord than do hardwoods. This fact must be considered when purchasing softwoods as a heating fuel. Table

#### Table 3-1. Btu Values per Unit for Common Fuels.

| | | |
|---|---|---|
| Natural Gas | Cu. Ft. | 1,000 Btu |
| | Thousand Cu. Ft. (Mcf) | 1,000,000 Btu |
| | Therm (100 Cu. Ft.) | 100,000 Btu |
| Propane | Gallon | 90,000 Btu |
| Butane | Gallon | 130,000 Btu |
| No. 1 Fuel Oil | Gallon | 136,000 Btu |
| No. 2 Fuel Oil | Gallon | 140,000 Btu |
| Electricity | Kilowatt hour (Kwh) | 3,413 Btu |
| Hardwood | Cord | 20 to 22 million Btu |
| | Pound | 8,6500 Btu |
| Softwood | Cord | 12 to 14 million Btu |
| | Pound | 8,600 Btu |
| Coal | Ton | 20 to 22 million Btu |
| | Pound | 10,000 to 11,000 Btu |

3-2 shows the number of Btu in an average cord of several common types of firewood. The Btu available for heating a living space is less than the amounts shown in Table 3-2 because of the heat energy used to evaporate moisture in the wood. In seasoned wood the available Btu will be about 15 to 20 percent less than the amounts shown.

All firewood contains some moisture, and this moisture utilizes some of the wood's heat to evaporate it. Therefore, the amount of Btu per cord shown in Table 3-2 must be reduced to account for the amount of heat lost in the evaporation process. In seasoned wood this loss will be about 15 to 20 percent. In "green" wood the loss can be 40 to 50 percent. To account for this moisture loss in the formula, simply take the amount of wood that is available for heat and multiply it by the Btu value of the wood you are using as shown in Table 3-2.

For example, if you are burning seasoned oak with an estimated moisture content of 15 percent, the wood available to heat the home is 85 percent. Multiply 22 million Btu times 85 percent:

$$22,000,000 \times .85 = 18,700,000$$

#### Table 3-2. Btu Heat Content for Firewood.

| Wood Variety | Number of Btu per Cord (in Millions) |
|---|---|
| Ash | 20 |
| Birch | 22 |
| Elm | 17 |
| Hickory | 25 |
| Maple | 20 |
| Oak | 22 |
| Pine | 13 |

Thus, in this cord of wood there are 18.7 million Btu of heat available.

## Efficiency

Determining the efficiency of the heating system is a crucial element in proper use of the fuel cost formula. It is difficult to determine the efficiency of a heating system. Efficiency depends on a number of variables including design, tuning, proper adjustment, and even the method of measurement. Establishing the "E" value for the formula becomes an educated guess.

Table 3-3 gives you an idea of the operating efficiencies for several types of warm air heating systems. These figures consider the loss of heat through the duct system, so they may appear to be low.

A new, well-tuned furnace system will operate at the high end of the efficiency spectrum. An older tuned furnace will operate in about the middle, and an older untuned furnace will function at the lower end of the scale.

## How to Figure Your Heating Costs

Now that we have shown you the formula and the variables that plug into it, let's work through an example. You can do this for your own heating system. If you are considering several different types of heating systems, you can use the formula to compare the relative cost of operating each type of system.

Suppose you are considering installing a natural gas furnace. It will be a new furnace, so its efficiency will be at the top end of the efficiency rating shown in Table 3-3. You can get an efficiency estimate from the furnace supplier, but beware of "sales puff" that may inflate efficiency claims. Efficiency in operation during a heating season will be less than laboratory tests, and some heat will be lost in the duct system. For this example, we will set efficiency at 70 percent.

Assume the fuel costs 4 dollars per thousand cubic feet (mcf), or 40 cents per therm. The Btu value per thousand cubic feet is 1 million Btu.

Table 3-3. This Chart Gives You a General Idea of the Operating Efficiencies of Common Heating Systems, Taking into Account Losses Through the Duct System. Newer Well-tuned Units Will Be at the High End of the Scale, While Older Untuned Units Will Be at the Low End.

| Heating System | Efficiency |
|---|---|
| Gas furnace | 50 to 70 perccent |
| Oil furnace | 50 to 70 percent |
| Electric furnace | 85 to 90 percent |
| Electric room heaters | 90 to 100 percent |
| Wood furnace | 40 to 70 percent |
| Electric heat pump | 120 to 200 percent |

Working through the formula, you come up with the following calculations:

$$C = \frac{F \times E}{P}$$

$$C = \frac{1,000,000 \text{ Btu} \times .70}{4.00 \text{ dollars}}$$

(Remember to express percentages as hundredths using the decimal point. Thus, 70 percent becomes .70 in the formula. Also, remember to express the cost in dollars. If you were figuring natural gas by the therm and it cost 40 cents per therm, that would be ".40 dollars" in the formula.)

$$C = \frac{700,000 \text{ Btu}}{4 \text{ dollars}}$$

$$C = 185,000 \text{ Btu per dollar}$$

Thus, in this example natural gas costs 185,000 Btu per dollar.

If you are calculating the Btu per dollar for wood using this formula, remember to account for the reduction in the wood's Btu output according to moisture content. The top line of the formula would read:

$$C = \frac{F \times E \times (1 - \text{moisture content})}{P}$$

If the wood is seasoned wood with about 20 percent moisture, this formula would be:

$$C = \frac{F \times E \times (1 - .20)}{P}$$

$$C = \frac{F \times E \times .80}{P}$$

## HEAT PUMPS AND EFFICIENCY

The efficiency of heat pumps is expressed a little differently than that of conventional heating systems. A heat pump might be "200 percent efficient." The maximum efficiency for anything is 100 percent. Efficiency figures for heat pumps, though, are calculated on the basis of how much heat the heat pump produces compared to the heat an electric resistance heating system would produce using the same amount of electricity. Thus, a heat pump that is "200 percent efficient" produces twice as much heat for the electricity consumed as would an electric heating system.

The heating efficiency of a heat pump over an entire heating season is expressed by the Seasonal Performance Factor (SPF). The SPF of the heat pump that is 200 percent efficient is 2.0. A perfectly efficient electric heater would have an SPF of 1.0. The higher the SPF, the more efficient the heat pump.

Another measurement sometimes used to express heat pump efficiency is Coefficient of Performance (COP). This figure is a less meaningful figure for comparing heat pump efficiences than the SPF. The SPF is a *seasonal average* whereas the COP generally is a laboratory measurement at a given outdoor temperature. Because the seasonal efficiency of a heat pump depends on the regional climate, the SPF will consider this variation if it has been calculated for a particular region.

The SPFs in most parts of the United States generally are between 1.25 and 2.0, depending on the region and the unit's design. The SPFs in your region for particular heat pump models you are considering should be available from heat pump dealers and suppliers.

When using the fuel cost formula to figure the Btu per dollars output of a heat pump, simply use the SPF figure in place of the efficiency figure. If the heat pump you are considering has an SPF of 2.0, the formula would be:

$$C = \frac{F \times 2.0}{P}$$

## SELECTING A HEAT PUMP

You have already been introduced to some of the numbers that will help you compare heat pump performance. The SPF tells you the average seasonal efficiency of the heat pump, and this figure is most useful when it is based upon your region of the country. The COP gives you an efficiency rating based upon a particular temperature.

Heat pump heating efficiencies vary for different parts of the country because of the way a heat pump works. A heat pump uses refrigeration techniques to remove heat from outdoor winter air and to release this heat into the living area. When outdoor temperatures drop below the freezing mark, so does the heat pump's ability to remove heat from outdoor air. When this happens, supplementary heaters of conventional design come on to make up the difference. On many heat pump models these supplementary heaters are electric resistance heaters, which operate much like an electric furnace. Naturally this reduces the heat pump's overall efficiency.

Significant advances in heat pump design make heat pumps suitable for most parts of the United States today. If you live in northern regions with harsh winters, be aware of possibly lower heat pump heating efficiencies in those climates.

Look at the manufacturer's COP and SPF figures for your area when selecting a heat pump. The higher these figures are, the more efficient the unit. A very large unit installed on a relatively small house will have a relatively high SPF. That unit will be oversized and will operate inefficiently overall, especially during the summer cooling season.

The cooling efficiency of a heat pump is measured similarly to air conditioners. A heat pump is rated with an Energy Efficiency Ratio (EER) for the cooling cycle. The higher the EER, the more efficient the cooling cycle for the unit.

# Chapter 4

# Heating-Cooling System Basics

There are three types of central heating systems: the *heating furnace,* the *heating and cooling furnace,* and the *heat pump* (also called the *reverse-cycle refrigeration system*).

## HEATING AND HEATING-COOLING FURNACES

The heating-only furnace has but one cycle—the heating cycle. If air conditioning is desired, it must be installed using window air conditioners.

Heating—cooling furnaces, on the other hand, have two cycles—heating and air conditioning. The heating-cooling furnace provides for central air conditioning in the summer months by allowing the burners to turn off so the air will pass by the heat chamber without being heated. The condenser turns on and begins pumping refrigerant into the evaporator, cooling the air as it passes through the furnace. The cool air will then use the same fan, ducts, and return air system as that used by the hot air in the winter. Most furnaces sold today have the capacity to work as heating-cooling furnaces if the owner desires central air conditioning. These furnaces are installed with the coil case (the part of the furnace housing the evaporator coils used to cool the air) attached. If the owner wants central air conditioning, the evaporator coils are inserted and other necessary changes are made to allow for it. If the owner does not want central air conditioning, the coil case is still normally installed with the furnace, without the evaporator coils. Instead of a heating-cooling system, the owner has a heating-only system. The installation of the coil case, however, means that the owner can, at any time, convert to central air conditioning rather easily.

Several differences are apparent between the two systems. The heating-cooling furnace will have a larger fan motor to facilitate the circulation of the heavier cool air in the summer. The heating-cooling furnace will also have a fan relay to bypass the fan limit switch. The fan limit switch controls the fan on the heating cycle by sensing the amount of heat in the heat chamber and switching on the fan when the heat chamber is hot enough. When the system is cooling, however, the fan limit switch would never turn on the fan, so a fan relay is installed for that purpose.

The coil case is a metal enclosure in the furnace that houses the evaporator coil. A heating-only furnace will not need a coil case, although it may have one, as previously discussed.

## HEAT PUMPS

A heat pump is basically an air-conditioning system that can be made to work in reverse. It has two coils—one inside the house and one outside—just like an air conditioner. When the heat pump is air conditioning, the inside coil is the evaporator and the outside coil is the condenser, as in the normal air conditioning system. The evaporator takes the heat from inside

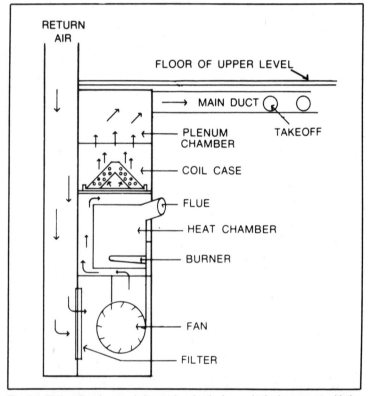

Fig. 4-1. This upflow furnace is located under the house in the basement, with the duct system running under the floor of the upper portion of the house. The arrows indicate the air flow through the system. If this upflow furnace were installed in the main level of a house, the main duct would be in the attic, and the return air would flow under the floor joists.

the house to the condenser, where the excess heat is dissipated into the outside air. When the system is heating, the coils switch. A reversing valve makes the inside coil become the condenser, and the outside coil the evaporator. Now the evaporator takes heat from the outside air and deposits it in the house at the condenser. The heat pump is now acting as an air conditioner in reverse. The usual air conditioner removes heat from inside the house and dissipates it outside. The heat pump, on heat cycle, removes heat from the outside and dissipates it inside.

## AIR FLOW IN FURNACES

To change the temperature of the air to the desired condition, the air must be in an enclosed area such as a room or house. To achieve the best quality in the conditioned air, it is usually necessary to draw in some outside air periodically to circulate with the air already moving inside the building. The purpose of this is to remove the odors and germs that are picked up in the air as it is circulated continuously in the same space. Certain facilities, such as hospitals and nursing homes, have regulations demanding that a specified amount of outside air be brought in and circulated.

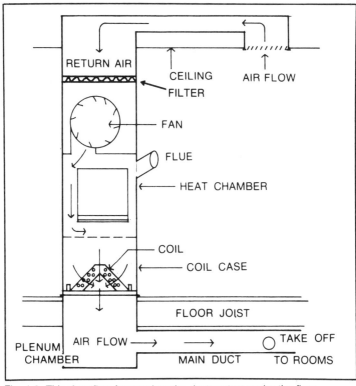

Fig. 4-2. This downflow furnace has the duct system under the floor.

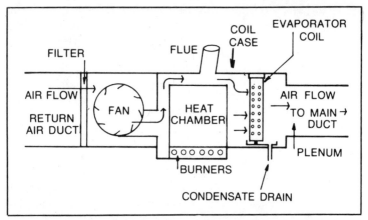

Fig. 4-3. This horizontal furnace may be used in the attic or crawl space under the floor. Notice that whether a furnace is upflow, downflow, or horizontal, the air flow through the furnace is the same.

Figures 4-1 through 4-3 show the basic heating-cooling furnaces. We will briefly consider the role of the major parts of the furnace here, and later in the chapter, we will go into more detail on each part.

The fan is used to move the air through the system. It pushes the air through the ducts and keeps the air circulating in the rooms. A squirrel-cage fan is the type normally used in central heating and cooling systems (see Fig. 4-4). There are two kinds of squirrel-cage fans: belt driven and direct drive.

The air moves from the fan past the heat chamber. Inside the heat chamber are the burners (on a gas or oil furnace) and the heat exchanger. The burners warm the walls of the heat exchanger. The air flowing through the heat exchanger picks up this heat and is warmed. In this manner the air can be heated without coming into contact with the burning fuel.

If a cooling coil is used, it will be located next to the heat chamber. The cooling coil is a part of the air conditioning unit on a heating-cooling furnace. The cooling coil, also called the evaporator, should have some sort of drain pan to carry the condensed water away from the furnace.

The plenum chamber is made of sheet metal and connects the furnace to the main supply duct. If the duct system is in the attic, the plenum chamber will extend above the furnace, through the ceiling, and into the attic, where it will connect to the main supply duct. On a downflow furnace the plenum chamber will extend below the furnace and will connect to the main supply duct below the floor (Figs. 4-1 and 4-2).

The main supply duct carries the air from the plenum chamber to the individual ducts, or runs. The main supply duct—often called the main duct, supply duct, or main trunk line—is the largest duct. It supplies all the runs which, in turn, take the air to each room. The main duct will extend from the plenum chamber to the connection, or takeoff, of the last run.

The runs are connected to the main duct and take the air to each room. The duct system can be located under the floor joists or in the attic. When a cement floor is used, the duct system is laid out first and cement is poured over it.

To keep recycling the air, some method has to be provided to return the circulated air to the unit for reheating or recooling. This is done with a return air duct. Connected at the bottom of the unit (or at the top on a downflow furnace), the return air duct draws air out of the room and takes it back to the furnace, where it is filtered and goes through the process again.

The following are the basic parts of a heating-cooling system in the order in which air circulates through them:

- Fan
- Heat chamber/heat exchanger
- Coil case/cooling coil

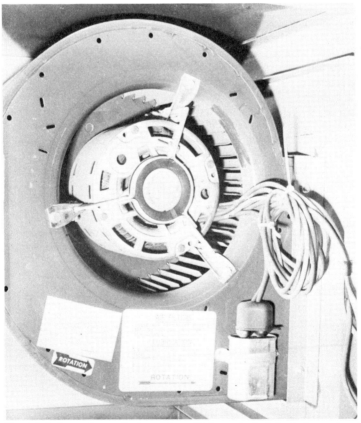

Fig. 4-4. A direct-drive squirrel-cage fan, with the motor installed in the center of the fan blades.

- Plenum chamber
- Supply duct
- Runs
- Room to be heated or cooled
- Return air duct
- Filter

From the last item the cycle goes back to the first item. These parts are the same in any heating-cooling system, whether the furnace is upflow, downflow, or horizontal.

## UPFLOW, DOWNFLOW, AND HORIZONTAL FURNACES

The upflow furnace is usually located in a basement, with the duct under the floor of the main part of the house. It may also be located on the main floor of a house, with the duct system in the attic. Upflow means that the air flows up through the furnace, from bottom to top. How the parts are arranged is shown by Fig. 4-1.

The downflow furnace (also called a counterflow furnace) is located above the duct system, with the furnace above the floor and the duct below the floor. The fan is located at the top of the furnace, and the air moves down, from top to bottom. The arrangement of parts in a downflow furnace is exactly opposite of those of an upflow furnace (see Fig. 4-2).

The horizontal furnace is normally used in the attic or under the floor. The fan is located at one end of the furnace, and the heat chamber, cooling coil, and plenum chamber are attached in a horizontal line (Fig. 4-3). Assembled downflow (counterflow) and horizontal furnaces are shown in Fig. 4-5.

## DIFFERENT FURNACES FOR DIFFERENT FUELS

There are several different types of furnaces: oil, gas, electric, wood, coal, and combinations of these. Each type of furnace is designed with special features required for the type of fuel it will burn. Each has its own operating technique, and each type of system has its own advantages and disadvantages.

### Gas Furnaces

The two main types of gas furnaces are natural gas and liquid petroleum (LP) gas. Basically the natural gas furnace is the same as the LP furnace, except the gas valves and orifices are different. The controls and operation of the two types of gas furnaces are the same. Natural gas has a lower pressure, and this makes it necessary to have a larger orifice than for LP gas. Some furnaces, but not all, are made so they can be changed from one gas to the other. This is done by changing the orifices and gas valve with a conversion kit.

If you live in a town which has a natural gas line, and it is available to you, this is often the cheapest fuel. If you live some distance from the city,

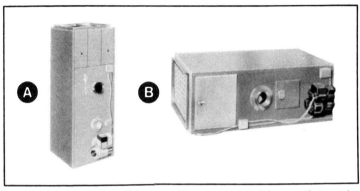

Fig. 4-5. (A) A downflow oil furnace. (B) A horizontal oil furnace that can be located in the attic or crawl space of a house to conserve living space (courtesy Rheem Air Conditioning Division, City Investing Company, 5600 Old Greenwood Road, Fort Smith, AR 72903).

you may not have access to natural gas. It will be necessary to use LP gas or some other fuel.

Liquid petroleum gas is stored in a liquid form, but the furnace burns the vapor. When LP gas is stored in a tank, a certain percentage will be in vapor form. As this vapor is gradually burned by the furnace, the tank's pressure will be reduced, and more of the LP will change to vapor by "boiling off." This fuel "boils" (changes from a liquid to a gas) at about −50°F.

In operation, the pilot light lights the burners when the thermostat calls for heat. After the burners are lit and the heat exchanger reaches a certain temperature, the fan controls come into operation. They will close the electrical circuit to the fan, turning it on and causing it to blow warm air through the duct system into the rooms of the house. The return air duct system removes the air from the rooms and returns it to the furnace to be reheated. This cycle continues until the rooms are warm enough, at which time the thermostat opens the control circuit and shuts off the gas valve. With the gas valve shut off the burners go out, and the heat chamber cools down. The fan control will open the electrical circuit, and the fan will stop.

## Oil Furnaces

Oil furnaces are similar to gas furnaces, since they have a fan control as well as a control that shuts the pump or burner off if the furnace gets too hot. The burner itself differs from a gas furnace in that the oil has to be pumped through the system, and the pressure has to be great enough to atomize the oil as it passes through the nozzle.

When the thermostat of an oil furnace indicates heat is needed, a high voltage transformer will produce an arc, igniting and burning the oil which is sprayed through this arc. It is very important to the operation of the furnace that these electrodes be set in the proper position (Fig. 4-6).

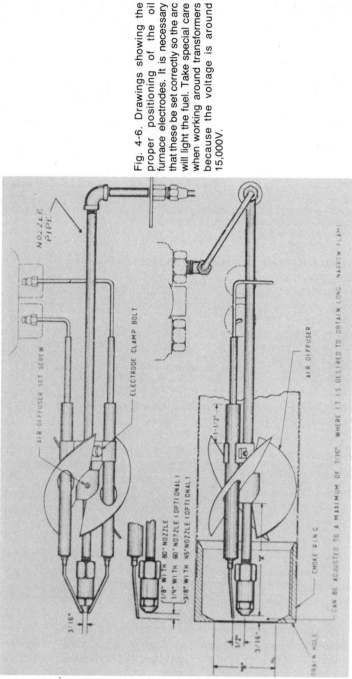

Fig. 4-6. Drawings showing the proper positioning of the oil furnace electrodes. It is necessary that these be set correctly so the arc will light the fuel. Take special care when working around transformers because the voltage is around 15,000V.

Soot buildup in the flue is another common problem with an oil furnace. This often occurs because the burner is improperly set. Frequently the air adjustment is out of position, or the pump has failed to put out the required amount of pressure. Either of these will cause soot to collect in the furnace and flue, resulting in oily smoke backing up in the house.

### Electric Heat Systems

The different types of electric heating systems include ceiling cable, baseboard heaters, and electric furnaces. Each of these has its advantages and disadvantages, but the practicality of any electric heating system depends on the price of electricity in the area.

**Ceiling Cable.** Electric ceiling cable is installed by stapling a heating cable to the ceiling of the house (Fig. 4-7). This is usually referred to as resistance cable. Plaster or some other recommended cover is put over the cable after it is installed.

When using this type of heat, special care must be taken to prevent breaking the cable. It is necessary to know where the cable runs before installing a new light fixture or anything else on the ceiling. When the cable is installed, it will have to be taken around anything that may be attached to the ceiling.

**Baseboard Heaters**. These heaters are placed around the rooms according to the amount of heat needed for each particular room. They

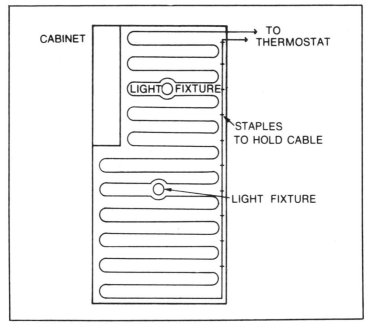

Fig. 4-7. Resistance electrical ceiling cable installed in the ceiling. Notice that the ceiling cable detours around obstructions such as light fixtures and cabinets.

operate by heating the air as it moves over a calrod element in the heater. As the air is warmed, it rises, and the cooler air takes its place. Heaters of this type are purchased according to wattage ratings. Advantages to baseboard and ceiling cable are that they do not need a flue or ducts, and each room has its own thermostat to control the level of heat. Baseboard heaters are excellent for supplementary room heating, as discussed in Chapter 15.

Baseboard units are easy to install because they simply fasten to the wall at the floor and connect to the previously installed electric circuit. To provide current for the baseboard heaters, it is possible to either bring current down through the wall from wires overhead or through the wall from underneath the house, depending on the existing wiring. The existing wiring should be checked to see that the wire is large enough to supply the heaters. If not, new wire will have to be installed. Any time electric heat is to be used it is especially important to have the house well insulated. Builders will often provide extra insulation if they know the house will be heated electrically.

Since ceiling cable and baseboard heaters do not have a duct system, they may be installed with less cost than other systems. It must be remembered, however, that if air conditioning is to be added at any time it may be desirable to have a central air conditioning system that requires a duct system. Therefore, it might be wise from a planning standpoint to install a furnace with a duct system so that central air conditioning can easily be added later.

**Electric Furnaces**. Electric furnaces operate with resistance heating elements installed in the furnace in banks, the number of these depending on the amount of heat needed. Unlike baseboard heaters or ceiling cable, which are room heating systems, an electric furnace requires installation of a duct system to carry the heat to the various rooms. It is also necessary to have a fan to force the air where it is needed. An electric furnace will not require a flue.

## COMPARING HEATING AND HEATING-COOLING SYSTEMS

The differences between a heating furnace and a heating-cooling furnace are few since the basic designs are the same. There are five main differences. The heating-cooling systems are distinguished by the following: a larger fan motor, a coil case, a heating-cooling thermostat, a fan relay connected in the electrical circuit, and an insulated duct system.

### Duct System

The reason for insulating the duct system of a heating-cooling furnace is for the protection of the duct system and house structure. During the summer when cold air is moving through the ducts moisture from under the house will condense on the ducts, causing water droplets to form on them. While this condition is tolerable for a while since the ducts are galvanized, eventually this moisture will cause the duct system to rust.

Another effect of this condition is high humidity under the house that can cause the floor and beams to rot.

This condition can be corrected in one of two ways. The first is to insulate the ducts. This may be practical, however, only if a heating-cooling furnace is being installed immediately after the house is built. Conversions from a heating-only furnace where uninsulated ducts have already been in operation for some time to a heating-cooling system can present problems, because insulating those ducts can be difficult. We recommend insulating all the ducts in a heating-cooling system with foil-backed insulation (recommended size is 1 inch of insulation inside the duct).

The second method is recommended only for an older house where central air conditioning is being added to the existing furnace. This method is to simply air condition under the house in the crawl space area during summer. This is not as involved or expensive as it might seem at first, because cool air is only blown under the house during the time the air conditioner is on. Since the house is already cool underneath, not much cool air is lost, especially if the foundation is tight. It is necessary to close all vents and openings in the foundation when using this arrangement. Put a duct takeoff onto the main duct, but do not attach a run to it. This opening can be left open, or you can provide for some method of regulation so it can be closed during the winter. If you want to regulate it, you could fashion a cap to go over the opening, or you might put a regulating floor register in the duct. Blowing air under the house is the most practical way to prevent sweating if you already have the ducts installed and have a tight foundation. In installing the duct system in a new house, however, you should insulate the ducts.

### Fan Motor

Cold air is heavier than warm air and has to be moved from place to place mechanically, whereas warm air will circulate from room to room by itself. Cold air will lie in one area and not move into another room; it will "pile up" instead of circulating. Because of these characteristics, the furnace fan will have to be speeded up in the summer months when the air conditioning unit is operating. The faster fan speed requires a larger motor. It is to accommodate the air conditioning cycle, therefore, that heating-cooling furnaces are required to have larger fan motors than heating-only furnaces.

### Coil Case

The coil case is simply the metal enclosure where the cooling coil is housed. It is sometimes necessary to add a coil case to convert a furnace which is already installed in the house. This would be the situation if the owner of a heating-only furnace later decided he wanted central air conditioning. In this case the furnace must be removed to put in the coil case, and the return air duct must be shortened enough to allow the furnace to go back in with the coil case's extra length. The easiest method of taking care of the coil case problem is to simply install the coil case when the furnace is installed, whether plans call for air conditioning at the time or not. When this is done, the coil can be easily inserted at any time. It saves the trouble of cutting the return air duct to make room for the coil case if the owner later decides he wants central air conditioning.

## Wiring

If the furnace has only two wires going to the thermostat, two more will have to be added before an air conditioner can be installed in the present system. One of the additional thermostat wires goes out to the air conditioning unit, and the other goes to the fan relay. If there is no fan relay, one will have to be installed.

Figure 4-8 shows the wiring diagram for a heating and cooling furnace. The R and C connections on the terminal board in front of the transformer are the main connections. The wire from the R terminal runs to the R connection, or feeder line, on the thermostat. In the diagram the terminal is connected to a heating thermostat. The right side of the diagram shows how the terminal is connected to a four-terminal heating-cooling thermostat.

The diagram also shows how the fan relay is wired into the circuit. The relay is connected by two blue wires, which are 24V. The power comes from the junction box and is 120V. Care must be taken when hooking this circuit together because there is a 24V coil and a 120V circuit is completed through the same relay. A wiring diagram for a heating furnace is shown in Fig. 4-9.

## FILTERS

Filters are very important in the heating and cooling system because they clean the incoming air and prevent dirt, lint, and other material from reaching the internal parts of the unit. Without the filters, dirt and lint will collect on the coil fins, thereby stopping up the openings and reducing air flow. If this occurs, the heating or cooling unit will not function properly. Naturally, since the filters remove all this dirt from the air they eventually become stopped up themselves and require cleaning or changing. If a filter is allowed to go unattended, it will eventually reduce the efficiency of the heating or cooling unit to the point of stopping the air flow and rendering the unit useless. To prevent this, a filter should be cleaned or changed three or four times during the year.

There are several places where these filters are located. Usually they can be found in the fan compartment at the point just before the air goes through the fan, or in the return air duct where the return air goes to the heating or cooling unit. See Figs. 4-1 and 4-2. Some units have a filter grille that can be removed to expose the filter.

## Disposable and Washable Filters

There are three main types of filters: disposable, washable, and electronic filters. The disposable filters are made to be used once and thrown

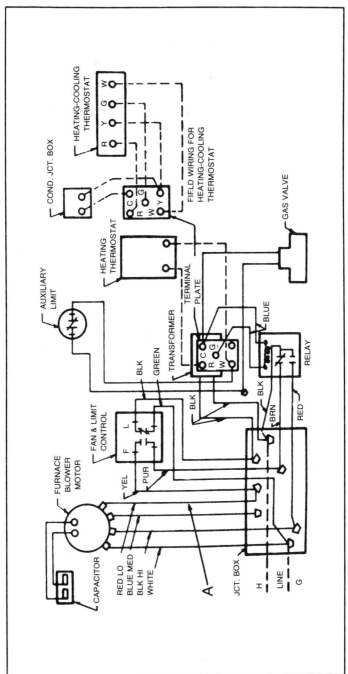

Fig. 4-8. The wiring diagram for a heating-cooling furnace.

73

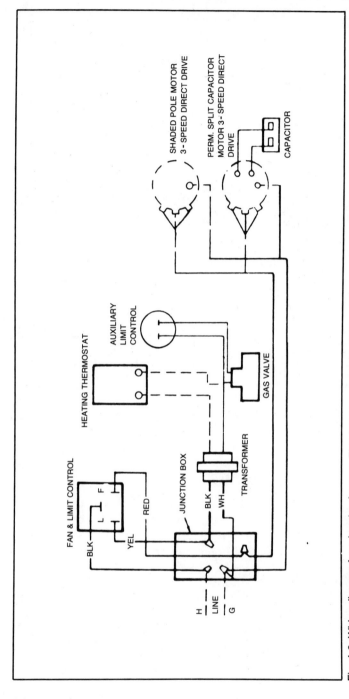

Fig. 4-9. Wiring diagram for a heating furnace. This furnace uses a fan limit switch, two-wire thermostat, and a direct-drive motor. The drawing shows how a running capacitor is connected, if one is used.

away when dirty. It is best not to wash them or blow them out with compressed air if they are dirty. They are normally made of fiberglass with a cardboard frame. The fiberglass removes the lint and dirt from the air that passes through. The size of the disposable filter is marked on one end of the filter. These can be purchased in most sizes at any building materials supplier and at many department and hardware stores.

Washable filters are made with aluminum filler or plastic foam. These filters can be cut to fit the system being used, or they can be bought precut. Care should be taken when washing these because they are prone to tearing. They should be washed with warm water and soap or cleaned without soap by running warm water through them in the direction opposite the air flow so that the force of the water removes the lint and dirt.

When replacing either a washable or disposable filter, take care to choose a replacement the same size as the old filter. If there is a 1-inch fiberglass filter in the furnace, replace it with a 1-inch filter, not a 2-inch filter, because a 2-inch filter will restrict some of the air flow and cause problems. The use of any size other than the original could cause furnace overheating because the air cannot carry the heat away fast enough. Sometimes a dirty filter will cause the same problem. Normally the only type of filter requiring replacement is the disposable type, and its size is marked on one end of the cardboard frame.

## Electronic Filters

Electronic air filters (Fig. 4-10) are the most delicate and the most expensive of the filters we will consider. Electronic filters have the advan-

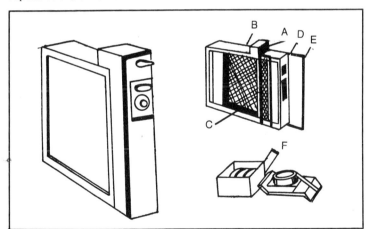

Fig. 4-10. Electronic air filter. (A) Electrical interlock that discharges cells to prevent electrical shock. (B) Frame which holds filter in the duct system. (C) Prefilter which stops lint and large material from entering the cells. (D) Cells that collect dirt. (E) After-filter which provides for even air flow. (F) Solid-state power pack with quick-disconnect and performance indicator to tell when the filter needs attention.

tage of trapping dust and pollen particles that would pass through an ordinary filter. For this reason an electronic air filter might be just the ticket for persons having allergy and hay fever problems. The main disadvantage is the cost of such a filter.

The electronic air filter operates in two steps. First, the air flows through a disposable or washable filter to remove all the large dirt, dust, or lint particles. The first filter is much like those covered so far in this section, and it will have to be cleaned and serviced at regular intervals as previously discussed. The real cleansing of the air comes in the second step, when the air passes through electrically charged plates which trap even the most minute dirt and dust particles. This is accomplished by using a stepup transformer that increases line voltage from 120V to 12,000V or more. This high voltage is applied between pairs of grounding plates (one positive and one negative) and causes an electrical attraction of all particles passing through this field.

The particles are captured on the plates, which means it will be necessary to clean them from time to time to ensure the best service. They should be cleaned with a special cleaning fluid or with automatic dishwasher cleansing solution following factory recommendations. The electronic filter usually has an indicator to tell the owner or serviceman when the filter needs service.

It is important to take care when working with electronic filters because of the high voltage. Usually a switch shuts off the power when the service door is opened, but the electricity should be disconnected just to be sure.

## FANS AND THEIR MAINTENANCE

There are two types of fans commonly used in heating-cooling systems: bladed and squirrel-cage fans.

### Bladed Fan

The bladed fan is normally used for the condensing-unit fans. It is cheaper to build than the squirrel cage and will move several cubic feet of air per minute. This type of fan is not very satisfactory, however, for moving air through the duct system because a bladed fan has to be excessively large to get the same amount of air through the ducts as a squirrel cage fan.

A bladed fan can be mounted on the motor shaft with the motor behind the condensing unit to pull the air through the condensing unit and blow it over the compressor. These fans can be used as single fans, or several can be used together. Sometimes a shaded-pole motor is used for bladed fans.

The bladed fan's main disadvantage, besides the size requirement, is the increase in noise that accompanies any increase in fan speed.

### Squirrel-Cage Fans

There are two types of blades usually found in squirrel-cage fans: the forward-type blade and the reverse type (Fig. 4-11). The blade can be

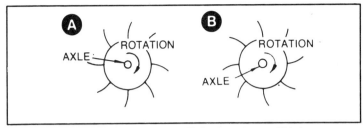

Fig. 4-11. (A) Forward-curved blades. (B) Backward-curved blades.

mounted on the motor shaft (direct drive), or it can be driven by a belt. The direct-drive fan is shown in Figs. 4-12 and 4-13, while the belt-driven fan is shown in Fig. 4-14. The type of blade used depends on the load and the amount of air circulation needed. Squirrel-cage fans usually are used to move air through the furnace duct system.

### Direct-Drive Fans

A direct-drive fan has the fan blades mounted directly onto the motor shaft, and the motor mounts inside the fan blades. See Fig. 4-13. A shaded-pole motor normally is used with direct-drive fans.

When service is needed, the cage and fan can be removed as a unit, or the motor itself can be removed if this is easier. Usually these jobs are not difficult, because there are only a few screws or bolts holding the fan in place. If this type of fan is used on a downflow furnace, the flue pipe may have to be removed before the fan can be removed. The wires that connect to the motor can be removed by pulling the connections loose at the motor. These should be marked so the correct wire will be replaced on the proper connection.

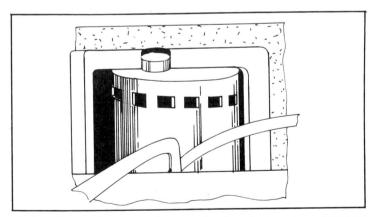

Fig. 4-12. This is a diagram of a direct-drive fan shaped-pole motor, as seen from above, as the fan cage is being removed. The speed of the motor can be changed by switching two electrical leads. A motor this dirty should be cleaned and lubricated to prolong its life.

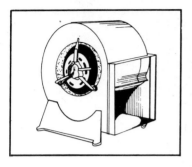

Fig. 4-13. A direct-drive squirrel-cage fan. The motor fits inside the fan blade assembly in a universal mounting bracket. When the motor is replaced, the new motor will have to be checked to be sure it will fit inside the cage and brackets.

The chief disadvantage of the direct-drive fan is that a motor must be used to replace an old motor that has the same size shaft and same speed as the old motor. The new motor does not have to be identical in all respects to the old motor, but it must fit inside the cage and in the mounting brackets.

### Belt-Driven Fan

The belt-driven squirrel-cage fan has a blade mounted inside the cage on a shaft. A belt pulley is attached to one end of the shaft, and the motor is mounted on the other side of the cage. A belt connects the fan shaft to the motor (Fig. 4-14). A split-phase motor is most often used with belt-driven fans, although several types of motors can be substituted.

The belt-driven fan can be removed from the furnace assembly by taking out the holding bolts and pulling the cage out. The motor can sometimes be taken off without removing the entire fan assembly. The motor can usually be removed without dismantling the flue pipe, although on a downflow furnace the flue pipe may have to be removed to remove the fan cage.

### Adjusting Fan Speed

Proper furnace operation depends on the fan operating at the proper speed. In some situations a fan speed set improperly can create numerous problems. If a fan is not set fast enough, the furnace may not create enough air pressure in the duct system to deliver air properly through the system. This can create cold rooms at the end of the duct runs. It also makes the furnace waste heat. Fan speed set too fast is less frequently a problem. Whistling sounds at the duct registers and excessive room drafts from the registers are signs of a fan set too fast.

The speed of a shaded-pole motor can be changed by switching wires in the junction box of the furnace. Changing these wires adds or removes some of the motor windings from the circuit. Follow carefully the furnace manufacturer's wiring diagrams and instructions. A wiring diagram for a shaded-pole motor is shown in Fig. 4-15. Shaded-pole motors generally are used in direct-drive fan applications.

Belt-driven fans normally adjust the fan speed by using a variable speed pulley on the motor shaft. This pulley can be adjusted to make the

Fig. 4-14. A belt-driven squirrel-cage fan assembly used on furnaces. The pulley on the motor can be adjusted by loosening screw A and turning flange B to increase or decrease the speed of the fan. Belt tighteners should be readjusted to compensate for changes in the belt's slack.

V-belt ride higher or lower in the groove, which decreases and increases the fan speed. Adjust the pulley by removing the belt and loosening the setscrew on the pulley shaft. The two halves of the pulley rotate, and by turning them you can change the size of the pulley groove. To increase the fan speed, turn the outer flange clockwise to make the pulley groove larger. Turning the flange counterclockwise makes the pulley groove smaller and decreases the fan speed. After the pulley has been adjusted, replace the belt and readjust the belt tension by changing the motor position.

## Fan Maintenance

The fan and motor should be cleaned and lubricated regularly. The fan blades should be cleaned, and dirt on the motor should be brushed away. You may have to remove the fan and motor assembly to do this cleaning. If the fan motor bearings have an oil hole or a cloth wick to permit oiling, place a few drops of SAE 10 oil in the appropriate spot. Lubricating the motor bearings located in each bell housing at each end of the motor will extend their life considerably.

You also should periodically check the fan belt for wear and tension. If you can move the belt more than about 1 inch when exerting light pressure upon the belt, it needs to be tightened.

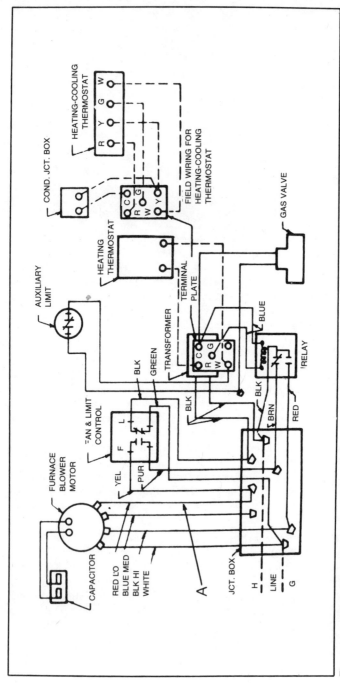

Fig. 4-15. Furnace field wiring diagram. At the left are the wiring connections for a direct-drive fan motor, also called a shaded-pole motor. To vary the speed of the fan, interchange the red and blue wires.

# Chapter 5

# Installing Central Heating Systems

There are several things to be considered when installing a system: the furnace location, the condensing unit location, electrical wiring for the unit, the flue for the furnace, the placement of the refrigeration lines, and the method of removing water from the coil case.

### FURNACE AND CONDENSER LOCATION

The best place for the furnace is in the center of the building to be heated. This helps to keep the air flow in the duct system at the proper level, while at the same time maintaining the most even heating possible throughout the building. This arrangement is very often not possible, and the furnace will have to be installed at one end of the building. The two branches of the main duct coming out of the plenum will be different sizes because of uneven air flow requirements. One of the branches may also be graduated—reduced in size—as the runs are taken off to the rooms. The reason for different sizes—one branch being graduated—is to maintain enough static pressure in the branches of the main duct to push the air into all the rooms.

The condensing unit, or condenser, should be placed within a specified distance from the coil case, depending on the manufacturer's recommendations. (Usually this is not over 35 feet from the coil. If more distance is required, larger refrigerant lines may be needed due to the pressure drop in the low-side lines. Information on this can be obtained from the wholesale or retail air conditioning dealer.)

The area around the condensing unit should be free of shrubs, over-hangs, or anything that will obstruct the air flow over it. The unit should be at least 18 inches from the outside wall. When choosing the side of the house on which to place the unit, remember that the hot afternoon sun will reduce the efficiency of the unit. Noise from the condensing unit should also be a factor in placing it. You would probably not want it under a window or by a patio.

## WIRING

To prevent overloading, a furnace or heating-cooling system is normally run on a separate electrical circuit and fused by itself. The wire will have to be a three-wire cable unless the unit is built for 120V. Check the instruction manual for specific wiring diagrams and wire size. If the unit is more than 50 feet from the breaker box, a heavier wire may have to be used to run electricity to the unit to minimize wire heat loss and voltage drop over the longer distance. The greater the distance between the unit and the breaker box, the more it will cost to run electricity to the unit.

## FLUE

Any combustible fuel (oil, LP gas, etc.) must have a flue to exhaust the fumes and gases resulting from combustion. (Electric furnaces will not have a flue.) The flue must extend above the roof of the house so it will draw properly. If it does not extend above the roofline there could be a downdraft. This would fill the house with smoke and gas. A taller building nearby may create irregular air currents which can make downdrafts. Even normal wind currents can cause downdrafts. On some days the flue may draw properly, and on other days a downdraft may occur. Most of these problems can be corrected by using a flue cap.

To determine if the flue on an oil furnace is creating a downdraft, check the door and burners. If the smoke is coming back through these, a downdraft could be present. On a gas furnace check the opening where the flue connects to the heat chamber. If a downdraft is present, heat will come out of this opening when the furnace is running. Another way to check for a downdraft is to hold a smoking rag next to the flue pipe. If the smoke goes up the flue, the flue is working properly; if not, a problem is present somewhere in the flue. Be sure to check all possible sources of trouble such as a plugged or disconnected flue pipe.

The materials used in the construction of flue pipe vary according to the manufacturer and use of the pipe, but they must be noncombustible. Flue pipe is normally constructed using two pieces of pipe, one with a smaller diameter than the other. These two pipes are separated and insulated from each other by a nonflammable material such as *asbestos*. In other words, the smaller pipe fits inside the larger pipe, and an insulating material is sandwiched between them. Because of the insulation, there is no danger of a fire being caused by the flue when it is passed through a roof or ceiling. Under no circumstances should ordinary metal pipe be used for the flue.

Flue pipe has self-locking joints to make an airtight seal. The pipe comes in different sizes and shapes for different installations. Before installing any flue, be sure to check the city building codes for fire regulations or specific restrictions.

## TYPES OF DUCT SYSTEMS

There are four basic types of duct systems recommended for heating and cooling installations: the graduated system, the extended-plenum system, the radial system, and the loop system. Sometimes combinations of these types are used.

### Graduated Duct System

The graduated system is normally used in a long house when the furnace is placed at one end of the house. This type of duct system would be ideal for a ranch-style home that is 70 feet long with the furance at one end.

Figure 5-1 shows the design of a graduated duct system. As the runs are taken off the main duct, its size is steadily decreased. The purpose for this reduction is to keep a steady static pressure built up in the main line. As the runs are taken off the main line, its pressure would reduce if the main duct were left the same size. By decreasing the size of the duct the pressure is kept high enough to push the warm air to the distant rooms. Generally the main duct should be reduced after every two runs are taken off, but sometimes the runs may connect too close together to allow a reduction after the second run. In this case three runs may be taken off before reducing (Fig. 5-2). Taking off more than three runs before reducing, however, will result in greatly reduced air flow in the last runs.

### Extended-Plenum Duct System

An extended-plenum system is shown in Fig. 5-3. With this system the plenum chamber is far enough from one end of the house to make it necessary for main ducts to be run from the plenum chamber in two directions. This system is normally used in combination with the graduated duct system discussed previously. If the plenum chamber were in the center of the house with the same number of runs off each main duct, the two main ducts would be the same size coming out of the plenum chamber and

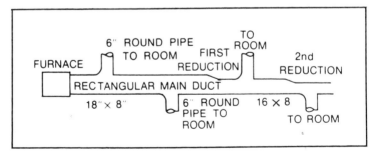

Fig. 5-1. A graduated duct system. Each time two runs are taken off the main duct, the main duct is reduced in size. This is to maintain the static pressure in the line to ensure the same air flow for the runs at the end of the duct as the ones closest to the furnace.

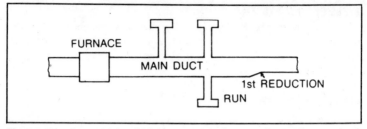

Fig. 5-2. Here the second and third runs are too close together to allow a reducer to be put between them. In this case it is permissible to take off the third run before reducing. If a fourth run were taken off before the reduction were made, however, that run would have a greatly reduced air flow due to a too-low static pressure.

would reduce in size as the runs were taken off. In most instances the plenum chamber is not in the center, and the two main ducts are not the same size (Fig. 5-3).

### Radial Duct System

Each run goes directly from the plenum chamber to a room with the radial duct system (Fig. 5-4). This type of system is easy to install because all of the runs are usually the same size and made of round pipe and elbows. The main considerations are the length of each run and the number of elbows in each run. The rooms most likely to be cold in this type of system are those fed by a duct with a large number of elbows and turns. Each turn increases the duct's resistance and decreases its air flow. For this reason the runs should be as straight as possible, and the furnace should be located in the center of the house. When installing a radial duct system, the runs that are longer and have more elbows should be larger. Dampers should be used in the runs to adjust the air flow.

### Loop Duct System

The loop duct system (Fig. 5-5) is normally used in a concrete floor. The furnace is at one end of the house, and the main duct goes in two

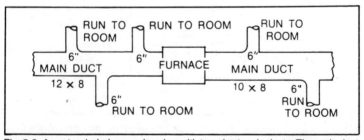

Fig. 5-3. An extended-plenum chamber with two short main ducts. The main duct on the left serves more runs than the one on the right. It is necessary in this situation to make the main duct larger on the side from which more runs are extended.

84

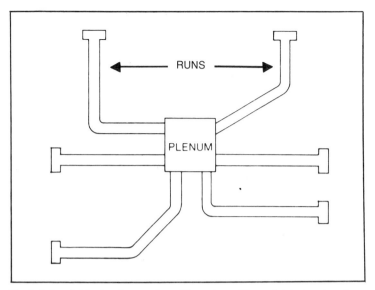

Fig. 5-4. A radial duct system as viewed from above. The radial duct system does not use main ducts, but has the runs connected directly to the plenum.

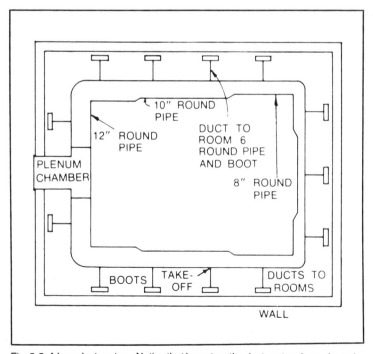

Fig. 5-5. A loop duct system. Notice that here, too, the duct system is graduated.

directions from the plenum chamber. As the runs to the room are taken off, the main duct size is reduced to keep the static pressure up. Round pipe should be used in this type of system to keep the cement from crushing the duct when the floor is poured, and the ducts should be tied down to prevent them from floating up when the cement is poured.

## SIZING THE DUCT SYSTEM

The size of the duct system is very important in a heating or cooling system. If one component of the duct system is the wrong size, none of the rooms will be heated or cooled properly.

The two most important physical properties that must be taken into consideration in sizing a duct system are air pressure and friction loss. The air pressure in a duct system is the force that keeps the air flowing through the duct and circulating in the rooms. The air pressure is created by the fan in the furnace as it blows the air through the furnace and into the duct system. The pressure in the duct system is exerted in all directions against the walls of the ducts and is called static pressure.

### Friction Loss

Friction loss refers to the loss in pressure the moving air experiences as it passes through the duct system. This loss occurs because of the resistance presented to the moving air by the sides of the duct system. Increasing the air flow will increase the friction loss, and decreasing the air flow will decrease this loss.

Friction loss can be reduced by using round ducts instead of square ducts, but there are disadvantages to using round duct in some systems. For instance, round duct takes up more vertical space to move a given amount of air than does rectangular duct. Table 5-1 shows that to move 1000 cfm (cubic feet per minute) of air requires a 16-inch round duct, but a rectangular duct 8 × 24 inches will also do this job, using only half the vertical space of the 16-inch round duct. If the duct were installed in a basement or crawl space under a house where 16 inches of vertical space could not be spared, the 8-inch-thick rectangular duct would have to be used.

A balance must be reached between getting a duct system too large (and not having enough static pressure to push the air through the ducts) and, on the other hand, getting a duct system too small (and having too much resistance and friction loss to allow the air to flow).

When planning a duct system, there are several other considerations. Things like the length of the main duct, the number of runs taken off the main duct, insulation for the main duct, 90° turns in the main duct, and the furnace air flow output must all be considered.

### Furnace Air Flow

The first step in sizing the duct system is finding out some important facts about the furnace. The physical dimensions of the furnace are needed

**Table 5-1. Required Duct Size as Function of Air Flow.**

| Flow, cfm | Supply Duct Size (Inches) Round | Rectangular | |
|---|---|---|---|
| 100 | 6 | 8 × 6 | 6 × 8 |
| 125 | 6 | 8 × 6 | 6 × 8 |
| 150 | 7 | 8 × 6 | 6 × 8 |
| 175 | 8 | 8 × 6 | 6 × 8 |
| 200 | 8 | 8 × 8 | |
| 225 | 9 | 8 × 8 | |
| 250 | 9 | 8 × 8 | |
| 300 | 10 | 8 × 10 | 10 × 8 |
| 350 | 10 | 8 × 10 | 10 × 8 |
| 400 | 10 | 8 × 12 | 10 × 10 |
| 450 | 12 | 8 × 14 | 10 × 10 |
| 500 | 12 | 8 × 14 | 10 × 10 |
| 600 | 12 | 8 × 14 | 10 × 12 |
| 700 | 12 | 8 × 16 | 10 × 14 |
| 800 | 14 | 8 × 20 | 10 × 16 |
| 900 | 14 | 8 × 22 | 10 × 18 |
| 1000 | 16 | 8 × 24 | 10 × 20 |
| 1200 | 16 | 8 × 28 | 10 × 22 |
| 1400 | 18 | 12 × 22 | 10 × 26 |
| 1600 | 18 | 12 × 24 | 10 × 28 |
| 1800 | 20 | 12 × 26 | 10 × 32 |
| 2000 | 20 | 12 × 28 | 10 × 34 |
| 2500 | 22 | 12 × 32 | 10 × 40 |
| 3000 | 24 | 12 × 38 | 14 × 32 |
| 3500 | 26 | 12 × 42 | 14 × 38 |
| 4000 | 28 | 14 × 44 | 16 × 38 |

so the furnace room can be built to house it. The normal air flow for the furnace should be determined, as well as the correct size for the plenum and return air duct. The furnace instruction sheet or the dealer can supply you with this information. Table 5-2 shows typical data for a furnace.

Figure 5-6 shows how the duct system is sized for a furnace with maximum output of 1150 cfm. The maximum output figure is the amount of air that flows through the furnace when the fan is on high speed. When the fan is on low speed, the furnace will have a lower output. The furnace will operate on high speed for air conditioning, on low speed for heating. Duct sizing should always be based on the maximum air flow.

The furnace in Fig. 5-6 is placed off center from the middle of the house. There are three runs taken off from the east side of the plenum and six runs taken off from the west side. The best way to arrange this duct

Table 5-2. Size of Furnace, Plenum Chamber, and Return Air Opening.

| | Model | Input (Btu/hr) | Output (Btu/hr) | Drive Type | Maximum cfm |
|---|---|---|---|---|---|
| Heaters | FG-1 | 140,000 | 112,000 | Belt | 1150 |
| | FG-2 | 160,000 | 128,000 | Belt | 1320 |
| Cooling Units | FGC-1 | 140,000 | 112,000 | Belt | 1600 |
| | FGC-2 | 128,000 | 128,000 | Belt | 2000 |

| | | Furnace | | | Plenum | | Return Air | |
|---|---|---|---|---|---|---|---|---|
| | Model | Height(in.) | Width (in.) | Depth(in.) | Width (in.) | Depth (in.) | Width (in.) | Depth (in.) |
| Heaters | FG-1 | 61 | 25 | 28½ | 23 | 20½ | 23 | 23 |
| | FG-2 | 61 | 25 | 28½ | 23 | 20½ | 23 | 23 |
| Cooling Units | FGC-1 | 61 | 25 | 28½ | 23 | 20½ | 23 | 23 |
| | FGC-2 | 61 | 25 | 28½ | 23 | 20½ | 23 | 23 |

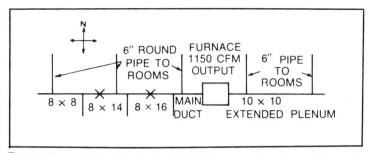

Fig. 5-6. How a duct system is sized. Each X represents reducers in the main duct system. The 10 × 10-inch extended plenum will carry enough air for the three runs on the east end. On the west side, the 8 × 16-inch main duct extends to the first reducer and is reduced to 8 × 14. The final reduction is to 8 × 8 inches.

system is to use an extended plenum (single-size main duct) on the east side and a graduated main duct on the west side.

### Air Flow Through Runs

To find the air flow through each of the runs, divide the furnace output in cubic feet per minute by the number of runs: 1150/9 = 128. This is about 125 cfm per run. Table 5-1 shows that to carry 125 cfm a 6-inch pipe is needed. Using a 6-inch pipe for all the runs means that the total air flow through the main duct to the three runs on the east side of the plenum will be 375 cfm (3 × 125). Rounding up to 400 cfm, Table 5-1 shows that a 10 × 10-inch rectangular duct or a 10-inch round pipe should be used for the main duct on the east side. The table also shows that a 12 × 8-inch duct can be substituted for this purpose if more space is needed underneath the duct.

On the west side, as already mentioned, a graduated main duct would be in order. Recall that a graduated main duct is reduced in size after every second run is taken off. This is done to maintain a sufficient level of static pressure in the main duct to push the air into the rooms that are fed by runs at the end of the main duct.

Since we have already allocated 400 cfm to the east side, we now have 1150 − 400 = 650 cfm for the west side. Rounding up to 700 cfm, this requires an 8 × 16-inch or a 10 × 14-inch main duct on the west side.

The reason for rounding up in all the sizing calculations is that if the ducts are a little large and the static pressure in the system should turn out to be too low to allow proper air flow, the fan motor can always be speeded up a little to increase the pressure. On the other hand, if the system is sized too small, the cold air will not circulate through the duct system when the air conditioner is operating. For this reason it is always better to round up rather than round down.

If an 8 × 16-inch duct is used to leave the plenum chamber, it should be extended enough to feed two runs. By the time two runs are taken off, static pressure will be reduced enough to require that the main duct be reduced in size to maintain a steady pressure for the diminished air flow through the main duct. Once 250 cfm (two runs × 125 cfm per run) are taken off for the two runs, that leaves 450 cfm to be carried by the remaining duct. The main duct should be reduced to an 8 × 14 behind the point where the second run is removed.

The 8 × 14-inch reduced main duct should be extended enough to allow two more runs to be taken off; then the main duct is reduced to carry 200 cfm (450 cfm − 250 cfm). An 8 × 8 is now used to feed the last two runs.

Instead of extending an 8 × 16-inch duct from the plenum for the main duct, a 10 × 14-inch duct could have been used and then reduced to 10 × 10 inches. Normally the main duct is reduced in width and the height is kept the same throughout the distance of the main duct. This is merely a matter of preference, though, and the height of the main duct can be reduced instead of the width, or they can both be reduced. The main considerations here are what duct sizes are available from the dealer.

## Sizing the Runs

The runs to the rooms should be at least 6-inch pipe (usually round pipe is used for the runs), and frequently 7-inch pipe will be used for the runs, depending on the furnace cfm output and the desired air flow to each room. Occasionally 5-inch round pipe is used for some installations, but we do not recommend using 5-inch pipe except in rare instances, because to air condition with 5-inch pipe is almost impossible. The cool air will not move through the smaller pipe due to excessive friction. If 5-inch pipe is installed on a central heating system and the owner later decides he wants to add central air conditioning, the runs will all have to be changed. Even without the air conditioning considerations, 6-inch pipe will heat more evenly and will create less air noise than 5-inch pipe.

If too much air flows through a register it may cause some noise, with the air whistling as it goes into the rooms. This condition can be corrected by slowing the fan speed a bit. Another way is to add an extra run to the main duct, which will have the effect of reducing the pressure and, hence, the air flow in all the runs off the main duct. The best place to take this extra run would be into a large room served by only one run. The added run will give more air flow to this room and make it warmer.

Figure 5-7 shows how the duct system would be sized for a furnace installed in one end of the house with the main duct extending from the furnace in only one direction. The cfm flow for the furnace in the previous example is rounded up to 1200 cfm, and the chart shows that an 8 × 28-inch or 10 × 22-inch duct would be needed to carry this air flow. The diagram shows that the main duct is reduced in size after every second run is taken off.

In our earlier example we took the number of ducts running off the main duct and divided that number into the furnace air flow to determine the air flow through each run. To be sure that you get the optimum air flow per run, however, it will be necessary to choose the number of runs by trying to

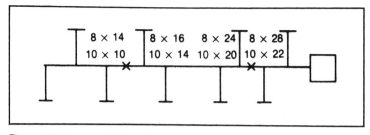

Fig. 5-7. Here the furnace is placed at one end of the house and a graduated main duct is used. In this case, figure about 375 cfm taken off (3 ducts × 125 cfm per duct) and reduce the main duct accordingly.

get a certain air flow value per run.

About 125 cfm is usually the optimum air flow per run. An air flow of 175 cfm per run can be tolerated and will work reasonably well with air conditioning; 200 cfm per run could drive you out of the house with the air noise from the registers. Thus, an 1800 cfm output furnace would warrant 1800/125 = 14 runs. If using 14 runs were not practical, it would be acceptable to use a different number of runs so long as the air flow per run remained in the 100-175 cfm range.

## PLANNING THE REGISTERS

When a heating-cooling furnace is installed, plan on using heating-cooling registers to bring the air into the rooms. The difference between a heating register and a heating-cooling register is that a heating-cooling register has more free-air area to allow the cool air to move more easily.

Usually the registers are placed along the outside wall (see A and B, Fig. 5-8) and under windows by doors, because these places are where the largest heat losses are. Sometimes in planning the duct system for a house, a register will have to be placed on an inside wall (C and D, Fig. 5-8), but this should be avoided if possible. Often, however, a two-story house will have registers located on inside walls for the upper stories, because running the ducts up to the second story through the outside walls would mean that there would be no insulation between the duct and the outside wall of the house. Naturally this would cool down the heated air going up the duct to the upper rooms.

Another good place to locate a register is in front of a glass or sliding door to the outside. Here a floor register is used. Usually if any room is larger than 12 × 12 feet, there should be two runs going to the room, and two registers will have to be installed somewhere in the room.

Any irregularities in the amount of air going through each run or any unevenness in the amount of heat going to each room can be corrected after installation by adjusting the dampers on the individual registers. These adjustments will allow more or less air to pass through the registers as needed.

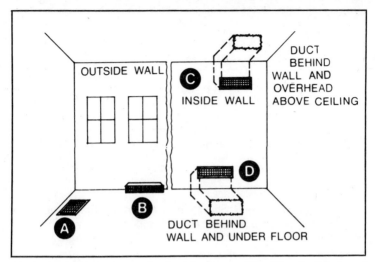

Fig. 5-8. For outside wall applications the floor register (A) or the baseboard diffuser (B) can be used. Notice that the floor register is away from the wall a few inches, while the baseboard register is against the wall. For use on inside walls the high wall register (C) or low wall register (D) can be used.

## DISTRIBUTION DIFFUSERS AND THEIR PLACEMENT

The lowly heat register, or diffuser, may not seem very important to the overall heating and cooling system, but it is. Diffusers are extremely important from the standpoint of appearance and performance. The diffuser has to be designed to do several jobs at the same time. It must direct the air flow into the room at the proper angle, conceal the register opening, control the amount of air that enters the room, and keep the air noise at a minimum.

Diffusers are connected to the part of the duct system known as the supply outlet, or boot. The supply outlet is merely the place where the run comes through the wall or floor in a room to supply air to that room. The diffuser connects to the supply outlet to help control and distribute the air flow as well as cover the boot.

There are many types of diffusers that can be used; we will consider a few of them. Some typical diffusers appear in Fig. 5-9.

Floor registers fit flat on the floor, several inches away from the wall. These are used when it is necessary to have the heat coming from in front of a wall. For example, if an outlet is needed under a picture window with draperies, a baseboard diffuser should not be used. When the drapes are closed they will cover the outlet. A floor diffuser will solve this problem by moving the air supply away from the wall and drapes.

With a baseboard diffuser the heat outlet comes through the floor next to the wall. The diffuser will fit over this opening up against the wall.

The ceiling diffuser is used if the duct system is run above the rooms rather than under the house. There are round and square ceiling diffusers on the market. A ceiling diffuser will distribute the air in all directions in the room, instead of just one or two directions as with the floor and baseboard registers.

High and low wall registers are used when the runs from the main duct come up through the wall. The low wall registers are just above the baseboard, and the high wall registers may be 6 feet or more above the floor.

When deciding on the location for the registers, the following will serve as a general guideline. If the heating season is longer than the cooling season, or if there is no air conditioner in the central system, the registers are usually placed on the floor (Fig. 5-10). On the other hand, if the cooling season is longer than the heating season, the registers are placed high in a wall or in the ceiling whenever possible. By placing the supply outlets higher in the room, the cool air will be allowed to drift down over the occupants.

In a return air grille the direction of air travel is reversed. The air comes from the room and goes through the return air grille on its way to the return air duct. The return air grille is larger and has more space for the air to pass through than most other registers. It must allow an adequate amount of air to pass through to the furnace. The return air grille must be at least as large as the return air duct. It is placed in the return air opening to conceal the return air duct.

Most diffusers have louvers that are either preset or adjustable. On preset louvers the direction of the air flow cannot be adjusted, but some

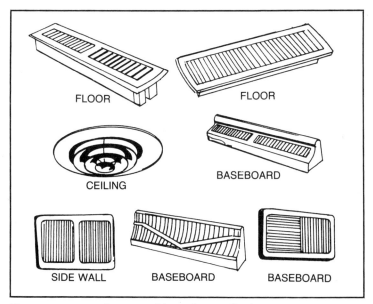

Fig. 5-9. Types of diffusers used for various applications.

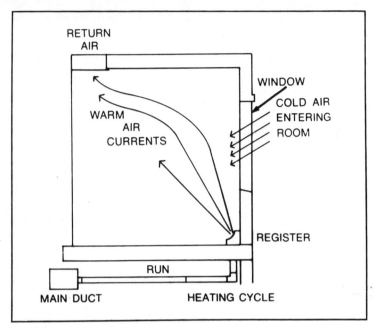

Fig. 5-10. Heating cycle. The warm air enters the room through the baseboard register and mixes with the cool air entering the room through the windows and walls. The air flows toward the return air register in the ceiling, and the return air duct carries this cooler air back to the furnace.

have a damper inside that can be set for the amount of air flow desired. Adjustable louvers on a diffuser allow a person to change the direction of the air flow and circulation. Some allow setting the amount of air flow and some do not.

The registers made for both heating and air conditioning have more space between louvers than plain heating registers. The extra space is necessary since the heavier cool air is more difficult to move through the louvers than warm air. With adjustable louvers on the diffuser this is not a real problem, because the space between the louvers can be increased to allow easier air flow.

### RETURN AIR SYSTEMS

The return air duct is just as important as the main duct. If the return air duct is too small the whole system will suffer. The furnace will not heat correctly because the fan can't move enough air to the unit, and the cooling system will also be affected. A return air system that is too small is a common fault with furnace installations, so the return air ducts and grille should be checked if the furnace is not working properly.

In a previous example the output of the furnace was 1150 cfm, and we rounded this figure to 1200 cfm. The return air duct must be able to carry

94

1½ times as much air as the main duct, so the size for the return air should be large enough to carry 1800 cfm. Table 5-1 shows that to carry 1800 cfm a 12 × 26-inch or 10 × 30-inch duct should be used.

To install a return air duct, a hole will have to be cut in the ceiling in a hall or main room near the furnace. A grille will be put in this hole. For a downflow furnace (Fig. 5-11) the return air duct will run from this grille, through the attic, to a hole above the furnace. (The return air duct would be under the floor for an upflow furnace.) The duct goes through the hole and fits onto the top of the furnace. The return air grille will cause problems if it is too small. The air moving through a small grille will make whistling and other noises. Be sure the grille has an air flow rating 1½ times the output of the furnace.

Round duct is often used for the return air because it is cheaper to buy, the space it requires is often unimportant in return air systems.

If you have a ranch-type house and the furnace is in the center, it might be more desirable to remove the air from both ends. In this case the return air duct is divided, and a return air grille is placed at each end of the house. With a 1200 cfm furnace each return air grille is placed at each end of the house. With a 1200 cfm furnace each return air duct should be capable of handling 900 cfm (1200 × 1½ = 1800, 1800/2 = 900 cfm). A 14-inch round pipe going to each grille will do the job.

Another way to install the return air system is to span two ceiling or floor joists with sheet metal, making a duct out of the space between joists. The main thing to consider is the space between the joists. For instance, a 2

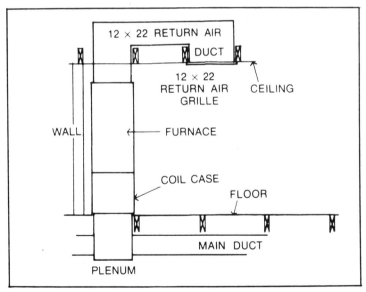

Fig. 5-11. The stack arrangement of a downflow furnace. Notice how the return air duct is run.

× 8-inch joist on 16-inch centers has a distance between two joists of only 14¼ inches and a height of 7¾ inches. Table 5-1 shows that less than 450 cfm of air could pass through the opening. Using two of these spaces would provide about 900 cfm capacity. The space between the floor or ceiling joists should never be used for a main duct or a run unless it is first lined with sheet metal.

Sometimes a return air duct is placed in one end of a closet and a false wall used as one side of the duct. Occasionally a partition wall can be used for a return air duct. The bottom or top of the wall has to be cut out and connected with the main return air duct. Make sure that all openings are sealed so air from the outside can't enter the duct. Remember that partition walls are not very thick, and one space 14¼ × 3⅝ inches will not allow much air flow (about 125 cfm per opening).

## BRINGING IN FRESH AIR

To guard against the circulated air inside a house becoming stale, fresh air is often brought in from the outside and mixed with the return air. If the fresh air is to come from the attic, you should be sure that there is no other system such as a range hood vent, sewer vent, or bathroom exhaust blowing air into the attic. The installation procedure is basically the same whether the fresh air is drawn from the attic or the outside.

A 2½ × 12-inch wall stack duct or a 4-inch round duct will bring in about 50 cfm of air, an adequate amount for most systems. The fresh air duct should be attached to the return air duct and should have a screen over its face to prevent bugs and other insects from entering the heating system. A damper should be installed in this duct to control the fresh air flow. If the fresh air cannot be drawn from the attic, it will be necessary to draw it from the outside. The same basic rules apply, the only difference being that the fresh air duct will have to extend to the exterior of the house through the roof or wall.

When a gas or oil furnace is installed in a new house, lenders or building codes may require that fresh air be available for the furnace. This is to keep the furnace from burning all the oxygen out of the house and creating a potential health hazard. The required duct is not connected to the furnace duct system, but is only an outside vent installed in the furnace room. (This is different from the fresh air duct installed in the return air system.) The easiest way to meet this requirement is to cut a hole through the floor in the furnace room and put a regulating floor grille in this hole. No ducts are necessary, and the amount of air coming through the vent can be controlled easily.

## INSTALLING A FURNACE

When you purchase the furnace, the dealer should be able to supply you with size requirements for the plenum chamber and return air duct, as well as the output rating. With the output figure you can size the duct and plan the runs to the rooms. Armed with your figures, dealer information, and duct system plan, draw up a bill of materials required to install the furnace. This bill of materials will include the plenum chamber, return air duct, main duct, reducers, takeoffs, elbows, boots, insulation for the ducts, etc.

### Furnace Room

You must know the dimensions of the furnace long before it is installed, so a furnace room can be constructed. There should be adequate distance between the wall and furnace on all sides. Eight to ten inches generally is sufficient, but check local building codes.

Sometimes before the furnace is installed the furnace room's floor, walls, and ceiling should be finished. It will be much easier to finish this room before installing the furnace.

Cutting the holes in the floor and ceiling for the installation of the plenum chamber and return air duct must be done before the furnace room is finally ready for the insertion of the furnace.

Not all furnace installations will require these holes. An upflow furnace installed in the basement may not have a furnace room, but only an opening somewhere nearby in the floor above to bring the return air down. A horizontal furnace will not require any opening unless the return air is

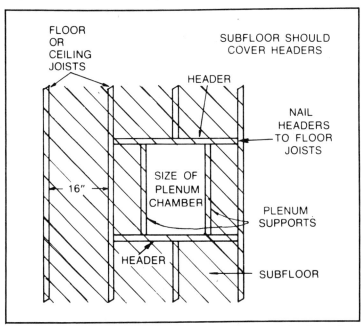

Fig. 5-12. Headers and plenum supports are installed around the plenum hole. The headers are made of the same size boards as the floor joists. When the subfloor is cut, it should cover all the floor joists, headers, and plenum supports. The hole should be cut about ½ inch larger than the biggest part of the plenum chamber.

brought through the house from a grille on the opposite side of the main living area from the furnace.

The downflow furnace will require an opening above the furnace for the return air duct and an opening below the furnace for the plenum chamber. An upflow furnace placed on the main house level will need an opening above for the plenum chamber and an opening below for the return air.

To cut the hole for the plenum chamber on a downflow furnace, set the plenum on the floor of the furnace room in its proper place and mark around it. The hole for the plenum is cut in the floor. Since this hole usually cuts through at least one floor joist, some bracing is needed to support the joist that is cut. This bracing is done by nailing headers to the joists. A header is a 2 × 6 inch board which runs at 90° angles to the floor joists and connects the cut joist to the two joists on either side (Fig. 5-12). This same procedure of measuring, cutting the hole, and installing the headers will have to be repeated to make the opening for the return air duct above the furnace.

### Installing an Upflow Furnace

An upflow furnace is usually installed in a basement with the duct system hanging from the floor joists beneath the floor of the main part of the house, but it can also be installed on the main floor of a house with the duct system in the attic (see Fig. 5-13). When the upflow furnace is used in connection with a duct system in the attic, the plenum chamber will have to extend from the furnace through the ceiling far enough to allow the main duct to connect to the plenum.

The return air duct will connect to the furnace at the bottom as shown in Fig. 5-14. The return air duct on upflow furnaces may be connected to a high-wall register and run through a wall to the furnace if the furnace is in the basement. Sometimes on basement installations the return air will be brought to the furnace through a floor grille. On main-level installations the return air duct will run through the floor beneath the furnace and go under the floor to a floor register as in Fig. 5-13.

### Installing a Downflow Furnace

The downflow furnace is usually installed above the floor with the plenum chamber extending through the floor and connecting to the main duct under the house. The return air duct runs through the ceiling and connects to the furnace top. After the plenum chamber and return air duct have been installed, the downflow furnace is moved into its place over the plenum, and the return air duct is connected.

### Installing a Horizontal Furnace

Horizontal furnaces are usually found in the attic or underneath the house in the crawl space. This system has two main advantages. Since the furnace is under the house or in the attic the space that would normally be occupied by the furnace can be used for something else. If it is installed

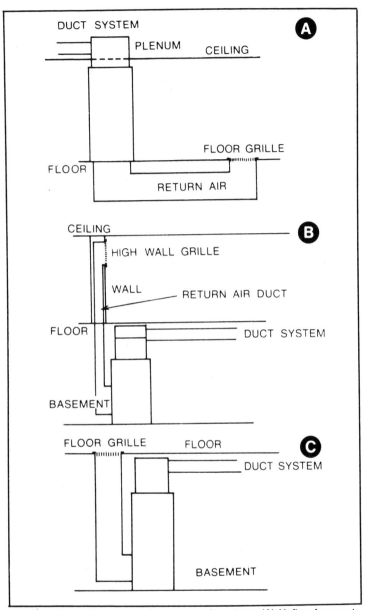

Fig. 5-13. Upflow furnaces and the return air systems (A) Upflow furnace installed in the main part of the house. The duct system goes into the attic, and the return air goes under the furnace and connects to the return air grille in the floor. (B) The furnace is in the basement, the duct system runs under the floor, and the return air is connected to a high wall register by the duct which runs through the wall of the room. (C) Alternative basement installation.

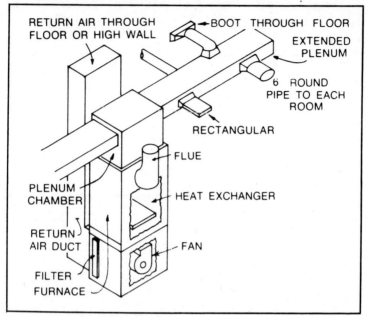

Fig. 5-14. Parts of an upflow furnace. Notice that the return air duct is connected to the furnace at the bottom.

under the house, the heat from the furnace will keep the water lines from freezing and help to keep the floors warm.

The disadvantages are in the area of service. If the furnace has to be repaired, it is necessary to crawl under the house or into the attic. If for some reason the furnace has to be removed, there has to be a service door large enough to move the furnace through. It may even be necessary on some furnaces to crawl under the house to merely change air filters. Moisture can also create problems if the house is built in a low place where water stands under the house.

The plenum chamber is installed at one end of the horizontal furnace, with the return air duct at the other. The furnace can be installed at one end of the house and a graduated-trunk duct system used to carry the warm air the length of the house (Fig. 5-15). Another way to install the furnace is to put the furnace in the center of the house at 90° angle to the duct system and run two main trunk lines from the plenum chamber as shown in Fig. 5-16.

The horizontal furnace is usually hung from the floor joists and suspended above the floor. Two horizontal furnace return air installations are shown in Fig. 5-17.

### Installing a Floor Furnace

A type of furnace that is used less frequently than the others, but nonetheless bears mentioning, is the floor furnace (Fig. 5-18). Floor fur-

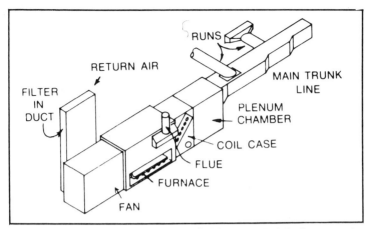

Fig. 5-15. This horizontal furnace is installed in one end of the house, and a graduated duct system is used to take the air to the runs.

naces are sometimes used in small houses where there is neither room to install a duct system nor space for a furnace. The floor furnace should be installed in the center of the house so the warm air can flow from room to room. The floor furnace is usually easier and cheaper to install than other

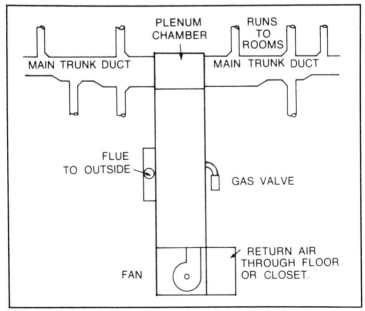

Fig. 5-16. Top view of a horizontal furnace, showing how a horizontal furnace, its plenum, and duct system are arranged if the furnace is located near the middle of the house. Here the furnace is installed at a 90° angle to the main duct branches.

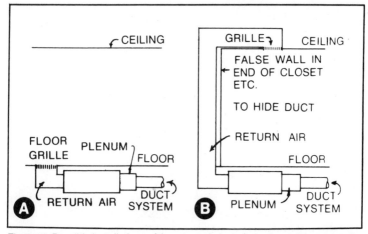

Fig. 5-17. Possible installations of the return air duct of a horizontal furnace under the floor. (A) The return air is connected to a floor grille. (B) Bringing the return air from the ceiling maintains the air flow in the room from the floor to the ceiling. To do this, the return air duct has been run to the attic through a false wall. The duct connects to a grille in the ceiling.

types because it doesn't have a blower, plenum chamber, or duct system. The return air system is built into the furnace.

Another type of floor furnace on the market has a blower than can be installed in a duct running from a room to the furnace (Fig. 5-19). This takes the cooler air out of the room and brings it to the furnace.

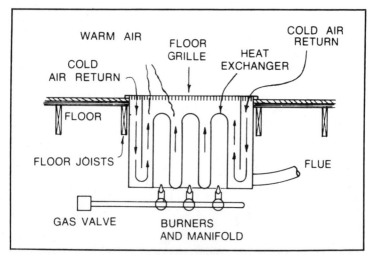

Fig. 5-18. No fan is used to circulate the air on this floor furnace; air circulation is by natural air currents. Warm air rises from the heat exchanger, and the cool air moves into the cold air return and is reheated.

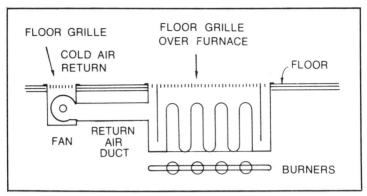

Fig. 5-19. This floor furnace has a fan and a return air duct. The fan will pull the colder air out of the room and take it to the furnace.

The disadvantages of floor furnaces relate to their air circulation. Since no duct system is used, heat is taken to the rooms only by the air currents in the house. This will center most of the heat around the furnace, and some of the rooms may be cold while others are hot.

To install this type of system, the furnace is placed in a hole in the floor cut to the size of the furnace, and a large floor grille covers the top of the furnace. The heat exchanger is typically located just under the grille.

## INSTALLING THE DUCT SYSTEM

On a downflow furnace there will be a hole in the ceiling for the return air duct and a hole in the floor for the plenum chamber. On the upflow furnace the plenum extends above the furnace. If the plenum extends through the attic, cut a hole for it. This discussion centers on downflow furnaces, but the techniques are the same for upflow furnaces.

### Installing a Plenum Chamber

Insert the plenum chamber in the hole with about an inch extending above the floor to be bent back for a flange to suspend the plenum in the hole (Fig. 5-20). If the plenum's vertical height is too much to allow it to fit (i.e., the bottom of the plenum touches the ground below the house), raise the plenum in the hole so it is above the ground at least a couple of inches. The excess can be trimmed off and the 1-inch flange fashioned as before. Be sure when trimming off the plenum that enough of the plenum chamber extends below the floor joist to connect the main duct.

Measure down the plenum from the top to mark the hole for the main duct. The main duct should hook into the plenum 2 inches below the floor joist. After measuring and marking, cut the hole for the main duct starter as in Fig. 5-21. If the main duct will extend from the plenum in both directions, two holes will have to be cut. Be sure to cut the hole on the correct side of the plenum. If the plenum is rectangular, it may not be possible to turn it

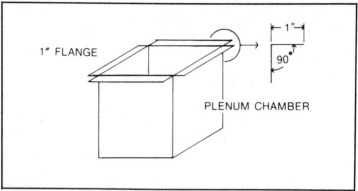

Fig. 5-20. The 1-inch flange is turned out on the top side of the plenum chamber to help hold it in position.

around. The hole in the plenum can be cut from under the floor, but it is much easier to cut it before the plenum is installed. Place the plenum through the hole in the floor and nail it down (Fig. 5-22).

### Hanging Ducts

The first step is to place the starter for the main duct in the plenum. There are commercial starters that you can purchase from your dealer to make this installation easier (Figs. 5-23 and 5-24). These have flanges (see Fig. 5-23) that anchor the starter in the plenum. The final anchoring of the starter is done with screws or pop rivets hooked through the plenum and the flanges.

Figures 5-25 through 5-28 show how the S-clamps and drive strips anchor the joints of the main duct to each other. When the starter has been installed, the second joint is attached using these strips. No pop riveting will be necessary to anchor the joints to each other.

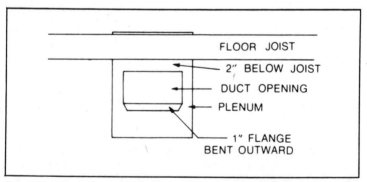

Fig. 5-21. Main duct opening in plenum. If the regular main duct section is used instead of a commercial starter, a 1-inch flange should be made at the bottom of the starter hole and bent outward at 90° to anchor the duct.

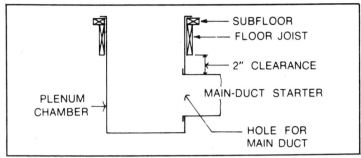

Fig. 5-22. Plenum chamber installation through floor. A 2-inch clearance is maintained between the floor joist and the main duct starter.

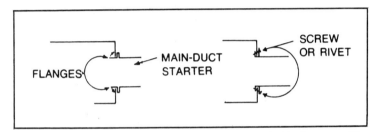

Fig. 5-23. A commercial starter is placed in the starter hole in the plenum, and the flanges are bent backward to hold the starter. The starter is anchored by pop riveting or screwing the flanges to the plenum chamber. Some commercial starters have flanges that rotate to anchor the starter to the plenum.

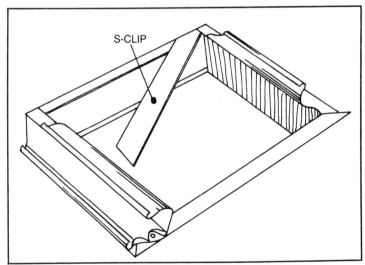

Fig. 5-24. Commercial duct starter. The starter is placed in the opening in the chamber and four S-clips snap in place to hold the edges of the duct starter to the edges of the hole in the plenum.

Fig. 5-25. Here two sections of duct are being joined together. An S-clamp has been attached to the duct section on the left, and the duct on the right has been inserted into the slot of the S-clamp. A drive strip (shown in Fig. 5-27) will be inserted on the top of the two channels and driven down the length of the duct to fasten the sections together.

The duct will now have to be hung from the floor joists temporarily. There are commercial clips and hangers that can be used for temporary purposes (Fig. 5-29), or you simply drive a nail into floor joists on each side of the duct and hang the duct from a wire strung between the nails.

The only purpose for hanging the duct at this time is to hold it up so another connection can be made. Later after the runs are connected permanent hangers should be attached. A permanent hanger can again be a

Fig. 5-26. At the top an S-clamp has been hooked onto the edge of the duct. On the left is the channel where the drive strip fits to hold the ducts together.

Fig. 5-27. The two lips running the length of the drive strip and bent toward the center hook into the two channels on the ducts (see Fig. 5-25). The tab on the end of the drive strip is bent forward at a 90° angle after the drive strip is installed to hold the drive strip in place.

Fig. 5-28. An S-clamp about 12 to 20 inches long used to hold the joints of duct together.

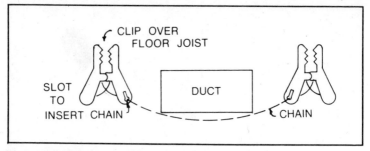

Fig. 5-29. Spring clamps sold as temporary duct hangers.

commercial product, or it can be simply some type of wire or sheet metal strap that has been nailed up (Fig. 5-30).

### Takeoffs and Reducers

At the point on the main duct where a room run is required, a takeoff is installed. The main duct should be held in position as the takeoff is marked. The duct must be lowered so the hole for the takeoff can be cut if the takeoff will go in the top of the duct. If the takeoff will connect to the side of the main duct, the hole can be cut while the main duct is suspended. Figure 5-31 shows how a takeoff is installed.

There are several types of commercial takeoffs available. Some clip into the hole that has been cut, and others have slotted metal clips that must be bent back to hold the takeoff (Fig. 5-32).

It is possible to make your own takeoffs from regular round pipe with one end crimped and the other end slotted in 1-inch slits 1 inch apart. These slits must be alternately bent inward and outward. When the homemade

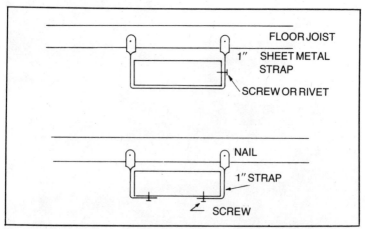

Fig. 5-30. For hanging the duct permanently, use one-inch wide scrap strips of sheet metal and nail them up at 4-foot intervals. Wire also works well.

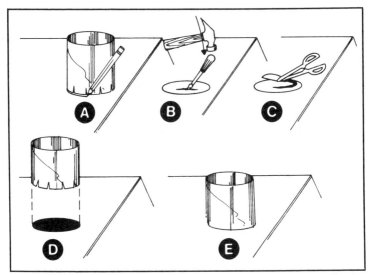

Fig. 5-31. Installation of a takeoff in a main duct. (A) Position the takeoff at the location on the main duct where you want to install it. Mark around the perimeter of the takeoff with a felt-tipped marker, a piece of chalk, or a soft lead pencil. (B) Using a screwdriver or a metal punch, start a hole in the duct large enough to begin cutting with a pair of tin snips. (C) Work from the hole, cutting out the perimeter circle with tin snips. (D) Insert the takeoff into the hole. (E) Fasten the takeoff to the main duct by folding back the tabs and anchoring it with screws or pop rivets.

Fig. 5-32. An adjustable commercial takeoff whose curve and direction can be altered by turning the joints as you would those on an elbow.

takeoff is inserted in the hole, every second tab will form an outside shoulder. The remaining tabs will form an inside flange that will later be bent backward to secure the takeoff (Fig. 5-33).

Generally the takeoff should be anchored to the main duct with pop rivets or screws. Care must be taken to cut the hole in the main duct the right size so the takeoff will fit. If the hole is cut too large, the shoulder will slip through the hole and the takeoff will not stay in position.

A reducer is used to make the size of the main duct smaller after every two, or occasionally three, runs are taken off. The reducer is a joint of duct about 18 to 24 inches long that attaches to the main duct (Fig. 5-34). The two ends of the reducer must be the same size as the two joints of duct to be connected. There are several kinds of reducers on the market, including reducers for round duct.

### Runs

The duct runs are that part of the duct system that takes the air from the main duct to the rooms. Round pipe is probably the most popular material for these runs, although square pipe can be used. To have sufficient capacity to move cool air conditioned air, round runs should be at least 6 inches in diameter.

Figure 5-35 shows how a run is put together. The runs snap together at the seams to form a sheet metal tube. You can buy insulating material made especially for duct runs that is precut to fit over the run joints. It usually is easiest to insulate the duct runs as they are being assembled.

The lengths of duct pipe that form the runs are only a few feet long. These lengths are joined together to make an entire run. The crimped end of one joint is pushed into the plain end of another joint, and the joints are fastened using screws or pop rivets (Fig. 5-36).

### Boots

The boot is the end of the run. It is the part of the duct system that connects to the room and from which air is sent into the room. There are

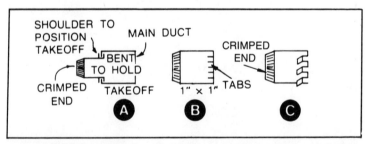

Fig. 5-33. (A) A commercial takeoff inserted in a main duct. The tabs on the inside must be bent outward to hold the takeoff. (B) A homemade takeoff can be fashioned from a short piece of round duct with 1 × 1-inch tabs cut in one end. (C) The tabs are bent inward and outward on the homemade takeoff. The outer tabs form the shoulder which fits against the outside of the main duct. A crimping tool forms the crimped end.

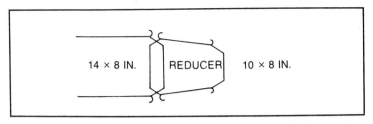

Fig. 5-34. This duct reducer connects to the main duct with S-clips and drive strips. This reducer reduces a 14 × 8-inch duct to fit a 10 × 8-inch duct.

several places the boot can come out into a room, but the most common place is along the wall at the baseboard (Fig. 5-37). If the boot is to come out at the baseboard, a hole the size of the boot must be cut in the floor from above (Fig. 5-38). In locating the exact spot to place the boot, the floor joist must be located so the boot can be attached to it. The boot is pulled through the hole from below one-half inch of the boot is allowed to extend above the floor for a baseboard register. For a flush floor register the boot is installed flush with the floor. Once in its proper location, the boot is nailed into the floor joist next to it. However, the initial installation is only temporary until the duct system is installed completely.

The boots that are installed at the baseboard are usually 2¼ × 12 inches or 2¼ × 14 inches, and they come with either 45°, 90°, or straight connections (Fig. 5-39). There are also several other types of boots for different register types. If a flush floor register is to be used, the boot must

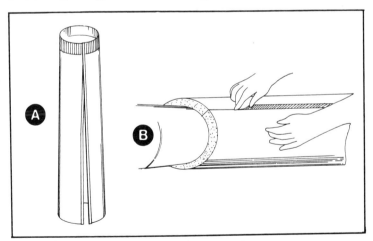

Fig. 5-35. (A) The run joints can be purchased from a furnace supply store ready to assemble. To assemble a joint, bring the two sides of the joint together. A locking seam snaps the two sides together, and a sheet metal tube is formed for a run. (B) The best time to insulate the duct runs is when you assemble them. Precut insulation can be purchased specially for this purpose, or you can use ordinary foil-backed home insulation and lots of duct tape to seal the seams.

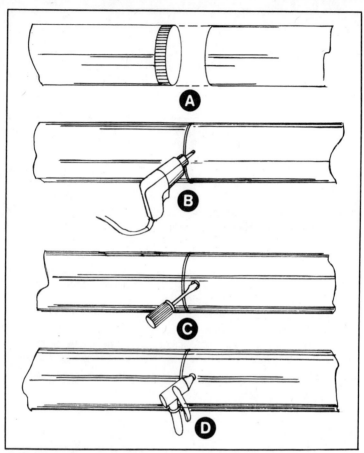

Fig. 5-36. Putting the runs together. (A) The crimped end of one run joint is placed inside the plain end of the second joint. Push the joints together tightly. (B) With an electric drill, drill a small hole through the two duct lengths. (C) These two joints are fastened with a screw or (D) with a pop rivet.

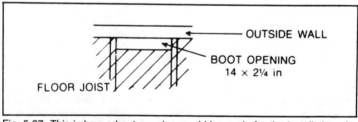

Fig. 5-37. This is how a boot opening would be made for the installation of a baseboard register. The outside edge of the opening touches the inside edge of the wall, and at least one side of the boot must be against one of the adjacent floor joists, where it will be nailed.

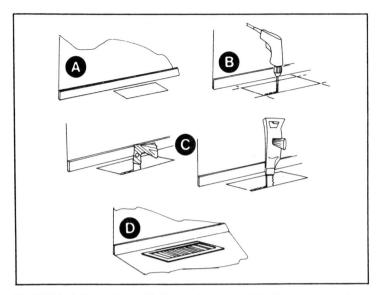

Fig. 5-38. Installing the boot. (A) After you have located the floor joist to which you will attach the boot, mark out a hole the size of the boot to be cut in the floor. (B) Drill three or more holes into the floor inside the marked-out area as a starting place for a saw. (C) Using a handsaw or a reciprocating saw, cut out the marked area. Pull the boot through the hole and nail it to the adjacent floor joist. (D) The final step—which you should put off until the floor covering is installed—is installation of the register.

be installed flush with the floor. An upflow furnace with the duct system in the attic would have ceiling diffusers, and boots would be installed flush with the ceiling. On all of these applications the boot should be located next to a floor or ceiling joist so the boot can be anchored.

The boot must be at least temporarily in place before the runs can be connected from the takeoffs to the boots. The length of the round pipe is then cut to fit, with a couple of inches extra for insertion, and is connected. When connecting joints of round pipe, takeoffs, and boots, always fasten them with pop rivets or screws.

The runs will have to be supported with hangers about 4 feet apart just as for the main duct. At times there will be special problems in connecting the runs and boots. Frequently an elbow will be required coming down from the boot to allow the run to connect properly. At other times a run may extend across a floor joist and require a straight boot to go into the room above.

Sometimes a collar will have to be used in installing a run. A collar is simply a short piece of round pipe to fill up any short gaps that may occur if the run turns out to be a few inches too short. Often an alternative to using a collar is to simply move the main duct a little toward the short side so the run will connect.

Fig. 5-39. This 90° boot connects to the run and extends through the floor. The baseboard register will connect to the top of the boot.

After the duct system has been installed, the furnace can be moved temporarily to the furnace room. If a coil case is being installed, it should be set over the plenum opening. When a coil case is not used, a noncombustible base is needed to protect the floor from the heat.

### Retrofitting Duct Installations

Older homes sometimes require substantial duct system modification for installation of central heating and air conditioning systems. Installing ducts in the second story of such homes particularly requires thought and imagination, because the houses often were not constructed with the duct system in mind.

Ducts can be run through closets or old large gravity flow furnace ducts to the second story. Sometimes a false wall can hide the duct. Figure 5-40 shows two possible methods of running ducts into a home's second story. Remember that you must carefully size the ducts, particularly if you are installing central air conditioning.

### Return Air

The return air duct that connects to the furnace is much like a plenum chamber above the furnace, and it must be anchored in place before the furnace is permanently installed (Figs. 5-41 and 5-42). After the furnace has

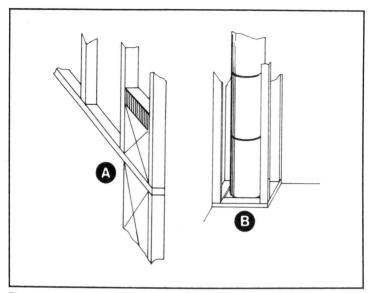

Fig. 5-40. (A) An upper-story run can be brought up through the wall studs by lining the interior space between the studs with sheet metal. (B) When necessary, upper-story ducts are run up a corner of a room, and an enclosure is built around them.

been put in place, the return air duct should be connected from the return air grille to the furnace. An opening will have to be cut in the return air duct over the furnace so a duct starter can be installed.

Build the air intake at the end of the duct between two ceiling joists by forming a wooden box around the return air opening in the room or hallway. Nail a piece of sheet metal to the top of this box and connect the return air duct; the joint should be insulated.

## Insulation

The main duct can be insulated on the inside or outside. The easiest time for insulating is before the ducts are installed. Each joint should be

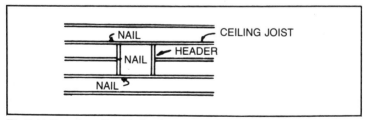

Fig. 5-41. Here the ceiling joist has been cut to install the return air duct above the furnace. The return air opening is prepared just like the plenum chamber opening, so headers must be installed.

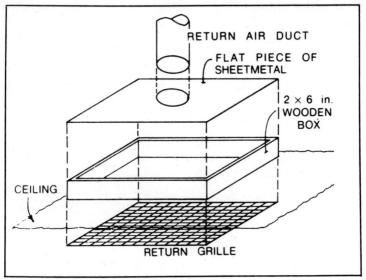

RETURN AIR DUCT

FLAT PIECE OF SHEETMETAL

2 × 6 in. WOODEN BOX

CEILING

RETURN GRILLE

Fig. 5-42. How the return air duct is connected to the return air grille in the ceiling.

wrapped in insulation before it is taken under the house to be connected. The insulation is wrapped around the duct and is taped with 1½-inch duct tape. See Fig. 5-35B. Sometimes wire is wrapped around the duct to make sure the tape doesn't come loose and let the insulation fall to the ground. As mentioned previously, the duct system must be insulated when air conditioning is used.

If the underside of the floor is to be insulated, this should be done after the runs and boots are installed so the floor insulation can cover them, too. If this is done, the ducts will not need to be wrapped in insulation, because the floor insulation will cover them. The plenum chamber, main duct, and return air duct will need to be insulated.

When the insulation is inside the duct, the outside measure must be enlarged to allow the same air flow to go through the duct. This enlargement should be the same as the thickness of the insulation (Fig. 5-43).

There are plastic sleeves that can be purchased which have insulation on their inner side and can be pulled over the pipe to insulate the runs. Another type of ready-made insulated duct is a flexible round duct with a plastic vapor seal on the outside and wire coil inside, with 1-inch insulation between. This type of duct is easy to handle because it is flexible. If it is used under the house, it must have a great deal of support. It seems to work out well for duct systems above the ceiling, and for return air ducts above the ceiling where the flexible pipe can rest on the ceiling joists.

**Shapes of Ducts**

Ducts come in three shapes: round, square, and rectangular. The round

116

duct will carry more air in less space, costs less, and takes less insulation than square duct of the same capacity. Its main disadvantage is that to carry large amounts of air (such as in a main trunk line), the diameter of the duct may be so large that it will extend too low in a basement or under the house.

Rectangular duct, on the other hand, can be almost any shape. This duct can be wide from side to side and narrow from top to bottom. Square and rectangular ducts are usually used for the main duct in a basement with limited head room, or under a house to allow more space between the duct and the ground.

Sometimes a combination of both types are used in the same system. The main duct is constructed from rectangular duct, and the runs are made of round pipe. Usually round duct is not used to run the duct system up a wall, because the wall generally is not wide enough for the round pipe. Rectangular wall stacks are commercially prepared for this purpose, however.

## Materials Used in Duct Construction

There are several materials used in ducts, including sheet metal, aluminum, fiberglass, clay tile, and cement blocks. The construction of the house plays a big part in the type of material used for the duct system. Sheet metal or aluminum usually is used in houses with a crawl space under the floor. Cement blocks or tiles are used under a concrete floor, although it is possible to use sheet metal ducts in concrete.

Fiberglass can be used for the duct system. If fiberglass duct is hung from the floor joists under the house, it will have to have more support than metal duct. Where fiberglass duct really comes into its own is in an overhead duct system. In this installation support is no problem, because the duct rests on the ceiling joists. Even with air conditioning, there is no need to insulate the fiberglass duct. When metal duct is installed in a system with air conditioning, it should be insulated to keep it from sweating and prematurely rusting the pipes. Fiberglass duct will not sweat like metal duct, because it is already insulated.

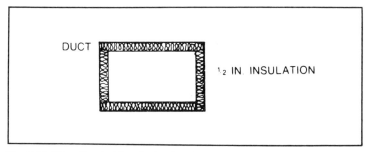

Fig. 5-43. When the duct is to be insulated on the inside, the outside walls of the duct must be larger to take into account the space taken up by the insulation. If 10 × 12-inch duct is needed to carry a given air flow, ½-inch insulation inside the duct will require on 11 × 13-inch duct. The insulation is glued to the metal.

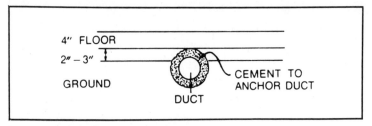

Fig. 5-44. How the trench is dug and the anchoring cement is poured for the duct. The cement around the duct will keep it from floating out and will help keep the duct from being mashed if someone should happen to step on it while pouring the floor.

### Installing Ducts in a Cement Floor

When pouring a cement floor for a building, the entire duct system must be installed before the floor is poured. The top of the ducts must be low enough so that there will be 2 inches of cement between the top of the ducts and the bottom side of the floor (Fig. 5-44). This means that if a 4-inch concrete floor is being poured, there will be 6 inches of concrete above the top of the duct. A trench is dug in the ground deep enough to lower the duct this much. All the runs must be installed in the same manner as any duct system, except that all the work can be done standing up instead of lying down and crawling around under the floor.

In a cement floor installation you will not be able to cut a hole next to a wall and install a boot as you otherwise would, because the boot has to be hooked up before the wall even exists. All that you have to measure by is the foundation. For this reason, if you plan to use baseboard registers you will have to know exactly how thick the wall will be when finished and where it

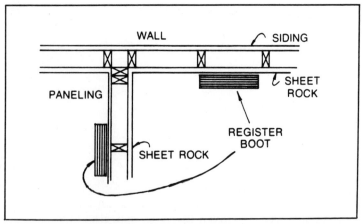

Fig. 5-45. It is especially important with a concrete floor that you know exactly how thick the finished walls will be so you can install the boot in the proper place before the floor is poured.

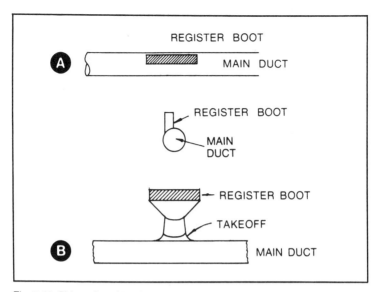

Fig. 5-46. This register boot A comes out of the main duct and extends to the top of the floor (or about ¼ inch below it). This installation might be used on a perimeter loop system. The installation in B would also be used for a perimeter loop system, but here a short takeoff and run are used before attaching the boot.

will be built in relation to the edge of the foundation. For example, you need to know if the wall will be started ½ inch from the edge of the foundation and whether wallboard or paneling will be used to finish the walls. The measure of all this must be determined, and you must install the boot so it will be at the edge of the wall when it is finished (Fig. 5-45). If a floor register will be used, it will not be necessary to be so exact in your planning and measurements. Figure 5-46 shows two methods of installing the boot with a perimeter loop system.

You must anchor the ducts in their trenches with some concrete. This is to prevent the duct system from floating to the top when the cement floor is later poured. To anchor the ducts, it is best to block them up about 2 inches from the bottom of the trench and then pour cement in the trenches to fill in around the ducts and cover the tops (Fig. 5-44). Be sure to work the cement under the ducts.

Before pouring the floor, brace the plenum chamber and place a cap over it if it does not extend above floor level. Put caps on the boots so they will not fill up with concrete. It is best to install the boots so that their tops are about ¼ inch below floor level. This will allow the cement finisher to go over the top of the boots to smooth out the floor. When the cement cures, the boots will show up in the cement, and the ¼-inch cement layer over them can be chipped out and the caps cut away.

Round duct is best for use in cement floors. It will not collapse easily from the weight of the concrete.

**119**

# Chapter 6

# Installing Central Air Conditioners

The air conditioner normally is installed after installation of the duct system and furnace have been completed. Figure 6-1 shows the major components and their locations of an installed furnace with central air conditioning.

Central air conditioning does not have to be installed at the time the central heating system is being installed. Often even a new installation will proceed in two steps. The central heating system is installed alone, with the capability of central air conditioning installation later. The homeowner decides to install central air conditioning at a later time. Sometimes central heat will be installed years before central air is added. In such installations central air may not have been planned into the central heat system's installation. When this is the case, modifications to the heating system components and duct system may be required to achieve a good central air system.

## PLANNING THE INSTALLATION

There are many planning considerations that you must consider before you install central air conditioning. On installation of a new heating-cooling system, these factors are considered during the initial system planning stages. When adding central air to an existing central heating system, these factors must be considered before you commit to the installation of central air. On installations of central air to older existing heating systems, the modifications required to accommodate central air sometimes are so extensive that it is not practical to install central air without installing an entirely new heating-cooling system. Room air conditioning may be the better alternative in such cases.

Central air can be installed in virtually every type of central forced-air heating system. Different components often are used depending on the type of furnace installation selected. For example, one type of evaporator coil is

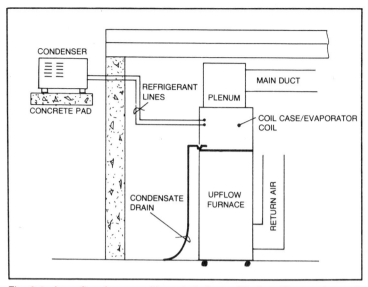

Fig. 6-1. An upflow furnace with central air conditioning. The condenser is located outside the house. The evaporator coil is inside the coil case above the heat exchanger of an upflow furnace. The condenser and evaporator are connected by two refrigerant lines, one which is larger than the other. A condensate drain takes away moisture that condenses at the evaporator coil.

used in a downflow furnace, and a different type is used in a horizontal furnace.

A coil case is required as part of the furnace unit for central air installations. The coil case is located next to the plenum chamber, between the heat chamber and the plenum. If the central heating system in your home has already been installed, and if it was installed without a coil case, you will have to add one.

The duct system will have to be capable of accommodating central air. Since cool air is more difficult to move than warm air, duct runs must be at least 6 inches in diameter. Some heating-only installations use runs of 5 inches in diameter, which generally are too small to adequately accommodate central air. If you are installing central air in an older two-story house, you need to do some careful planning or running the ducts to the upstairs rooms. The cool air will be difficult to push into the upper rooms in the best of circumstances. It may be impossible to accomplish the task using ducts run inside wall partitions, because these generally do not have enough capacity to handle cold air. You may want to consider running the ducts up a corner and building a wall to hide them, as discussed in Chapter 5.

When central air is installed, the duct system may have to be insulated to prevent the ducts from sweating and rusting out. Without insulation harmful condensation will form on the ducts, and they will deteriorate in time. You can avoid insulating the duct system if you open an air conditioning vent into the space where the ducts are run (crawl space, basement, or attic) to keep the air around the ducts cool as well. You will need to insulate this space for energy efficiency. Sometimes this is cheaper than insulating the ducts. Other times it is impractical, and the ducts must be insulated.

Before you install central air on an existing heating system, check the fan size to be sure it is sufficient to supply the required air. Unless enough air moves across the coil, it will operate inefficiently or it may freeze up. As a general guide, you can check Table 6-1. Your furnace supplier or cooling system manufacturer should be able to give accurate air flow requirements for your particular products.

When planning an air conditioner installation, select a unit that will be energy efficient and will help keep future electricity bills low.

## CONDENSER LOCATION AND INSTALLATION

When planning the installation, you must decide where you will place the condenser/compressor unit. Condenser location is discussed briefly at the beginning of Chapter 5. This unit will be located outdoors, and it should be placed somewhere that it will receive good air flow around it. Avoid locating the condenser in a corner where there are building walls on more than one side of the unit. Such locations are common, however, and can be suitable. The condenser should have a minimum distance of 18 inches to the nearest wall, with 24 inches of clearance preferred (Fig. 6-2).

The condenser is placed on a 3½-inch or thicker concrete pad. This pad should be a few inches larger than the condenser on all sides. Take care to make the pad level when pouring the concrete.

Once the pad has been prepared, set the condenser unit upon the pad. When setting the condenser, make sure the condenser fan will be blowing air away from nearby building walls. The air flow should not be directed toward nearby walls.

## COIL CASE

The easiest way to assemble the coil case is to begin with a prefabricated coil case assembly (Fig. 6-3). Although you can make your own coil

Table 6-1. Evaporator Coil Air Requirements.

| A/C Size (Tons) | Approx. Air Flow Required (CFM) | |
|---|---|---|
| | | When installing central air conditioning, be sure the furnace fan has enough air flow capacity to meet the air conditioner's needs. This chart gives you a general guide to air flow requirements, in CFM (cubic feet per minute). When adding a central air system to an existing heating-only furnace, you may have to install a larger fan. |
| 1½ | 600 | |
| 2 | 800 | |
| 2½ | 1000 | |
| 3 | 1200 | |
| 3½ | 1400 | |
| 4 | 1600 | |

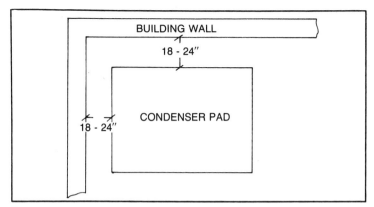

Fig. 6-2. The condenser is installed outdoors on a 3½-inch-thick concrete pad. This pad should be a few inches larger than the condenser on all sides. To ensure proper air flow around the condenser, the pad should be 18 to 24 inches from nearby building walls. If you can, avoid placing the condenser in a corner like this one.

case from sheet metal, it generally is much easier to use a prefabricated unit. You should use a prefabricated coil case on a downflow furnace. The furnace will sit on top of the coil case, and structural strength is important. All seams should be drilled and fastened with sheet metal screws or rivets.

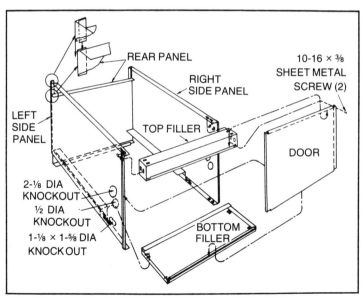

Fig. 6-3. This diagram shows how a coil case is assembled. You can purchase a ready-to-assemble coil case from a commercial supplier, or you can have a sheetmetal shop make one for you.

If the furnace has previously been installed without a coil case, you will have to make room for the coil case installation. Usually the best way to accomplish this task with a downflow furnace is to disconnect the present furnace and return air duct and remove them entirely from their installed

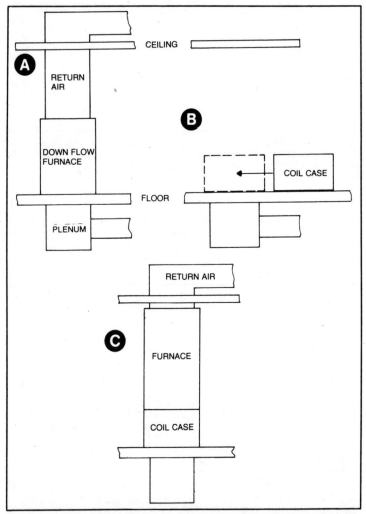

Fig. 6-4. Adding a coil case to a downflow furnace in preparation for air conditioning installation. (A) The downflow furnace has been installed as a heating-only furnace. Note that the return air duct has been extended a considerable length downward to meet the furnace. This duct will be shortened to make room for the coil case. (B) The furnace is disconnected and removed to make room for the coil case. The coil case is placed over the plenum. (C) The furnace is placed on top of the coil case. After shortening, the return air duct connects to the furnace. The furnace wiring is reconnected.

locations. Be sure to mark the electrical wires and terminals so wiring can be reinstalled easily. Assemble the coil case and set it in place above the plenum (Fig. 6-4). Set the furnace on top of the coil case, and be sure seams between the furnace and coil case are tight. The return air duct is reconnected to the furnace, but it will have to be shortened first to account for the increased height of the furnace-coil case assembly.

With an upflow furnace, the conversion is somewhat easier. The furnace will not have to be moved (Fig. 6-5). Generally an upflow furnace without a coil case will employ an extended plenum chamber to take air from the furnace up to the main duct. This plenum can be shortened to make room for the coil case. The coil case is installed on top of the furnace. The plenum is shortened and reconnected to the coil case. Make sure all seams are tight.

## EVAPORATOR COIL

Once the coil case is installed on the furnace, the evaporator coil can be inserted into it. One side of the coil case is a removable panel that must be removed to insert the coil. Figure 6-6 outlines the primary steps of inserting the evaporator coil into the coil case.

Install the coil supports. These can come in a variety of forms, such as metal bars or sheet metal configurations. On an upflow furnace, these coil supports fit on the flanges above the furnace heat exchanger. On a downflow furnace, they will span the hole cut for the plenum chamber.

If the furnace opening is larger than the coil itself, sheet metal baffles are used to make the opening smaller. These baffles direct the entire furnace air flow through the coil.

When the supports and baffles, if needed, are installed, insert the evaporator coil into the coil case and fit it into place. The coil case panel can be replaced to close the coil case.

## CONDENSATE DRAIN

The bottom of the coil case has a drain pan that slopes toward a condensate drain outlet. During the cooling season the cooling coil will sweat a considerable amount, so it is important that this drain be unclogged and connected to a drain hose that will remove this condensate from places where it could create problems.

A *P-trap* is installed in the drain line to prevent the loss of furnace air through the drain (Fig. 6-7). The drain itself can be constructed of either rigid tubing material, such as copper tubing, or more flexible tubing. The line should not be connected to sewer lines, because sewer gas might back up through the drain and enter the furnace air. The line is attached to the condensate drain on the coil case using a fitting sized for the drain outlet.

## INSTALLING REFRIGERANT LINES AND CHARGING

There are two ways to install refrigerant in air conditioning systems: the conventional system and the precharge system. The conventional

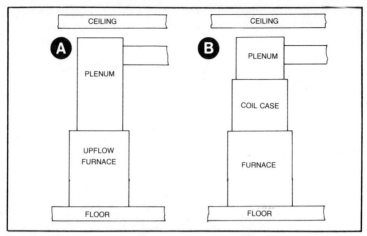

Fig. 6-5. The addition of a coil case to an upflow furnace. (A) The plenum chamber extends from the furnace to the main duct, and in most installations it will have plenty of length for shortening. (B) Once the plenum has been shortened, the coil case is installed between the plenum and the furnace. All components are reconnected.

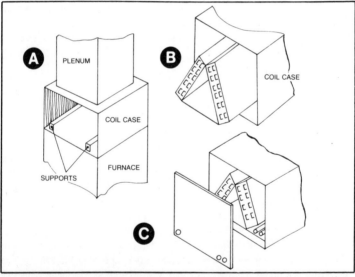

Fig. 6-6. Installation of the evaporator coil. The coil case usually has a panel or a door that can be removed to permit installation of the coil. (A) When the panel is removed, install the coil supports, which fit into the flanges on the furnace. Install sheet metal baffles that direct air flow through the coil. (B) Slide the coil into the coil case and set it into position. (C) Replace the coil case panel. Normally the panel can be replaced before the condensate drain or refrigerant lines are connected. Once installation is completed and you are sure you will not have to reopen the panel for a time, check all seams to be sure they are tight.

126

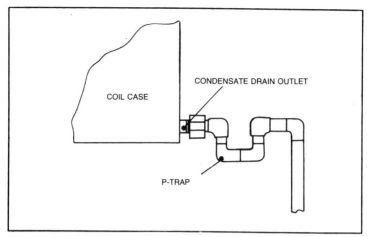

Fig. 6-7. A condensate drain is constructed of any suitable tubing material. Copper tubing makes an excellent durable drain line. A P-trap can be fashioned using copper elbows and fittings. The drain line is attached to the drain outlet with a fitting nut. Be sure to install the line so that water will drain naturally.

system has to have the refrigerant lines cut and welded as the air conditioner is installed. The tubing is purchased separately from the coil and condensing unit. The precharge unit, on the other hand, comes from the factory with a charge of refrigerant (often called gas) already in the coil and condenser.

## Conventional System

On the conventional system all of the joints for the refrigerant lines will have to be cut and fitted together. Usually this type of system is used on larger units and where the furnace and condensing units are over 30 feet apart.

The coil is placed in the coil case at the furnace, and the condensing unit is set. The refrigerant lines (Fig. 6-8) can then be run between the two units. The condensate drain is now installed on the drain pipe of the coil pan and run outside the house or into a drain. A P-trap should be installed somewhere in the drain line to keep the cool air from going out the drain. This drain can be run with copper tubing, iron pipe, or plastic pipe.

The high-side refrigerant line is usually run with soft copper tubing, while the low-side line is usually run with hard-drawn copper tubing. Soft copper tubing could be used to run the low-side line, also. Tubing and its installation are discussed in Chapter 1. The high-side line is the smaller of the two lines, coming out of the bottom of the condensing unit and going to the coil. The low-side line runs from the coil to the compressor. Tighten all connections after installing the lines.

Service valves will have to be installed in the lines unless these valves have already been built into the condensing unit. Figure 6-9 shows the drier

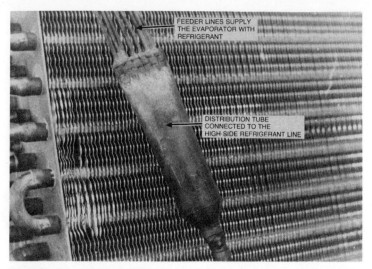

Fig. 6-8. The evaporator coil and, in the foreground, the feeder tubes that connect the refrigerant lines with it.

and sight glass that must also be installed on the high side if they are not already part of the condensing unit.

After the service valves have been installed in their locations close to the condensing unit, the gages can be hooked up to the service valves, and

Fig. 6-9. The drier is placed in the high-side line just before it leaves the condensing unit. The sight glass enables you to see the refrigerant as it moves through the system. When there are bubbles in this glass, the system may be low on refrigerant. The drier and sight glass can be placed just before the expansion valve or capillary tube.

the system can be charged (Fig. 6-10). Open the service valves and bleed a small amount of refrigerant into the system from the refrigerant cylinder by opening and closing the low-side valve on the gages. With the vapor in the system, check all the connections for leaks. Fix all of the leaks by bleeding the system and tightening or rewelding the connections.

Check for leaks at 25, 50, and 75 psi pressure. The pressure is increased in the system by putting more vapor into the lines; the unit should not be running.

After all the leaks have been fixed and the pressure checked, bleed refrigerant from the system and attach a vacuum pump to the center charging hose on the gage manifold. Tighten all hose connections, start the vacuum pump, and open the manifold valves. This is known as evaluating the system. It removes the air and moisture from the system.

When the vacuum has cleared the system, the valves on the gage manifold should be closed and the vacuum disconnected. The center charging hose is then connected to the service drum, and the valves are opened. The air in the charging hose should be bled by loosening the connection at the manifold and letting the air escape. Retighten the hose and charge the system with vapor without starting the unit. Check for leaks, bleed the charge, and pull the system on a vacuum again.

Before charging the system for the last time, place a thermometer in the register of the duct closest to the plenum chamber. Start the unit and record the temperature of the air coming through the duct. Leave the unit on and begin to charge the unit by opening the low-side valve on the charging

Fig. 6-10. Low- and high-pressure gages installed on the unit.

manifold for a few seconds. Close the manifold valve and read the low-side gage. If the unit is charging, the low-side gage should indicate a higher pressure than before the charging was started. (Due to the vacuum in the line, there will most likely be a negative pressure reading at this point.) Turn the low-side manifold valve on again for a few more seconds, then shut it off. Repeat this procedure slowly, taking gage readings after each charging to see if the pressure on the low-side gage is coming up. After you have given the system only a few charges, you should get a pressure reading on the head pressure gage (high-side gage), and a positive pressure reading should appear on the low-side gage.

Continue charging the system in this manner until the low-side pressure gage reaches 50 psi. At this point check the thermometer and record the temperature of the air coming through the duct. This temperature should begin to drop somewhat as the pressurized evaporator and condenser begin to cool the air. At 50 psi of pressure the unit may be approaching a full charge. Most units should charge at 69 psi, but some will reach full charge at 55 psi. To determine when the unit has reached full charge, you will have to keep an eye on the thermometer. The outside temperature plays an important role in determining when the unit reaches full charge, so the thermometer is generally used even if the repairman knows at what temperature or pressure the unit will probably reach full charge.

To determine when the unit has reached full charge, continue charging the unit as before. After every charge from the service cylinder, check the thermometer. The temperature of the thermometer will continue dropping as long as the unit is taking a charge, but when the temperature drops to its lowest point and begins to rise, you have the unit overcharged. A second way you can usually determine that you are getting the unit up to charge is that water droplets will begin to form on the low-side line.

When you determine that the unit is overcharged a little, loosen the connection where the low-side charging hose connects to the manifold. Bleed the refrigerant until the lowest temperature is reached. Still another aid in determining a fully charged system is to place a clamp-on ammeter around one of the hot lines coming into the contactor, as shown in Fig. 6-11. The ampere reading will be low when the unit is starting to charge and will increase steadily as more refrigerant is put into the system. The information plate or the instruction manual gives an ampere rating for the unit under normal operation. As the unit becomes fully charged, the ampere reading will begin to reach the proper value.

When the system is at full pressure, the last step is to check all the lines and connections for leaks. If no leaks are found, close the service cylinder, manifold, and service valves. Replace all caps and plates on the unit and check to see that the unit is cooling properly. Check to see that the thermostat will shut the unit off by moving the thermostat to a higher setting. If a leak is found, you will have to bleed the lines, fix the leak, pull the system on a vacuum, and recharge.

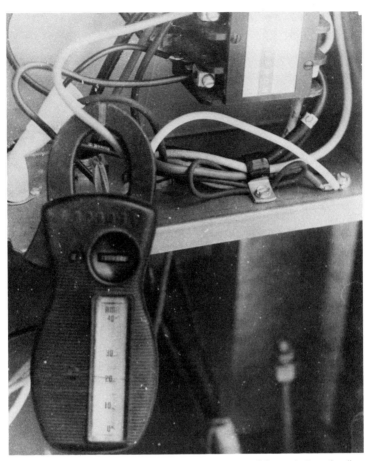

Fig. 6-11. The ammeter has been placed around one of the main lines feeding the unit. The nameplate on the condensing unit will give you the amperage reading for the unit. If the unit is not fully charged, the reading will be below the reading stamped on this plate. As the unit is charged, the reading will rise.

Sometimes the unit will stop running when the system is being charged. This may be caused because the thermostat is not set low enough to keep the unit running, or it may be caused by the presence of a low-pressure control on the condensing unit. The low-pressure control (if there is one) may shut down the unit when it is first being charged because there isn't enough pressure in the system. If the unit has a low-pressure control, just keep charging the system until the pressure gets high enough to keep the unit running. A unit with a low-pressure may not start, due to the vacuum. If this is the case, run enough refrigerant into the lines to bring the pressure up and start the unit.

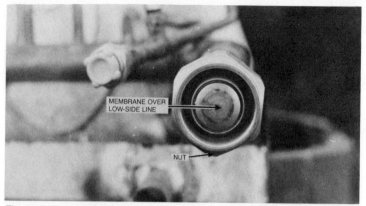

Fig. 6-12. The quick-disconnect fitting with the plastic cap removed. The center membrane is punched out when the fittings are connected. The nut pulls the connections together.

## Precharge System

The other type of system is the precharge system. With this system the evaporator coil and condensing unit are fully charged with refrigerant when they come from the factory. The evaporator coil and condensing unit have special fittings welded on the ends of the lines to prevent the gas from escaping. These are known as *quick-disconnect* fittings, and they have membranes in their centers that are punched out as the fittings are tightened (Fig. 6-12). The fittings come with plastic caps in the ends of the fittings that must be removed. When connecting the fittings, hand-tighten them and be careful not to cross-thread them. Follow the manufacturer's instructions.

Usually there is a 90° elbow at one end of the low-side line as shown in Fig. 6-13. This fitting is connected to the evaporator coil. The high-side line

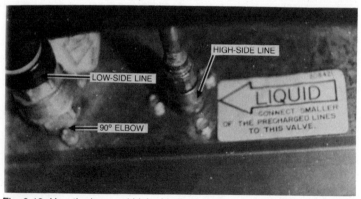

Fig. 6-13. How the low- and high-side lines connect to the coil. The 90° elbow helps connect the low-side line in close places.

Fig. 6-14. The quick-disconnect joints are in place here. The larger line is the low-side line, and the small line is the high-side line. (A) The low-side line with a snifter valve installed by the factory. (B) The low-side gage hose is connected to the service valve to check the pressure. (C) The high-side line with the hose from the high-side gage connected to the snifter valve.

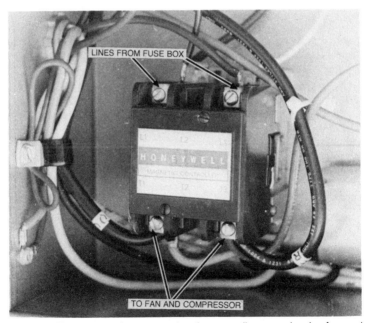

Fig. 6-15. The contactor is connected to the power lines, condensing fan, and compressor. The lines from the fuse box connect at this terminal. This terminal is where the lines leave the contactor to go to the fan and compressor.

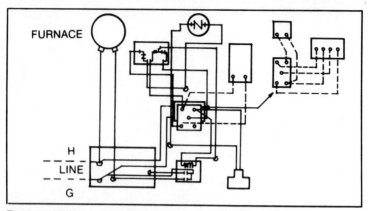

Fig. 6-16. Wiring diagram for heating and cooling system.

is connected to the coil and bent to fit into the space provided. The lines are then run out to the condensing unit. Be sure when making any of these connections that there isn't any dirt between them.

After all the connections have been made, they should be checked for leaks using a commercial leak detector or soap bubbles. If a leak is found, the connection should be tightened as quickly as possible to avoid losing any refrigerant.

There are usually service valves on the lines near the condenser. Figure 6-14 shows a type of service valve known as a *snifter* valve. To check the gas in the system, the caps are removed from the valves, and the gages are attached. The pressure should be near 69 psi. If the pressure is low, make an amperage check to be sure the system needs more refrigerant. If it does need more refrigerant, start the unit and install the service cylinder. Charge more refrigerant into the system following the charging procedures given previously. You will not have to bleed out the gas that is in the system—just add to it. When the amperage check determines that the unit is fully charged, remove the service cylinder and gages, replace all caps, and check the system for leaks.

### THERMOSTAT AND POWER WIRES

Figure 6-15 shows the contactor where the power wires are connected to the condensing unit. Lines are run from the breaker box to this contactor. The contactor is prewired into the condensing unit so that the wires leaving the contactor go to the condensing unit. In this way power is supplied to the condensing unit through the contactor.

There are two wires from the thermostat that must be connected to the condensing unit. One wire from the thermostat connects the Y-terminals (the cooling terminals) on the terminal board and thermostat, and the second wire connects the C-terminals (the common terminal connected to the transformer in the furnace). A wiring diagram is shown in Fig. 6-16.

# Chapter 7

# Thermostats

The *thermostat* is the control center for the heating and cooling system. The thermostat "tells" the furnace or air conditioner when to turn on and off. For decades the thermostat was a neglected part of the household heating and cooling system. With the changing demands on heating systems and the rising cost of fuel, the thermostat has attracted much attention. Unlike years ago when you could buy a thermostat that simply went "on" and "off," today you can buy thermostats that resemble miniature computers in their capabilities. State-of-the-art thermostats today automatically set the thermostat temperature forward and back according to preset programs.

## THERMOSTATS AND ENERGY SAVINGS

The single most important factor behind the increasing awareness of the importance of the thermostat to the heating system has been rising fuel costs. If the thermostat is set at a lower setting during the heating season and higher during the cooling season, energy costs will be less. You will probably save about 3 percent on your heating bill during the winter for each degree you lower the thermostat setting. Those savings can mount up, especially with rapidly escalating fuel costs. Homeowners should keep thermostats set at 65° to 68° during the heating season and 78° to 80° during the cooling season.

Because of this emphasis on energy conservation and turning down the thermostat, automatic set-back thermostats have become very popular. These thermostats automatically change the thermostat setting at preset times during the day, thereby reducing fuel costs. Table 7-1, prepared by the U.S. Department of Energy, shows the savings to be achieved using an automatic set-back thermostat. The savings can be substantial.

Set-back thermostats are not the only way to achieve energy savings with your thermostat. Proper installation (never on an outside wall) and

Table 7-1. Set-Back Thermostat Savings.

| City | Percent Savings at Set-back of: | |
| --- | --- | --- |
| | 5° | 10° |
| Atlanta, GA | 11 | 15 |
| Boston, MA | 7 | 11 |
| Buffalo, NY | 6 | 10 |
| Chicago, IL | 7 | 11 |
| Cincinnati, OH | 8 | 12 |
| Cleveland, OH | 8 | 12 |
| Columbus, OH | 7 | 11 |
| Dallas, TX | 11 | 15 |
| Denver, CO | 7 | 11 |
| Des Moines, IA | 7 | 11 |
| Detroit, MI | 7 | 11 |
| Kansas City, MO | 8 | 12 |
| Los Angeles, CA | 12 | 16 |
| Louisville, KY | 9 | 13 |
| Madison, WI | 5 | 9 |
| Miami, FL | 12 | 18 |
| Milwaukee, WI | 6 | 10 |
| Minneapolis, MN | 5 | 9 |
| New York, NY | 8 | 12 |
| Omaha, NE | 7 | 11 |
| Philadelphia, PA | 8 | 12 |
| Pittsburgh, PA | 7 | 11 |
| Portland, OR | 9 | 13 |
| Salt Lake City, UT | 7 | 11 |
| San Francisco, CA | 10 | 14 |
| Seattle, WA | 8 | 12 |
| St. Louis, MO | 8 | 12 |
| Syracuse, NY | 7 | 11 |
| Washington, DC | 9 | 13 |

**This table was developed by the U.S. Department of Energy to demonstrate expected savings in various cities from set-back thermostats. These figures are based on a basic home temperature of 65 degrees with nighttime set-backs of 5 degrees and 10 degrees for an eight-hour set-back period.**

routine maintenance will ensure that your thermostat is properly functioning and operating your furnace efficiently.

## TYPES OF THERMOSTATS

Thermostats are classified according to the amount of voltage they are capable of handling. For example, common thermostat voltage ratings are 24V, 120V, and 240V. You must be sure when buying a thermostat that you get a unit with a voltage rating that matches that of the circuit you will connect to the thermostat.

A *line voltage* thermostat generally is a 120V or 240V thermostat. This type of thermostat is wired directly into the power line of the heating unit.

Figure 7-1 is a wiring diagram showing a line voltage thermostat connected into a heating system circuit. Line voltage thermostats are generally used in electric room heating systems. Line voltage thermostats and their installation are discussed in Chapter 15.

The *low voltage* thermostat is most commonly used in central heating system installations. This type of thermostat is powered by a low voltage control circuit of 24V. The thermostat is not wired directly into the main power circuit of the furnace. Instead, the thermostat is connected into a separate low voltage control circuit that uses a system of relays to turn the main high voltage circuit on and off. A wiring diagram of a low voltage thermostat installation is shown in Fig. 7-2.

A *heating-only* thermostat is installed with central heating systems that do not have central air conditioning. These thermostats contain control circuits only for heating cycles and not for cooling cycles.

A *heating-cooling* thermostat is installed with central heating and air conditioning. This thermostat has control circuits for both heating and air conditioning cycles. If you install a central air conditioning system, you must install a heating-cooling thermostat.

A *set-back* thermostat, also called a clock thermostat, allows the homeowner to have two different thermostat settings at various hours. The thermostat automatically switches itself from one setting to the other.

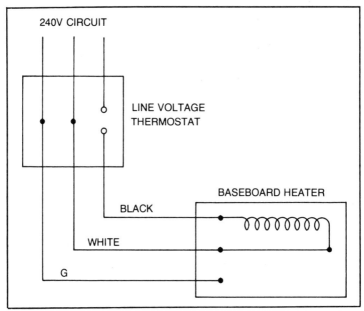

Fig. 7-1. A line voltage thermostat is wired directly into the power line supplying the electric resistance heaters. In this case a 240V line voltage thermostat is used because the power supply line is a 240V circuit. Line voltage thermostats also are available in 120V sizes.

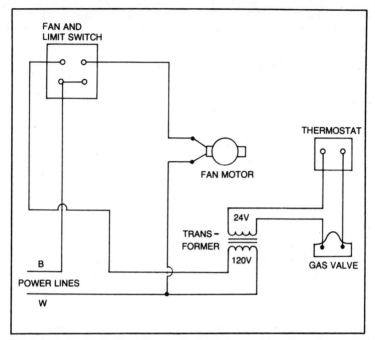

Fig. 7-2. A simplified wiring diagram illustrates how a low voltage thermostat controls a furnace. The type of furnace shown here is a heating-only gas furnace, but the principles are the same with other types of furnaces and for air conditioning installations. The 120V power supply powers the fan and other electrical components of the furnace. A transformer steps down this voltage to 24V for the thermostat circuit. The thermostat is connected to the gas valve—an electrical relay. When the thermostat calls for heat, the 24V circuit is closed, sending power to the gas valve. The relay on the gas valve is energized, and the gas valve opens.

These thermostats are very useful in saving energy, because they automatically lower the house temperature at preset times. Set-back thermostats are available in heating-only and heating-cooling models. The heating-cooling models, as with regular thermostats, are somewhat more expensive than the heating-only types.

A *two-stage* thermostat is used when you want the heating units to come on in stages rather than all at once. The thermostats discussed to this point are all *single-stage* thermostats that turn on the entire heating system when the thermostat calls for heat. Two-stage thermostats are commonly used in electric furnace installations, heat pumps, and recently in supplementary wood furnace installations. A two-stage thermostat is shown in Fig. 7-3.

The two-stage thermostat avoids turning on the entire heating system each time the thermostat calls for heat. For example, in an electric furnace when the thermostat calls for heat, two heating elements might turn on. If

Fig. 7-3. A two-stage thermostat has two sets of contact points for the heating cycle (shown at A) so that only one set of heating elements will come on unless the temperature continues to drop. This thermostat is also a heating-cooling thermostat and has a separate set of contact points for the cooling cycle. (B) is the thermostat anticipator, which is discussed later in this chapter.

those units were not enough to bring up the house temperature, the second stage would be activated. The final two elements would turn on. The two-stage thermostat is generally set so the second stage comes on a couple of degrees lower than the first stage. Two-stage thermostats normally are also heating-cooling thermostats.

A two-stage thermostat should always be used in heat pump installations and generally should be used in electric furnace installations. Two-stage thermostats will save energy. They activate only as much of the heating system as is needed to control the house temperature. In a heat pump the second stage of the thermostat controls the supplementary heat.

## THERMOSTAT INSTALLATION

When installing a thermostat, always follow the instructions of the furnace manufacturer and the thermostat manufacturer. These instructions are usually complete and tell you step-by-step how to install and wire the thermostat for your particular furnace installation. Furnaces and thermostats differ in their terminal labeling and in the number of wires required for the thermostat cable.

Thermostat location is important for the comfort of a home's occupants and for the furnace's efficiency. Locate the thermostat on an inside wall where it will receive good air flow. Do not place the thermostat on an outside wall or where it will receive direct drafts of outside air—for example, when the outside door is opened. Do not place the thermostat in the kitchen or any other room of the house subject to unusual heat sources that will affect its temperature sensing.

Installing the thermostat is as simple as installing an electrical outlet box. Some thermostats require that you first install an electrical box at the thermostat location. This will generally not be required with a low voltage thermostat.

Locate a spot about 5 feet up the wall where you want the thermostat placed. Drill a hole. The thermostat cable will run from the thermostat through the studs to the furnace terminal board. Depending on where the furnace is located, you will have to drill a hole between the studs into the basement or attic to run the cable through. Be sure to purchase the proper type of thermostat cable. This can be bought at a furnace supply store. Feed the thermostat cable from the furnace through the studs to the wall hole.

Run the cable through the thermostat baseplate. Tie or hold the cable in some way so it will not slip back down the wall.

Install the baseplate on the wall, and be sure it is level. You can use a small level that can be purchased or fashion a makeshift plumb bob using a heavy washer and string. Hang the plumb bob beside the baseplate to see if it is straight.

Connect the thermostat cable wires to the appropriate thermostat baseplate terminals, according to the manufacturer's instructions. Connect the corresponding wires to the furnace terminal board. For a discussion of connecting a thermostat to the furnace terminal board, see Chapter 11.

## SELECTING A SET-BACK THERMOSTAT

Basic set-back thermostats start at prices about two to three times the cost of a quality heating-cooling thermostat. They generally pay for themselves in two to three years. The simplest set-back thermostat permits the thermostat setting to be changed a limited number of times per day—generally between one and three set-back periods. The more elaborate models are electronic systems that can change settings many times per day using different temperature settings. Some models can be programmed for set-back periods a week at a time—with different settings for each day.

Set-back thermostats currently are eligible for a 15 percent federal income tax credit for energy conservation. Your income taxes will be reduced by 15 percent of the thermostat's cost. While you do not have to itemize your deductions, you must have 67 dollars qualifying energy conservation expenditures in the tax year so take any credit.

Cost, convenience, and lifestyle are factors to consider when choosing a set-back thermostat. Analyze your daily living patterns to determine how many set-back periods per day you will want. If the set-back periods will change daily, think about a one-week programmable model. Make sure the thermostat can be reset easily to different set-back periods and the controls are easily accessible to override the clock settings.

Purchase a heating-cooling model if you have central air conditioning. While almost all set-back thermostats are available in heating-cooling as well as heating-only models, the advertised models frequently are heating-only versions. Heating-only thermostats will not work on a central air conditioning system. Similarly, if yours is a two-stage heating system (a heat pump, for example), be sure to purchase a compatible thermostat. A regular heating-cooling set-back thermostat will not fit a two-stage heating system.

## INSTALLING THE SET-BACK THERMOSTAT

Many set-back thermostats will be installed as replacements for existing thermostats, and for that reason this section describes the removal of the existing thermostat. If you are installing a set-back thermostat in a new installation, begin directly with the discussion of the new thermostat's installation. Each thermostat will be different, so you should rely upon the manufacturer's installation instructions.

Installing a set-back thermostat is like installing any thermostat in many respects. Location should be chosen carefully. Be sure you install the thermostat level. The thermostat is sensitive, so handle it carefully. Before you begin, turn the furnace off. Turn off the power to the furnace at the fuse box or breaker box by removing the fuse or tripping the circuit breaker.

Be sure you have a thermostat of the proper voltage for your application before installation. Set-back thermostats usually are 24-volt ones that cannot be used for line voltage thermostats on 120V circuits. Likewise, a heat pump system requires a two-stage thermostat. Most set-back thermostat models will not work for this application.

### Removing the Old Thermostat

Turn off the heating system power supply at the fuse box or breaker box. Remove the thermostat's front cover.

Remove the thermostat itself. Some thermostats come in two parts—a main body and a wall mounting plate. The body of the thermostat will be attached to the wall mounting plate by screws or another mechanism. When a wall mounting plate is used, the thermostat wiring terminals are generally located beneath the main thermostat body. On some thermostats, once the thermostat cover is removed, the thermostat wiring terminals are exposed. If yours is a thermostat with a mounting plate so that the terminals are not exposed when the cover is removed, loosen the screws holding the thermostat body and remove it from the wall mounting plate. Note the thermostat anticipator setting on the old thermostat. This figure is the anticipator setting you should use initially when installing the new thermostat.

Identify the thermostat terminals with tags. These tags should be labeled with the terminal designation of the old thermostat. Then remove the wires from the terminals of the old thermostat and the wall mounting plate. You can begin installing the new thermostat using the existing thermostat wiring.

Some set-back thermostats require that you run a new wiring cable from the furnace terminal board. On some models this is necessary to provide power to the thermostat timer mechanism. Locate the thermostat wiring cable connected to the furnace terminal board. Make a note of which wires are connected to which terminals. Connect the new cable to the end of the old cable. Pull the old cable out with the new cable trailing behind it. This will put the new cable in place without having to drill new holes or fish in the dark for existing ones.

You should now be ready to install the new thermostat. If the terminal labels on the new thermostat do not match those on the old thermostat or on the furnace terminal board, consult your thermostat installation instructions to determine the terminals to which the cable should be connected.

### Installing the New Thermostat

Pull the cable through the thermostat base and attach the base to the wall. The base must be level as in any thermostat installation.

Connecting the wires to the thermostat terminals is the next step. The wires will generally be connected to the thermostat terminals so that they match the corresponding labeled terminal on the furnace terminal box or on the removed thermostat.

Complete the installation by mounting the thermostat body on the baseplate, if appropriate for your model. The thermostat has a heat anticipator that you should adjust to match the amperage rating of the furnace thermostat circuit. This rating usually can be found on the furnace's nameplate. You might check the thermostat terminal board for an amperage rating, or you can set the anticipator for the setting of the thermostat that you removed.

If you install a single-stage, set-back thermostat on an electric furnace, you may have to install jumpers on the furnace relays so that all the heating elements will come on. This is explained in Chapter 11.

### THERMOSTAT MAINTENANCE

Once properly installed, the thermostat requires little maintenance to ensure proper functioning. Remember that the thermostat should be installed level, and you should check occasionally to be sure it remains level.

The thermostat anticipator must be adjusted when installed to match the low voltage circuit to which it is connected. Two common types of thermostat anticipators are shown in Fig. 7-4. After initial adjustment, you may want to readjust the anticipator to keep the furnace heating your house evenly as it should.

The anticipator is a part of the thermostat that helps prevent the furnace from overshooting the preset thermostat setting. Before the room temperature reaches the preset thermostat setting, the anticipator causes the thermostat to turn off the heating portion of the furnace. The fan continues to blow and raises the room temperature the final degree or so to reach the thermostat setting. The anticipator prevents wide swings in the home's temperature.

The anticipator has a scale with numbers generally running between .1 and 1.0. It has an indicator or a pointer that notes the present anticipator

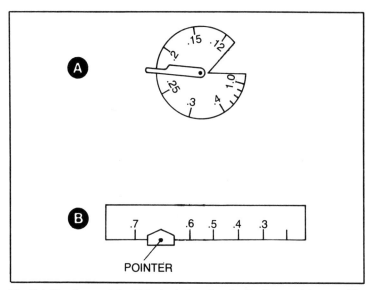

Fig. 7-4. The thermostat anticipator is found under the thermostat cover. The anticipator is set by moving the pointer. Two common types of anticipators are illustrated in (A) and (B).

setting. Moving this pointer changes the anticipator setting. The numbers on the scale represent the amperage rating of the thermostat circuit. If you install a furnace that has a .2 amp thermostat low voltage circuit, the anticipator should be set at .2. The thermostat circuit amperage rating should be marked on the gas valve or on the furnace terminal board.

You will find the words "longer" and "shorter" near the anticipator indicator. If you set the anticipator toward the "shorter" direction, the furnace will shut down sooner. Dust off the thermostat periodically to maintain top performance. Remove the thermostat cover. Dust the bimetallic coil and the inner workings of the thermostat. Run a strip of paper between the thermostat contact points (if yours is not a mercury switch thermostat) while the points are closed. Check all wires and connections. Tighten them with a small screwdriver.

# Chapter 8

# Humidifiers

Humidity control is a very important part of modern climate control systems. Unfortunately, it is often overlooked. If your heating system does not have a humidifier or if the humidifier is not working properly, you probably won't have to repair it immediately. However, a properly working humidifier is important to the comfort of your home during the heating season, and the humidifier can save you money on your heating bill.

### THE IMPORTANCE OF HUMIDITY CONTROL

Probably the primary reason to have a humidifier as part of your heating system is not the fuel savings, but the comfort it gives the occupants. Heated winter air is dry, leading to several undesirable effects upon the house and its occupants. One of the most obvious effects of winter's dry air is the abundant static electricity that is annoying to everybody. Furniture tends to dry out and will crack in extreme cases. Dust is excessive, and an occupant's allergies may be aggravated. Noses and throats often become dry and scratchy, especially after a night's sleep.

These problems are the result of low relative humidity inside the home. Cold winter air has a low moisture content. When that air is heated by the home heating system, it becomes capable of holding much more moisture. Its relative humidity drops. Inside air with low relative humidity speeds evaporation of moisture inside the home and dries out the surroundings.

A humidifier adds moisture to the air and increases relative humidity to bring it to a comfortable level. A relative humidity of between 30 and 60 percent makes occupants feel the most comfortable. Static electricity charges may not be eliminated unless the relative humidity is above 50 percent. When the outdoor temperature drops really low, it may be difficult for the average humidifier to raise the relative humidity inside the house beyond 20 to 25 percent. The ability of a humidifier to keep the relative humidity high during really cold weather is a factor you should consider in selecting a humidifier. If you want to be sure that higher humidity is maintained during the winter, you should consider installing a sprayer-type or a forced air evaporative-type humidifier.

## FUEL SAVINGS

Most homes will experience some energy savings by adding an automatic humidifier to their heating systems. Whether you will save depends on your home and its construction. The primary factor is whether the home is well sealed from air infiltration.

The humidifier saves fuel because of the principles already discussed. At levels of higher relative humidity the evaporation is slowed because of the moisture saturation of the surrounding air. The human body undergoes constantly a process of moisture evaporation as perspiration evaporates from the skin surface, and this evaporation cools the skin. When the relative humidity is higher, this evaporation is slowed. The skin feels warmer.

When the relative humidity inside the home is higher, the occupants feel warmer because of the slower evaporation process. You can turn down the thermostat on your furnace a few degrees and not sacrifice any comfort for the occupants. Because mositure is not evaporating from their bodies as rapidly, they feel as warm as before.

The fuel savings can be significant as a result of lowering your thermostat. A rule of thumb is that you will save about 3 percent on your heating bill for each degree you lower the thermostat. For a homeowner able to lower his thermostat from 72° to 68° with the operation of a humidifier, this represents a fuel savings of approximately 12 percent.

The fuel *costs* of humidifier operation are important and mostly overlooked. There is a significant *heat loss* involved in the operation of a humidifier. This heat loss may or may not be significant enough to offset the fuel savings gained by turning down the thermostat.

Humidifier operation involves the evaporation of water into the air flowing through the heating system. When water becomes water vapor, it does so only after absorbing a certain amount of heat energy. This heat energy comes from the output of the heating system. The energy loss must be subtracted from the energy saved by dialing down the thermostat to arrive at a net energy savings that represents the real savings of humidifier operation.

It takes more than 8000 Btu of heat to evaporate 1 gallon of water. In the average home a humidifier will evaporate about 1 gallon a day for each room in the home. This is the amount of heat energy lost in the evaporation process.

Even with this heat loss, the humidifier will give a net energy savings. For each 10 percent increase in a home's relative humidity, the thermostat can be lowered 1° without any comfort loss to the occupants. As previously discussed, each degree lower on the thermostat will cut fuel consumption by about 3 percent. An increase in relative humidity from 10 percent to 50 percent initially gives you a savings of 12 percent, less the amount of heat lost by the water evaporation process. In the home sealed in an average manner, this loss is much less than the 12 percent saved by lowering the thermostat. Humidifier operation thus results in a net fuel savings, although it will be less than 12 percent.

The key to the question of overall fuel savings is how well the home is sealed. If the home is tightly sealed, the relative humidity inside stays fairly constant without the continual addition of new moisture from the humidifier. When this occurs, the heating system experiences much less heat loss due to the evaporation of water into the furnace air.

If the home is not well sealed, the inside air constantly is being replaced with dry outside air. This means the furnace air must constantly evaporate large quantities of water to keep the relative humidity inside up to desired levels. A poorly sealed home will lose more heat through the constant water evaporation process of a humidifier than it will save by lowering the thermostat inside.

## SELECTING A HUMIDIFIER

When you choose a humidifier, you should know the effectiveness you want the humidifier to have. If you want the relative humidity maintained around the 40 to 50 percent level even during the coldest weather, you may want to consider a sprayer-type humidifier. Cost may be an important factor. Evaporative humidifiers that rely on natural evaporation cost less to purchase than forced-moisture humidifiers that spray a water mist into the furnace air stream. You must know the size of your house, the square footage, number of rooms, and heat load, if possible. These items will help you choose a humidifier that has the capacity to handle your house. From the furnace nameplate you should determine the model and capacity of your furnace.

Give some thought to the ease of installation and locations in the plenum chamber or main duct where there is ample room for installation. Sometimes the amount of space the humidifier requires or its configuration will determine the type of humidifier you can install in your heating system.

## TYPES OF HUMIDIFIERS

This book focuses on humidifiers that are installed in the heating system ducts. The room humidifier or the *console humidifier* does not require duct installation. This humidifier is contained in a cabinet and sits in a room. The humidifier normally has a water pan, a water absorption system, and a fan to draw room air through the water absorption system (a sponge belt, for example) and push it out into the room. The console humidifier has the advantage of easy installation. Its disadvantages are that the humid air may be distributed unevenly throughout the home, and it takes up space in the living area of the home.

There are several types of furnace humidifiers. The water supply is

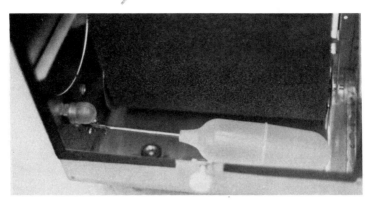

Fig. 8-1. This float system controls the water level in the reservoir. The sponge rubber belt picks the water up from the reservoir and carries it into the air stream, where the air can absorb it as it moves through the duct system. This type of humidifier needs a humidistat to control the moisture.

normally in a pan at the bottom of the humidifier. The water is brought to the pan through a water line connected to a float system which maintains a constant water level (see Fig. 8-1).

The humidifier has a pickup element that will hold the water to be absorbed by the dry air passing through the system. This pickup element can be a roller with bristles (Fig. 8-2), a sponge belt (Fig. 8-3), or plates made of an absorbent material (Fig. 8-4). The pickup element is rotated by a low voltage electric motor. The amount of moisture absorbed by the air will

Fig. 8-2. With this humidifier the entire mechanism is connected to the bottom of the main duct as close as possible to the furnace. The water flows into the lower part of the pan. The correct water level is maintained with a float. The bristles pick up water from the pan and move it into the air flow, where it is picked up by the passing air. A motor turns the bristles when the fan is on.

Fig. 8-3. A view of the top half of the sponge belt humidifier shown in Fig. 8-1. The belt is the absorbent element of this humidifier that puts the moisture in the air flow.

depend on the amount of moisture already in the air and the air temperature. Air with a higher moisture content or a lower temperature will take less moisture from the humidifying system.

There are two classifications of humidifiers. The evaporative humidifier has the air passing over or through the pickup element, taking the moisture from the element by evaporation as it goes. This is the type of humidifier shown in Figs. 8-2 and 8-4. The plastic bristles pickup the moisture as they move through the reservoir. These bristles carry the moisture up into the air flow. The dry air absorbs the moisture as it passes through the bristles. The bristles are turned by a motor that is wired in the circuit with the furnace fan so that when the fan shuts off, it will shut off the humidifier. A humidistat may also be wired in the circuit to shut off the humidifier when the desired moisture level is achieved and turn it on when the ambient air is excessively dry. In this case the humidstat would be located in the return air duct.

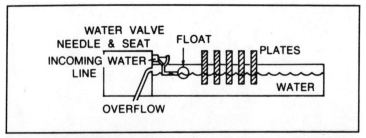

Fig. 8-4. In this humidifier the plates absorb moisture from the reservoir. The air flows around the plates and picks up moisture. Notice the float system and overflow to control the amount of water in the reservoir. This humidifier would be installed in the plenum chamber or warm air duct. It does not have an electric motor to turn the water-absorbing plates and therefore is less efficient than some other evaporative humidifiers.

The other classification, called a forced-mosiure humidifier, forces the moisture into the air as a mist so the air can absorb it and carry the extra moisture into the rooms. The latter type has to have some type of pump to spray the water mist into the air. This type also has to have a humidistat to shut off the pump when the correct amount of moisture is obtained. If the humidistat isn't used, too much moisture may become present in the air, and water will form on the inside of the walls. Also, the excess moisture will cause clothes, shoes, and carpets to mold.

Halfway between these two types is the forced-air humidifier shown in Figs. 8-1 and 8-3. This humidifier has a spongelike belt held in position by rollers. As the belt turns, it picks up water from the reservoir and carries it up toward the top roller. The furnace air is forced through the sponge material and picks up the moisture before going to the duct system.Both forced-moisture humidifiers and evaporative humidifiers with motorized pickup elements may be controlled by a humidistat. The humidistat senses the air's relative humidity and turns the humidifier on and off (Fig. 8-5).

Humidifier motors may be 24V or 120V. Humidistats can operate either type. A humidistat usually operates on a 24V volt circuit if it is located in a room, but the humidistat will probably control a 120V circuit if it is close to the furnace (in return air duct, for instance). Figures 8-6 through 8-8 show wiring diagrams and transformers for humidistats.

## HUMIDIFIER INSTALLATION

There are several types of humidifiers on the market, but we will only cover a few here because they are basically connected in the system in the same way. The humidifier should be placed in the warm air side of the duct system because warm air will absorb the moisture better than cool air.

### Evaporative Humidifiers

The plate-type humidifier is usually installed in the plenum chamber because this is where the air is warmest. It should be installed so that the air flows around and through the plates (see Fig. 8-9). The pan extending into the plenum must be level so the water will not spill into the plenum. Any water overflow should run out an overflow valve and away from the plenum. The most common cause for water overflow is the float sticking due to mineral deposits building up on the needle and seat. This float system is housed in a tank on the end of the humidifier. The top can be removed for cleaning.

The pan has a mark where the water level should be maintained to allow the plates to absorb enough water. The water level can be changed by adjusting the float. This is made possible by the use of a wing nut and adjustable arm on the float (Fig. 8-10).

The installation of humidifiers with motorized pickup elements is shown in Fig. 8-11. These normally are installed in the main duct near the plenum chamber. A sheet metal baffle directs the air flow into the pickup element.

Fig. 8-5. The humidistat dial can be set to increase or decrease the amount of moisture in the air. This control is usually installed in the return air duct or in a room or hall where the air can move freely over the control.

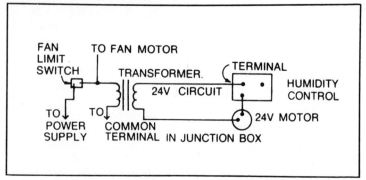

Fig. 8-6. How a 24V transformer is connected to the fan circuit to operate the humidifier motor. When the fan limit control turns the fan on, power is supplied to the 24V transformer, and the motor on the humidifier will start.

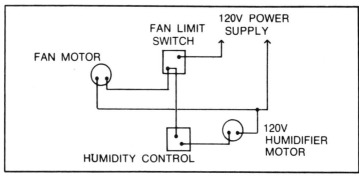

Fig. 8-7. This humidifier motor operates on a 120V circuit. When the fan limit switch reaches the proper temperature the switch will close and the fan will run. If the humidity is below the humidistat setting and the fan is on, the humidifier motor will run.

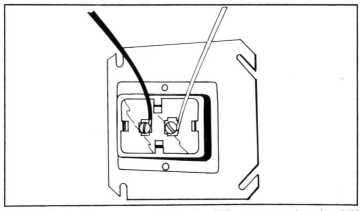

Fig. 8-8. The transformer connects to the humidifier motor to reduce the 120V line voltage to the 24V for powering the motor.

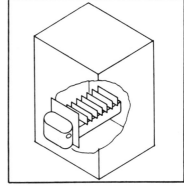

Fig. 8-9. A plate-type humidifier installed in the plenum chamber. The pan must be level so water will not spill over into the furnace.

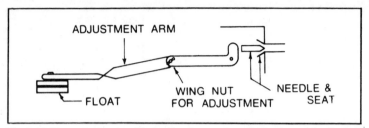

Fig. 8-10. The water level on this float system can be adjusted by moving the float up or down.

The water source for the humidifier should be a nearby water main, and a valve must be placed in the line to control the water supply to the humidifier. One way to do this is to install a saddle valve as shown in Fig. 8-12. Drill a hole in the water line large enough for the valve tube to go through. Place a gasket over the valve tube and place the tube over the hole so that the gasket is between the pipe and the tube. Install the bolts and fasteners and tighten the unit. Be careful to drill the proper size hole in the water line so that the gasket will seal.

The saddle valve should only be used on iron pipe, not for soft copper line. Using this arrangement on copper line will result in a flattened copper water line and a leaking system. There are other types of valves that can be installed on both iron and copper pipe.

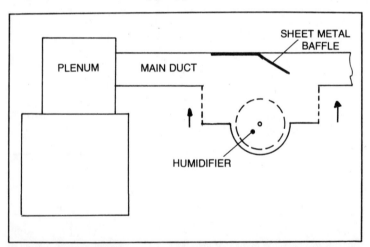

Fig. 8-11. Humidifiers of the most common evaporative types are installed on the underneath side of the main duct leaving the plenum chamber. To install these humidifiers, you simply cut a hole in the bottom side of the main duct large enough for the humidifier to fit into. The humidifier is then fastened to the duct system, and water line and power supply connections are made. To increase the efficiency of an evaporative humidifier, you can make a simple baffle from sheet metal to direct air flow over the humidifier. This baffle is attached to the top inside surface of the main duct and is installed before the humidifier is attached.

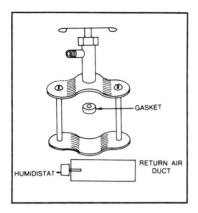

Fig. 8-12. A saddle valve used to tap an iron water line. The water should be shut off and a hole drilled in the water line. The valve has a tube that goes into the hole, with a gasket to keep it from leaking.

After the valve is connected, the line to the humidifer can be installed. A compression fitting will make this connection. The nut and ferrule are placed on the line so that the line will come in contact with the valve properly. Place the line in position and hold it against the valve while moving the ferrule and nut into position on the valve. Tighten the nut while applying pressure on the line. The nut will seal the ferrule as the pressure is applied. Take care not to cross-thread the nut. The reason for applying the pressure while tightening the nut is to prevent the line from slipping back and causing a leak.

### Forced-Air Humidifiers

The float system is about the same as in units already discussed. The main difference with the forced-air humidifier is that there is a small fan pump to move the air over the material that picks the water up. The pump humidifier sprays a mist into the plenum chamber. Here the warm air picks up the moisture and carries it to the rooms. The water line and valve should be about the same as discussed earlier. The pump motors on these humidifiers are usually designed for 120V.

Figure 8-13 shows a forced-air humidifier mounted on the outside of the plenum chamber. Two round or square holes have to be cut in the plenum to connect to the humidifier. The air moves out of the plenum chamber through the humidifier and returns to the plenum. This humidifier has its own fan to move the air through it and back into the plenum. It should be wired into a circuit with a humidistat to turn off the humidifier when the air has enough humidity.

In another type of forced-air humidifier an opening the size of the face of the humidifier must be cut in the plenum. The humidifier is attached to the side of the plenum with screws.

A knockout panel in the side of this humidifier (Fig. 8-14) must be removed and a thimble (Fig. 8-15) installed. The thimble is held in place by the flanges. A second thimble must be installed in the return air duct. A flexible hose (Fig. 8-16) connects the two thimbles to create an air flow

153

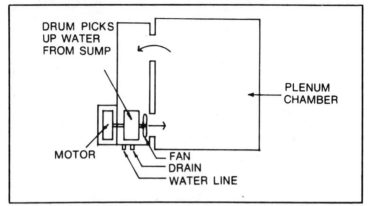

Fig. 8-13. Forced-air humidifiers attached to a plenum. The fan moves air through the humidifier. The humidistat can be installed in the return air duct.

from the plenum chamber through the humidifier and up to the return air duct. A damper is placed in one of the thimbles to control the air flow.

This type of humidifier uses the furnace fan to move the air through it. The plenum chamber has a positive pressure, and the return air has a negative pressure. Because of the differences in pressure, the air will flow from the plenum up into the return air, passing through the humidifier as it goes.

## HUMIDISTAT

The purpose of the humidistat is to shut off the humidifier when there is sufficient moisture in the air and turn it on again when the air is too dry.

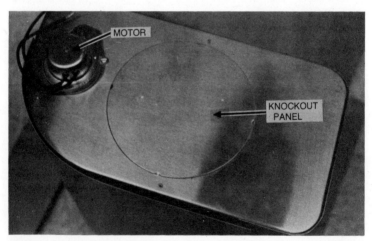

Fig. 8-14. The knockout panel has to be removed so a thimble can be installed. A 24V motor operates the humidifier.

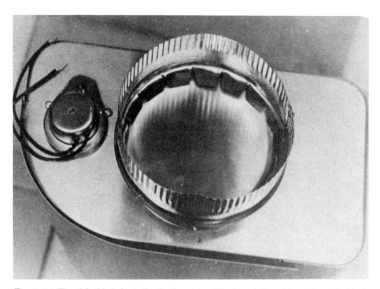

Fig. 8-15. The thimble is installed in the side of the humidifier. Place the thimble in the hole and bend the flanges over to hold it in place.

Fig. 8-16. After the first thimble is installed in the plenum, the thimble in this photo should be placed in the return air duct. The flexible hose is connected to both thimbles to form an air duct between them. Take care when installing these thimbles not to cut the holes too large in the return air duct.

The humidifier motor only operates when the furnace fan is turned on. Some humidifiers will work just fine if they are wired so that every time the fan comes on the humidifier comes on. Others must use a humidistat to keep the moisture content of the air from becoming too high; the humidistat is merely a second switch in the circuit. The humidifier with the humidistat control is wired into the fan circuit just like the other humidifiers, but when the fan comes on and the humidistat control senses that adequate moisture is already present in the air, the humidifer will not run. Later, when the humidistat circuit closes, the humidifier will start, but it will shut off again when the fan stops.

The motor for the humidifier will be either 24V or 120V. The instruction sheet with the humidifier will give this information. If the circuit is 24V, there will be a transformer to reduce the furnace fan's 120V circuit to 24V (Fig. 8-17). When a 120V motor is used to run the humidifier, the hot line is run from the fan limit switch to the humidistat and humidifier motor (Fig. 8-18). The other wire is connected to ground. The motor on the humidifier will only operate when the fan is running and the humidistat points are closed.

The humidistat can be installed in the return air duct or in a room in the air flow. Figures 8-19 and 8-20 show parts of a humidistat designed to operate in the return air duct on a 24V circuit.

## SERVICING THE HUMIDIFIER

A humidifier should be thoroughly cleaned and serviced at least once a year. One of the main problems encountered with a humidifier is the lime and mineral deposits left behind on the unit as the water evaporates. These deposits are left on the plates, belts, or any parts that are used to carry the moisture into the air stream .

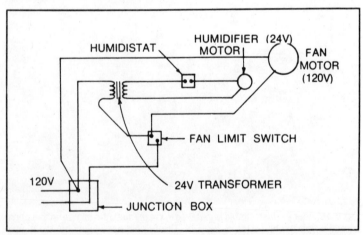

Fig. 8-17. This is how a humidifier and humidistat are connected in the fan circuit. When the fan runs, the humidifier uses a 24V motor, so a transformer is required.

156

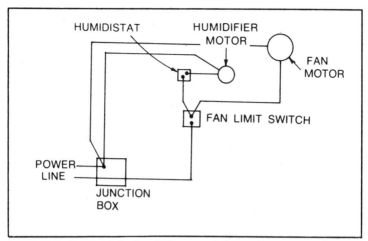

Fig. 8-18. In this circuit the humidifier motor is for 120V, so no transformer is used.

Since the buildup of such deposits can hamper the effectiveness of the humidifier, it is necessary to clean the unit. Besides building up on the part of the unit carrying water to the stream of air, the minerals can deposit themselves on the float, needle, and seat. This will cause the float to become heavier and allow the water to raise to an undesirable level. Mineral deposits can also cause the needle and seat to stick open, causing the humidifier to overflow.

When servicing the humidifier, the water supply should be shut off, and the humidifier should be removed from the duct system. It can then be cleaned and replaced. Scrape the mineral deposits away from the float, needle, and seat. Clean and replace pickup elements if required.

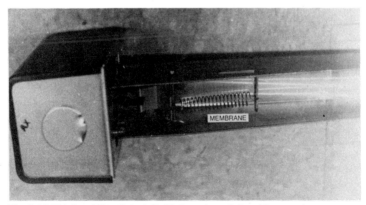

Fig. 8-19. This humidistat is installed in the return air flow. The membrane senses the humidity in the air and either opens or closes the contact points to run the humidifier. The spring holds the proper tension on the membrane.

Fig. 8-20. Humidistat with the front panel removed to show the terminals.

## TROUBLESHOOTING THE HUMIDIFIER

Possible causes of humidity being too low are:

- Mineral buildup on plates or sponge belt.
- Water shut off.
- Humidistat set too low.
- Humidifier motor burned out.
- Float stuck.
- Loose electrical connection.
- Bad transformer.

If the humidity is too high, suspect:

- Humidistat stuck.
- Broken spring or membrane on humidistat.
- Dirt and lint buildup on membrane.
- Humidistat set incorrectly or located in a dry place.
- Water leak into the duct system.
- Float valve stuck open.

Possible causes of humidifier overflow include the following:

- Float not set correctly.
- Float stuck open.
- Humidifier not level.

# Chapter 9

# Servicing Gas Furnaces

When servicing a furnace, always turn off the furnace electrical power by tripping the furnace circuit breaker. The only exception is when electrical power is necessary to perform tests. Also, shut off the gas line except when required to be open for tests.

## GAS VALVE OPERATION

The gas valve (Fig. 9-1) meters the correct amount of gas to the burners. The pressure setting of the gas valve is of major importance, because if it is set too high, the flame in the burner will burn improperly, wasting gas. Some manufacturers do not include gas valve pressure regulators on their furnaces, and the gas pressure must be adjusted at the regulator on the tank or line hookup.

The gas valve opens when the thermostat calls for heat. It also has a safety function in that it shuts off the gas supply to the burner when the pilot light goes out. This shutoff feature prevents the toxic gas from being pumped into the room if the furnace burners quit.

In most furnaces the *thermocouple* on the pilot light is the "master switch" on the gas valve. A thermocouple is a device that generates electricity when heated. Normally the thermocouple is heated by the pilot light. The thermocouple's electrical output holds closed an electrical relay that supplies current to the gas valve. The current supplied to the gas valve opens the valve. If the pilot light goes out, the thermocouple stops supplying current to the relay. The relay, in turn, stops supplying current to the gas valve. The valve thus closes, shutting off gas to the burners whenever the pilot light goes out.

In order to relight the furnace, you must first find the pilot light and gas valve. On the gas valve there is a red button or a knob which you push down while lighting the pilot (Fig. 9-2). After the thermocouple has been warmed

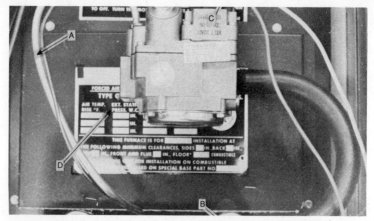

Fig. 9-1. Gas valve. (A) Pilot light tube and thermocouple line running from the gas valve to the pilot light and thermocouple at the burner. (B) Manifold connecting the burners to the gas valve. (C) Location of connection of the two thermostat wires to the gas valve. (D) Metal plate that gives furnace data.

by the pilot light, it will allow the burners to light at the proper time. The size of the flame for the pilot light is also regulated by the gas valve.

### Leaking Gas Valve

Sometimes the gas valve leaks. To check for a leaky gas valve, disconnect the manifold from the gas valve and screw a half-union into the

Fig. 9-2. The gas valve controls the flow of gas to the burners. The low voltage solenoid coil opens the gas valve when the thermostat calls for heat. The control knob stops the flow of gas through the valve. This knob is turned to the "pilot" position and pushed down to hold the pilot light valve open and allow the pilot light to be lit.

connection where the manifold was removed. The half-union adapts the pipe fitting for the manifold to a ¼-inch flare connection so a hose and gage can be installed. Turn the valve on and watch the gage. If pressure is indicated, it means the valve is leaking.

A valve that leaks should be replaced since it will let gas leak out through the burners and into the room. When these fumes reach the pilot light, they will ignite. If the pilot light is out and the valve is leaking, it will fill the room with gas, which could be ignited by a light switch, match, or spark.

### Closed Valve

One of the main causes of failure of the burners to light is the gas valve not opening to send gas to them. There is a coil in the gas valve that opens the valve when the thermostat calls for heat. If this coil is bad, the gas valve won't open. To check the coil, remove one of the wires from the terminals on the gas valve and place the two leads from an ohmmeter on the terminals (Fig. 9-3). The meter should move to indicate that there is not an open circuit.

If the coil checks out to be good and the voltage to the coil is correct (24V), disconnect the manifold at the gas valve, install a gage, turn on the gas valve, and turn on the furnace using the thermostat (this assumes the pilot light is on). You should get a pressure reading on the gage. No pressure indicates the gas valve is frozen closed and should be replaced. If the gas valve does open, check from the gas valve to the orifices.

### GAS BURNERS

There are several types and designs of burners. Basically, they are similar in style. Figure 9-4 shows a typical burner assembly. The manifold carries the gas from the gas valve to the orifice. The gas sprays out through the orifice into the burner housing where air is mixed in. The mixture goes through the slots in the burner where the gas burns. Figure 9-5 gives a closer view of the burners.

The size of the hole in the orifice depends on the type of gas being burned. For natural gas the orifice hole is quite large, but for LP the hole will be smaller. Usually the gas supplier will have the correct size orifice for the type of gas to be used.

The orifices can be changed by removing the burner and unscrewing them (Fig. 9-6). They can be cleaned with a brush or compressed air.

The number of orifices and burners depends on the size of the furnace in Btu. Each orifice also has a Btu rating that indicates how much gas will pass through the orifice.

The burner usually slips over the orifice, and there is an air adjustment at this point (Fig. 9-5). Another type of air adjustment is shown in Fig. 9-7. By loosening a screw, the air adjustment can be opened or closed.

If the air adjustment is closed too much, the flame on the burner will burn yellow and will not give off as much heat as it should. Also, the burner

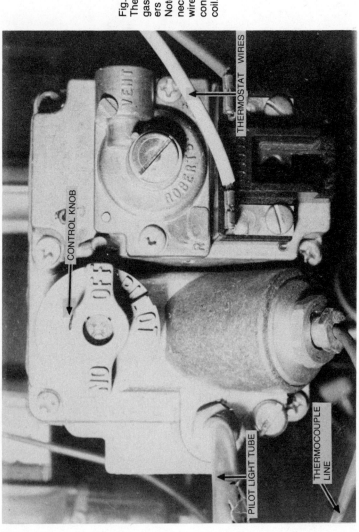

Fig. 9-3. A top view of the gas valve. The burners are underneath. The gas valve is connected to the burners by a manifold (not visible here). Note the two thermostat wires connected to the gas valve. Remove the wires from these terminals to run the continuity check on the gas valve coil.

CONTROL KNOB

THERMOSTAT WIRES

PILOT LIGHT TUBE

THERMOCOUPLE LINE

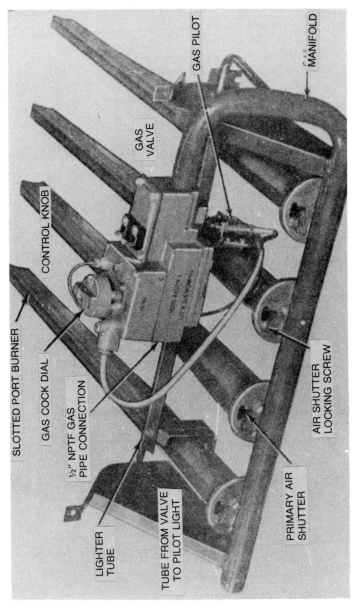

SLOTTED PORT BURNER

GAS COCK DIAL

CONTROL KNOB

GAS VALVE

GAS PILOT

MANIFOLD

½" NPTF GAS PIPE CONNECTION

LIGHTER TUBE

TUBE FROM VALVE TO PILOT LIGHT

PRIMARY AIR SHUTTER

AIR SHUTTER LOCKING SCREW

Fig. 9-4. Illustration of burner assembly showing gas manifold carries the gas from the valve to the burners.

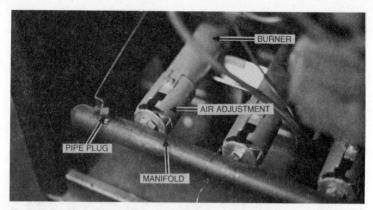

Fig. 9-5. Burners and manifold. The manifold takes the gas into the burners. The burners extend into the heat chamber where the gas and air mix before burning. The pipe plug can be removed to check gas pressure on the manifold. If the pressure is too low, the gas will not give off enough heat. If the pressure is too high, the flame will be jumping off the burners. For proper air adjustment it is necessary to loosen the screw and move the air adjustment sleeve in or out.

Fig. 9-6. The orifice can be unscrewed from the manifold for cleaning.

Fig. 9-7. To make the adjustment with this type of gas burner, it is necessary to loosen the screw and turn the outside flange. By turning it counterclockwise, the amount of air can be decreased. Each burner has to be adjusted separately.

164

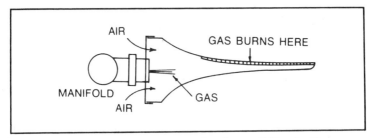

Fig. 9-8. How the gas burner is connected to the manifold and orifice.

will smoke and accumulate soot. The collection of soot in the heat chamber or the flue will cut down on the efficiency of the furnace. Another possible result of improper air adjustment is a tendency of the flame to burn inside the burner body or in front of the orifice.

As the gas passes through the orifice and burner, it pulls in air, and the air then mixes with the gas (see Fig. 9-8). Sometimes dust, dirt, or lint will collect in the throat of a burner and partially block the air. The burner may become clogged with soot, or parts of the burner could become spotted with rust. For these reasons the burners should be cleaned regularly.

Cleaning can be done by removing the burner assembly as shown in Fig. 9-9 and cleaning it with air. Care should be taken not to bend or break the burners as they are being cleaned. Figure 9-10 shows burners that can be removed easily by removing two screws at the bottom of each burner.

### Lighting the Burner

When lighting the burner, the thermostat should be turned down and the gas valve turned on. The knob on the gas valve should be turned to

Fig. 9-9. Removing the burner assembly. To do this, remove the two screws on each side of the burner. Shut off the gas at the tank and disconnect the line at the gas valve. Disconnect the thermostat wires. The burner assembly can then be removed. Some burners slip off the manifold, while others are held on with two screws. The pilot light bracket (arrow) can also be removed.

Fig. 9-10. This burner assembly has been removed from the furnace and is shown upside down. The two screws (arrow) at the bottom of the burner can be removed to allow the burner to slip off.

Fig. 9-11. Here the burner assembly can be seen with the thermocouple extending from the pilot light housing. The pilot light cap directs the flame over the thermocouple. The pilot light tube is part of the burner, but extends out toward the pilot light. The flat part of the burner with the slot in it is where the gas burns.

"pilot" position. On some valves the knob must be pushed down until the pilot is lit. On other gas valves there is a red button which has to be pushed down and held until the pilot heats a safety element that makes the pilot continue to burn. (After the pilot light has burned long enough to warm the thermocouple, the thermocouple circuit will hold the gas valve in the proper position, as in Fig. 9-11.)

Usually the pilot light is between the burners and is difficult to reach. A wire with a clip or hook on the end can be used to hold the match (Fig. 9-12). A soda straw can also be used for lighting the pilot.

If the pilot light burns but goes out when the knob or button is released, chances are the knob or button wasn't held down long enough. If several attempts have been made to light the pilot light and it fails to stay on, the connection should be checked where the thermocouple connects to the gas valve (Fig. 9-13). If all connections are tight, the thermocouple will probably have to be changed.

Once the pilot light stays on, turn the knob to the "on" position. Turn up the thermostat, and the burner should light. If the pilot goes out—which often happens in a new installation or when the gas line has been opened—there is probably air in the line, and the procedure will have to be repeated. All of the connections should be checked with soap bubbles for a peak if the pilot repeatedly goes out.

## Checking Gas Pressure

The gas pressure can be checked at the manifold by removing the plug (Fig. 9-14). Sometimes there is a ¼-inch plug in the gas valve. This plug is usually located in the bottom of the gas valve, just before it goes into the manifold. You check the pressure by removing the plug from the manifold on the valve and installing a pressure gage.

Another way to check the pressure is to remove one burner and the orifice and then screw a fitting in where the orifice was removed. Now the gage can be connected to the fitting and the pressure checked.

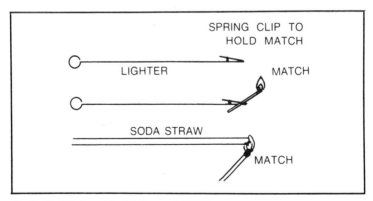

Fig. 9-12. Aids to safely lighting a pilot light.

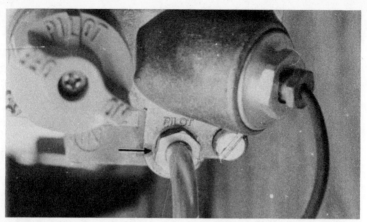

Fig. 9-13. The arrow points to the connection where the pilot light tube connects to the gas valve. The connection must be removed or loosened before the pilot light can be removed. Check this connection if you are having trouble keeping the pilot light lit.

In making the check, the gas valve should initially be turned to the "off" position. After the gage has been installed, relight the pilot light. Turn the gas valve to the "on" position and set the thermostat so the burners will light. After the burner is lit, take the gage reading.

For checking the gas pressure, use a special gage that reads in inches of a glass tube water column. With each instruction manual for a furnace, there will be a chart telling how the gas pressure should be set.

If the pressure is too low and you have LP gas, set up the pressure regulator on the tank. If turning up the tank's pressure regulator does not increase the pressure on the manifold, the furnace may have another pressure regulator on the bottom of the gas valve (Fig. 9-15). This regulator is set by the factory, but it will have to be advanced if the pressure is still too

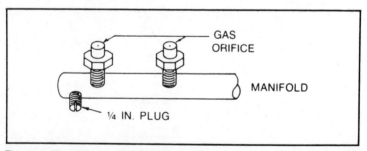

Fig. 9-14. The orifices connect to the manifold as shown here. The size of the hole in the orifice depends on the type of fuel being used. The ¼-inch plug may be removed, and test equipment may be installed to test gas pressure at this point. The pressure is changed by adjusting the regulator on the main line. The pressure will vary with the different types of fuel used.

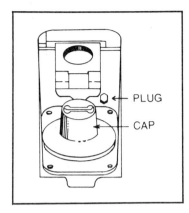

Fig. 9-15. Remove the cap to adjust the pressure on the gas valve. The plug can be removed to connect a gage to check the gas pressure on the manifold. Not all furnaces have such a regulator built into the gas valve. If a furnace doesn't have a gas valve pressure regulator, the regulator at the tank will have to be adjusted to change the gas pressure at the manifold.

low. If the gage indicates the pressure is too high, one regulator will need to be reset for a lower pressure.

It is sometimes against the gas supplier's policy to allow anyone but a company repairman or representative to change or adjust the pressure regulator on the tank. Often the determining factor is which party has ownership of the tank. If the homeowner owns the tank, an outside repairman is usually allowed to adjust it. If the gas supplier owns the tank, outside repairmen are often not allowed to adjust it. Where a city operates as a natural gas supplier, frequently no one other than a city representative is allowed to adjust a supply pressure regulator. Be sure to check on these restrictions before making adjustments.

Let us assume you are allowed to make the adjustments. For most pressure adjustments, start with the pressure regulator closest to the furnace. Most times this will correct any pressure problems.

When an LP gas tank is used and the distance from the tank to the furnace or furnaces is greater than usual, there will be a high-pressure regulator at the tank and a low-pressure regulator just before the gas line goes into the house. This added regulator means that there are now three regulators which must all be in adjustment for the pressure to be correct. The best way to approach this situation is to try to adjust the gas pressure using the regulator on the gas valve, if there is one. If this doesn't work, call the gas supplier and find out what the policies are on pressure regulator adjustments. If they give you the okay, continue adjusting the regulators, working from the gas valve to the supply tank. Otherwise, have them come and adjust the pressure.

After making the proper adjustments, turn off the gas valve, remove the gage and fitting from the manifold, and replace the plugs. Turn on the gas valve, light the burner, and check for possible leaks. Also, check the air adjustment if any pressure changes were made.

If there is no plug in the manifold, one of the burners can be used to install the gage for making the check. Make certain that all the fittings are tight and that the hose does not come off while the gas valve is open.

The gage used to check the gas pressure is a special type. Usually the gas company will have such a gage and will set the pressure on the furnace if you contact them.

## PILOT LIGHT

The pilot light should burn constantly unless there is an electric igniter to light the burners. The pilot light serves to hold the gas valve on a standby basis so that when the thermostat calls for heat, the gas valve will open and let the gas flow through the manifold to the burners. As the gas flows through the orifices into the burners, it mixes with the air being drawn in. When the air and gas mixture comes out the opening in the burner, the pilot light will ignite the gas.

When the pilot light is not burning, the gas valve will not open, no matter how cold the room gets. This is a safety device. If the gas valve were able to open, and if the pilot light happened to be out for some reason, the gas would flow out into the room instead of burning in the furnace.

There are several types of pilot lights, but basically they are all the same. They have to be installed in such a manner that when the gas valve opens and the gas flows through the burner, the pilot light will ignite the burner. This makes it very important to have the pilot light set correctly. This setting is made at different locations on the gas valve. Your dealer can give you the setting location and specifications for a specific furnace.

Sometimes if the pilot light flame is set too low, if it is dirty, or if it is out of adjustment, there will be too much gas in the combustion chamber, and there will be a small explosion when the pilot is lit. If the trouble seems to come from an accumulation of soot, check the burner air adjustment to be sure it is set correctly. This trouble might also be caused by a dirty pilot light.

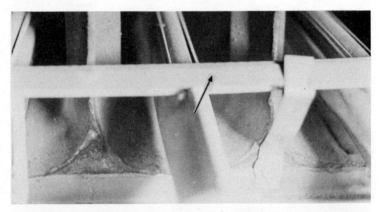

Fig. 9-16. The horizontal tube near the center of the photograph is the lighter tube. The lighter tube is connected to the manifold ahead of the burner so the gas will pass through the tube first. The pilot light will light the tube. The tube, in turn, will light the burners.

To clean the pilot light, loosen the line going to the pilot light as it leaves the gas valve. The gas valve should be turned to the "off" position. Loosen the thermocouple line and disconnect both lines. Remove the screws or bolts that hold the pilot in position (Fig. 9-11). Remove the pilot light and the thermocouple from the burner. Loosen the compression nut and remove the pilot light line so the orifice and pilot light can be cleaned with compressed air. Sometimes the only way to reach the pilot light is to remove the entire burner assembly.

## Lighter Tubes

Lighter tubes (see Fig. 9-16) are used where multiple burners are connected to the manifold. The lighter tube is connected to the manifold before the gas reaches the burner. The tube has a small orifice in it and a place where the gas is mixed with air. After being mixed, the air and gas mixture flows through the lighter tube until it comes to the small opening in the tube where the pilot light ignites it. The full length of the tube is lit. It, in turn, lights each burner as the gas flows through the opening in the burner.

Some burners are designed so they will light each other, and still other systems have two pilot lights. There are also electric pilot lights.

## Removing the Pilot Lights and Burners

To remove the pilot light and thermocouple, the screws that hold the manifold to the furnace usually have to be removed. Usually there are two at each side of the manifold. Sometimes the burners can be removed by just loosening the screws.

The gas line from the tank will have to be shut off, or the gas will have to be shut off at a valve at the regulator. The gas line to the assembly can then be removed at the gas valve. Detach the thermocouple and pilot light from the burner as previously described. Remove the connection from the pilot light and clean the orifice.

Fig. 9-17. The connector holding the orifice and pilot light can be removed if the pilot light orifice has to be cleaned. The thermocouple is pressed into the bracket that holds it into position. To remove the thermocouple, pry it out with a screwdriver and push a new one into position. Be sure the thermocouple extends high enough into the pilot light flame.

Fig. 9-18. In this type of gas valve the transformer is under the fan relay. This transformer supplies 24V for the coil which opens the gas valve. On transformer/relay assemblies used in heating-cooling units, the relay may bypass the fan control when the air conditioner is turned on.

If the thermocouple has to be removed from the bracket, it can be pulled out. A new one can be pressed into place (Fig. 9-17).

Replace the pilot light and the thermocouple and position them on the burner, making certain the thermocouple is in proper alignment so the pilot flame will contact the thermocouple tip. Connect the burner and thermocouple line to the gas valve and pilot light tube, making certain all connections are tight. Then replace the manifold and gas line. Finally, turn on the gas and check all joints for leaks with soap bubbles.

## TRANSFORMERS

Transformers can be found in many places on the furnace or air conditioning unit. Usually they are located close to the power supply line. The transformer has a *primary* winding and a *secondary* winding. The primary connects to the 120V power main, and the secondary connects to the low voltage circuits to operate the thermostat, fan relay, and gas valve. When a transformer reduces the voltage from a high to a low value, as in this application, it is called a *stepdown* transformer.

In furnaces the transformer usually reduces the voltage from 120V to 24V (or sometimes 12V volts). The condensing unit may require a voltage reduction from 240V to 24V. When it is necessary to change a transformer, it should be replaced with an identical kind. Figure 9-18 shows a typical transformer and relay installation.

In a central heating and air conditioning system, the furnace transformer will also supply the voltage for the coil of the condensing unit contactor which turns the condensing unit on and off. One runs from the thermostat to the contactor coil on the condensing unit, and the other wire returns to the other side of the transformer secondary.

The transformer can be checked using a voltohmmeter. Set the meter on a voltage range higher than 24V and place the two leads from the meter on the two secondary terminals. The meter should read 12V or 24V, depending on the transformer. When running this check, power must be applied to the transformer primary circuit.

A second method of checking the transformer is to disconnect the primary leads from the power supply, set the ohmmeter on R × 1 and place the two leads of the meter on the primary terminals (Fig. 9-19). If the meter gives a resistance reading, the primary winding is good. The low-voltage (secondary) side can be checked the same way. If the transformer is good, then check the transformer connections and power supply.

Another ohmmeter test is to connect one of the ohmmeter leads to a secondary terminal and the other lead to the transformer case. A reading on the meter means the transformer is shorted out. All ohmmeter tests must be made with the power off to avoid damaging the ohmmeter.

## FAN CONTROLS

The fan control is usually located near the heat exchanger. When the temperature reaches a preset temperature, the fan control points will close and the fan motor will start. The warm air will move out of the heat exchanger and into the duct system and rooms.

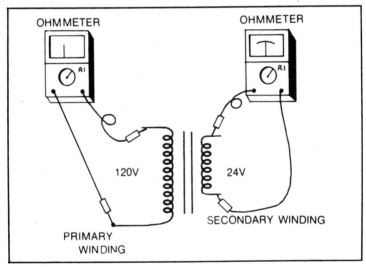

Fig. 9-19. Checking the transformer with an ohmmeter. When resistance can be read or the pointer moves across the scale to zero, check for a short from one transformer terminal to the transformer case. If the meter hand moves, the transformer has shorted out; if not, the winding is good. Now check the other winding in the same manner. When the two ohmmeter leads are connected to the transformer terminals and the resistance reading is infinity, the circuit is open inside the transformer. Be sure the power is disconnected when running this check.

Fig. 9-20. The fan control and limit control are shown here. As the furnace heats up, the round dial turns to switch the fan on. If the furnace gets too hot, the dial will turn farther and will open the limit switch, shutting off the power to the transformer. Some of these controls have two hands or levers that can be adjusted to control the temperature at which the fan comes on. The third lever is the limit control. It is set by the factory and should not be tampered with.

There are several types of fan controls. One type has a limit control built in with the fan control (Fig. 9-20). If the fan doesn't come on or the furnace gets too hot, the control will disconnect the power to the transformer and the gas valve will close, putting the burner out.

Some controls include two levers that can be adjusted to turn the fan on or off at the desired temperature. Usually one of these levers will be set at 125° F and the other will be set around 110° F. When the temperature in the heat chamber rises to 125° F, the control will trip the fan switch, and the fan will run. If the upper setting is too low and the fan is turned on too soon, it will blow cold air. If the upper setting is too high, the limit switch may cut the burner off before the fan removes the warm air from the heat chamber.

Both of these problems can be solved by readjusting the temperature level at which the fan turns on. Do not attempt to adjust the factory setting on the high-temperature shutoff (limit control).

If the two fan temperature levers are set too close together, when the fan comes on it will immediately cool the heat chamber to a temperature that will shut off the fan. For example, if the high setting is 115°F and the low setting is 110°F, the fan will come on when the temperature in the heat chamber reaches 115°F. When the fan starts, it will blow the cooler air from the return air duct into the heat chamber and cool the heat chamber to, say, 106°F. The fan will immediately shut off. The burners will warm the heat chamber again and kick the fan on, and the cycle will be repeated. This is known as *short cycling*, and it can be prevented by adjusting the fan controls so that there is at least a 15° to 20° difference between the high and low settings.

When the fan continues to run without stopping, the difficulty could be caused by a bad fan control. If the thermostat includes air conditioning as well as heating, the control could be at the setting necessary for air conditioning. With the dual-purpose thermostats there are usually two settings: "automatic" and "on". If by mistake the control is set to the "on" position, the fan will run continuously. This is desirable with air conditioning, but not when heating, because part of the time the fan will be blowing cold air into the room. When the thermostat is set to "automatic", the fan will cycle with the furnace.

If the control is defective, the problem might be in the switch or the sensing device. In either case it is necessary to remove the control. To do this, first shut off the power to the furnace. Next, remove the screws in each corner of the control. The wires on the terminals of the control will have to be removed. Removal can be done by inserting a small screwdriver in the

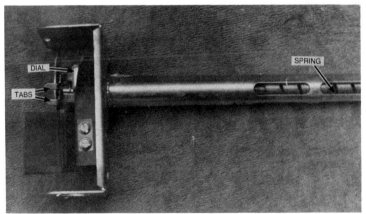

Fig. 9-21. Top view of fan control. The sensing device senses the temperature of the heat exchanger. As the spring expands due to the heat, it will turn the dial and open or close the fan switch and limit switch. The dial operates the switches. The two tabs adjust the temperature at which the fan turns on and off.

slot above or below the terminal and releasing the wire. The wire can then be pulled out. The wires should always be marked, or the color of the wires should be written down so the wires can be returned to the proper place. The control can then be removed from the furnace.

Upon examination of the sensing unit inside the control (Fig. 9-21), if the spring is found to be broken or stuck, the control will have to be changed. It will also need to be changed if the switch is bad.

The new control may not be exactly like the one that is removed. Some of the controls have three wires and some will have four wires. If, for example, it is necessary to replace a three-wire control with a four-wire control, place a jumper wire from the "hot" wire to the bottom of the fan side or the limit side (Figs. 9-22 and 9-23), depending on which side the "hot" line is connected to.

If a four-wire control is needed, the jumper is not used. One "hot" wire should go to the fan side of the limit control, and the remaining "hot" wire should go to the other side of the limit control.

Often bimetal switches are used for the fan and limit controls (see Fig. 9-24). The switch used for the fan control closes when the temperature rises to about 125°F, and the one used for the limit control opens when the temperature rises to 225°F. These controls cannot be adjusted.

## TROUBLESHOOTING GAS FURNACES

This section summarizes the troubles found in gas furnaces and the causes of the troubles. You should familiarize yourself with this section now; later it will serve as a handy reference.

### Burner Won't Light

● Power supply to furnace disconnected.
● Voltage on secondary side of transformer insufficient.

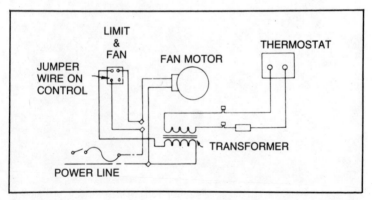

Fig. 9-22. A wiring diagram for a heating furnace without an air conditioner. Jumper wires may have to be used on the fan-limit control when changing controls.

176

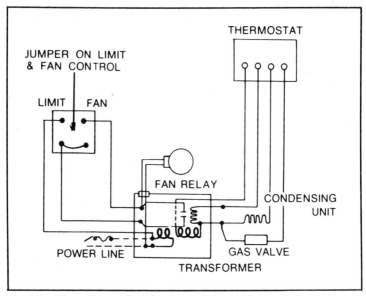

Fig. 9-23. Wiring diagram for a heating and air conditioning unit.

- Loose connection on transformer primary circuit.
- Bad transformer.
- Loose or bad thermostat wire.
- Bad thermostat.
- Bad gas valve coil.
- Gas valve not opening.
- Gas valve turned off.
- Pilot light out.
- Bad thermocouple.
- Bad high-limit switch.

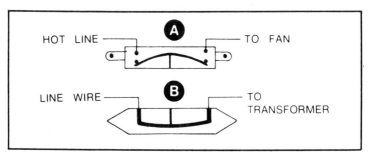

Fig. 9-24. (A) The fan control closes when the temperature rises. When the control cools it will open, breaking the circuit to the fan. (B) The limit control has the points closed because the temperature is below a preset level. When the points are open, the power is disconnected from the transformer.

### Pilot Light Won't Stay Lit

- Gas valve not set correctly.
- Tank out of fuel.
- Dirty pilot light.
- Bad thermocouple.
- Thermocouple not in pilot light flame.
- Pilot light adjusted too low.
- Moisture frozen around outside regulator.

### Burner Explodes When Lighting

- Pilot light set too far away from burner.
- Pilot light tube dirty.
- Pilot light set too low.
- Leaky gas valve.
- Improper gas pressure.
- Wrong pilot light for furnace.

### Yellow Flame at Burners

- Air adjustment set wrong.
- Dirty burners.
- Air restricted at burner air adjustment.
- Bad burners.
- Gas pressure set wrong.
- Dirty orifices.

### Fan Won't Run

- Fan motor burned out.
- Fan limit switch bad.
- Bad fan bearing.
- Broken fan belt.
- Fan belt too loose.
- Bad capacitor on motor.
- Foreign material in fan.
- Fan stuck.
- Loose fan wire.
- Internal overload on motor open.

### Furnace Won't Heat House

- Furnace too small.
- Broken fan belt.
- Loose fan belt.
- Fan stuck.
- Bad motor.
- Loose fan blade.

- Fan limit switch bad.
- Fan running too slow.
- Dirty air filter.

## Furnace Continually Cut Off by Limit Switch

- Bad limit switch.
- Fan not running.
- Fan turn-on switch set for too high temperature.
- Loose belt.
- Loose fan blade.
- Obstruction in fan blade.
- Bad bearing in fan or motor.
- Dirty air filter.

## Fan Making Noise

- Fan blade out of balance.
- Loose blade.
- Fan blade too close to motor housing.
- Bent shaft.
- Bent housing.
- Loose mounting bolts.
- Foreign objects in fan.
- Fan running too fast.

# Chapter 10

# Servicing Oil Furnaces

When servicing a furnace, turn the electrical power supply off and shut the fuel supply line except when these need to be open to perform a test. In an oil-burning furnace the fuel oil is put under pressure by a pump and sprayed through nozzles. It mixes with air as it travels through the burners and into the firebox, where the combustion process takes place. In the burner, igniters form an electrical arc that lights the oil and air mixture. In an oil-burning furnace the fuel oil is put under pressure by a pump and sprayed through nozzles. It mixes with air as it travels through the burners and into the firebox, where the combustion process takes place. In the burner, igniters form an electrical arc that lights the oil and air mixture.

### OIL BURNER BASICS

The gun type burner shown in Fig. 10-1 is the one used most often on residential heating units. The canister extension, or barrel, on the burner sticks through the wall of the furnace into the firebox, where the oil burns. The barrel houses the spray nozzles and igniters (Fig. 10-2).

The fuel oil furnace is usually made somewhat differently than the gas furnace. The firebox is constructed of thick steel lined with fire brick (Fig. 10-3) or of stainless steel. This is made necessary by the intense heat concentrated at the end of the barrel.

The controls on an oil furnace are basically the same as those on a gas furnace, but there are more controls on an oil furnace. The oil furnace has two transformers: one that steps up the line voltage from 120V to 10,000-15,000V, and another that steps the line voltage down from 120V to 24V.

### STORING AND TRANSFERRING THE OIL

The oil is stored in a tank either outside the house or in the basement. If you are considering installing an oil furnace, check the city building code

Fig. 10-1. Gun-type oil burner. The pump brings the oil from the tanks and raises the pressure to spray it through the nozzles. The barrel of the burner houses the spray nozzles and igniters. This part of the burner sticks inside the firebox.

Fig. 10-2. This is the burner as seen looking into the end of the barrel. This end of the barrel sticks into the firebox.

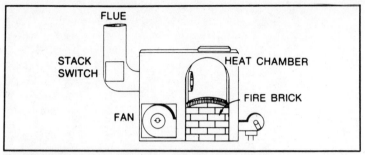

Fig. 10-3. The gun-type oil burner installed in a furnace. The fire brick serves to prevent the concentrated heat from burning through the firebox. The stack switch is installed in the flue to sense the heat going up the flue.

to determine the regulations governing the storage of fuel oil. These laws may affect location of the tank. Probably the easiest way to check on this is to contact a local fuel oil dealer.

An advantage of locating the tank outside is that any possible messes involving the tank will not occur in the house. Another advantage is that the tank can be placed high enough to permit gravity flow of the fuel to the furnace pump. Without gravity flow, the pump may have to be primed if it ever runs out of fuel.

One disadvantage to outside storage is that if you live in an area where the temperature frequently falls below zero, the oil may thicken and not flow properly. Another problem caused by outside storage is the possibility of moisture entering the tank.

There should be a filter somewhere in the fuel line between the tank and the pump. Access to this filter is provided by a cutoff valve at the tank. After shutting this valve, the filter may be removed and cleaned. The filter should be drained and cleaned at regular intervals as part of the routine maintenance. If you are servicing someone else's oil furnace, it is a good idea to clean this filter just for insurance.

There are two different fuel line systems used: single-line systems and double-line systems. In the single-line system all of the oil that flows to the pump is burned by the furnace. In the double-line system one line carries the oil from the tank to the pump, and the second carries the unburned fuel back to the tank. In this system only a portion of the oil flowing into the pump goes to the burner; the rest returns to the tank.

### BASIC SERVICING

The motor for the system runs the blower and pump. It is usually located on one side of the burner (Fig. 10-4). To remove the pump for repair, remove the plate on the bottom of the burner as shown in Fig. 10-5; then disconnect the pump from the motor shaft by loosening a screw in the coupling. Finally, remove the external bolts holding the pump in place and remove the pump.

With the plate removed you can also service or repair the motor, igniters, and nozzle. The motor can be removed by loosening the fan blade setscrew and pulling the motor out. To remove the igniters and nozzle, check to be sure that the power is off, then unplug the wires from the transformer. Usually the nozzle and igniters are held in place with a setscrew that must be loosened. Next, disconnect the fuel line running between the pump and nozzle, and the nozzle can be removed. The igniter and nozzle assembly is shown in Fig. 10-6 during removal, and in Fig. 10-7 after removal from the burner unit. Take care when removing the assembly not to break the igniters.

The igniters should be scraped and cleaned with sandpaper and replaced in the proper position. The nozzle should be removed and cleaned with compressed air. To remove the nozzle, unscrew its end using the proper size wrench. On some units there will be a screen behind the nozzle that should be cleaned at the same time.

The pump raises the pressure of the oil so it will atomize as it leaves the nozzle. The high voltage from the transformer produces an arc at the igniter ends, and the oil begins to burn, (see Fig. 10-8). If the arc doesn't light the oil, the stack switch in the flue will not sense any heat through the flue and will shut down the burner. This is to keep the pump from pumping oil into the firebox when the oil is not burning. The stack switch is the counterpart of the thermocouple and pilot light on gas furnaces.

Figure 10-9 shows the proper settings for the nozzle and electrodes for one burner assembly. Check the manufacturer's specifications for the burners on your furnace. These settings have to be accurate so the electrodes will arc, and as the fuel is sprayed through the arc, the fuel will light.

Fig. 10-4. Oil burner. The transformer steps the voltage up from 120V to around 10,000 to 15,000V. The motor runs the pump and the blower for the air to the burners. The air duct has an adjustment at the bottom to regulate the air flow to the burners.

183

Fig. 10-5. This burner has the plate removed, allowing access to the fan and nozzle. The squirrel-cage fan forces the air through the burners.

The electrodes can be adjusted by loosening the setscrew and turning the electrodes and moving them in or out as required. Then the screw is retightened. Normally the arc can be heard or seen if the door to the furnace is open and the furnace kicks on. Be sure to tighten all connections and check the electrode connections. If the electrodes are cracked they should be replaced.

Fig. 10-6. Here the igniters and nozzle assembly are being removed from the burner.

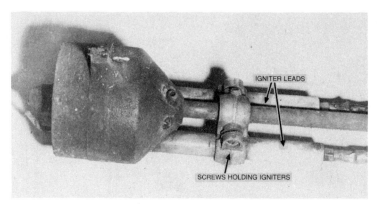

Fig. 10-7. The igniter and nozzle assembly after removal.

## SERVICING PUMPS

The pump is usually connected to one end of the motor shaft. To check the pressure on the pump, remove the ¼-inch plug from the pump housing as shown in Fig. 10-10. A standard pressure gage (measurements in pounds

Fig. 10-8. The high voltage from the transformer causes an arc across the two electrodes. As the nozzles spray the oil through the arc, the oil will burst into flames.

185

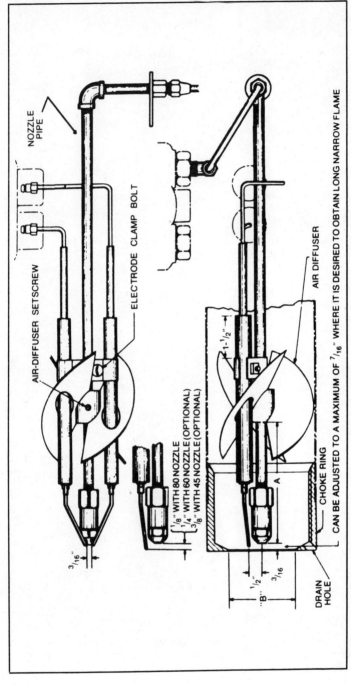

Fig. 10-9. Illustration of nozzle settings. These are the settings which will apply on most oil-burning furnaces.

FUEL LINE

OIL FILTER

CAP NUT

PLUG

Fig. 10-10. The pump is connected directly to the motor shaft. The fuel line goes to the burner nozzle. To adjust the pressure of the pump, remove the ¼-inch pipe plug and install a pressure gage. Remove the cap nut to make the necessary adjustments.

per square-inch) can then be installed by hooking it into this fitting. Start the furnace by setting the thermostat up until the furnace comes on.

The correct pressure is usually about 180 psi, but check the manufacturer's specifications. To adjust pressure, remove the cap nut and turn the adjusting screw underneath it. To increase pressure, turn the adjusting screw clockwise; to decrease pressure, turn this screw counterclockwise. After correcting the pressure, turn off the furnace and replace the plug and cap nut.

To remove the pump, loosen the coupler on the end of the motor shaft and remove the two studs in the pump housing (Fig. 10-11). Then remove the pump by pulling it straight out. Do not pry too hard on the casting; it could break the pump housing.

To gain access to the gears inside the pump housing, remove the eight bolts on the end plate of the housing (Fig. 10-12). The end plate can then be removed, revealing the screen underneath. Before the end plate can be replaced later, the mated surfaces will have to be scraped and cleaned, and a new gasket will have to be installed.

In Fig. 10-13 you can see an example of the sludge buildup that may occur on the screen. Sludge restricts the flow of oil to the pump and must be removed. Clean the screen by placing it in fuel oil and brushing it with a household brush.

The internal plate that covers the gears and motor shaft is located under the end plate (Fig. 10-14). This plate, which is part of the pump housing, can be removed by removing the five bolts that hold it down. When removing this plate, take care to prevent springing or bending the plate. If you have difficulty removing it, you may want to tap it with a wooden mallet or plastic hammer to make it come loose.

Fig. 10-11. The pump is removed from the motor shaft by removing the hold-down bolts which go into the holes (arrows). Be sure to remove the setscrew in the coupler which connects the pump shaft to the motor shaft.

Fig. 10-12. To get to the inside of the pump, remove the eight studs and remove this end plate. Take care to prevent breaking the casting. A new gasket will have to be installed when the end plate is replaced.

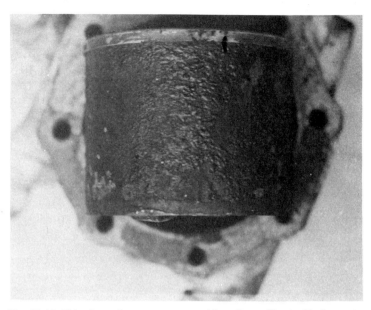

Fig. 10-13. This shows the screen removed from its position inside the pump housing. Here the sludge buildup on the screen is very evident. When cleaning this screen with a brush and fuel oil, be careful not to punch a hole in the screen.

Fig. 10-14. The plate inside the pump may be removed by removing the five studs. Under the plate are the gears and motor shaft. The plate is part of the pump housing.

Fig. 10-15. This is the back side of the internal plate. Notice the groove where the oil enters the suction side of the pump. The divider separates the gears.

The surface on the back side of the plate is machined, so a gasket is not used. The plate is grooved on the back side so the oil can be picked up (Fig. 10-15).

The gears and gear housing could be worn so badly that the oil bypasses the gears, and the proper pressure can't be reached. The parts of

Fig. 10-16. The gears of the pump are revealed by removing the internal plate. The motor shaft is keyed to the inside gear, which drives a ring gear.

the pump may have to be replaced before the pressure can be held. These parts are all machined to a close tolerance, so gaskets aren't used. Figure 10-16 shows the gears in position. Figure 10-17 shows the intake port where the oil enters the gears, and the exhaust port where the oil leaves the gears.

## OTHER SERVICING

The fan switch on an oil furnace serves the same purpose as on a gas furnace. When the heat in the heat chamber reaches a certain temperature, the fan switch will close, and the fan will blow the hot air through the duct system.

The *limit switch* is used to keep the furnace from getting too hot. If the fan doesn't start, the limit switch will turn the furnace off to avoid over-heating in the heat chamber.

These controls can be made as one unit, or they may appear separately. The previous chapter gives further information on these controls.

The *stack control* switch operates the burners on an oil furnace just as the thermocouple and safety pilot relay operate the pilot light and burners on a gas furnace.

When the thermostat calls for heat, the stack relay turns the igniters on and starts the pump. In some units the igniters stay on even after the oil has begun to burn, and in other units the relay will shut the igniters off. The heat going up the flue heats the probe from the stack switch, and the pump relay

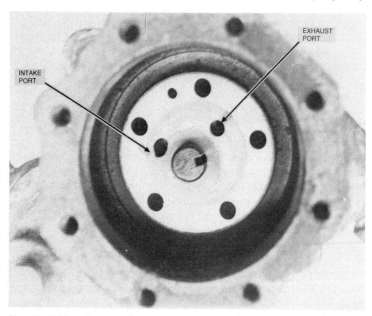

Fig. 10-17. Here the gears have been removed to show the intake and exhaust ports. The pump forces the oil through these into the lines toward the burners.

191

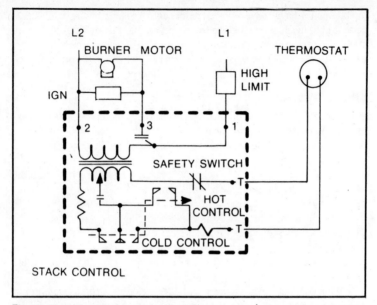

Fig. 10-18. Wiring diagram for a two-wire thermostat with a stack control. The area inside the box is the stack control.

is held on. If the igniters do not light the fuel and the stack control doesn't heat up in the proper amount of time, the control will turn off the pump and igniters. This prevents the pump from filling the firebox full of unburned oil.

A button on the front of the stack control is pushed to get the stack control to recycle. Then any oil in the firebox is removed and the burners are lit. Figures 10-18 and 10-19 show wiring diagrams for two- and three-wire thermostats used with stack controls.

## OIL BURNER EFFICIENCY TESTS

The operating efficiency of an oil furnace can be measured in a series of tests. These tests measure the amount of smoke and soot the furnace produces, as well as the furnace flue temperature and the carbon dioxide level in the flue gases. By comparing these measurements to an established norm, the homeowner or serviceman can determine how well the tested furnace is working and what adjustments need to be made to increase efficiency. These tests should be conducted annually on an oil burner in conjunction with a preseason tune-up.

The oil furnace testing devices are shown in Fig. 10-20. The basic testing devices can be purchased as a single kit that consists of the following: a flue thermometer, flue gas analyzer, smoke pump, soot comparison scale, and instructions. It is very important to follow the manufacturer's instructions for your testing devices. In the following paragraphs we will summarize the basic procedures commonly followed in such tests. If the

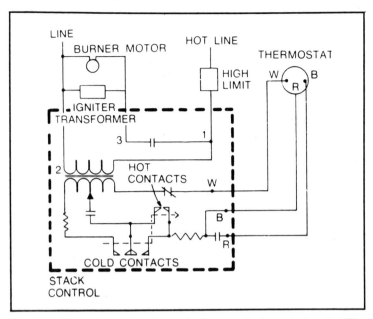

Fig. 10-19. Wiring diagram for a three-wire thermostat using a stack control. The area inside the box is the stack control.

instructions supplied with your kit follow different procedures, adhere to those procedures.

Testing kits can be purchased at heating supply or furnace supply stores. Their cost may be prohibitive to the average homeowner planning to test his furnace once a year.

### Test Preparations

Drill or punch a hole about ¼ inch in diameter in the flue about 12 to 24 inches from the flue outlet at the furnace. This hole should be ahead of the draft regulator (Fig. 10-21). When the tests are complete, block this hole with a large sheet metal screw or with a sheet metal flap attached to the flue with a sheet metal screw.

The furnace needs to be warm to conduct the tests. Set the thermostat above room temperature so the furnace will run for about 20 minutes.

### Smoke Test

The smoke test indicates the amount of smoke the furnace is producing. Heavy smoke production indicates the furnace is not operating efficiently and is wasting fuel. The smoke is produced when the fuel is not burning completely. If permitted to continue and to build up, the smoke will produce soot on the heat exchanger. This prevents the efficient transfer of heat from the combustion chamber to the room air.

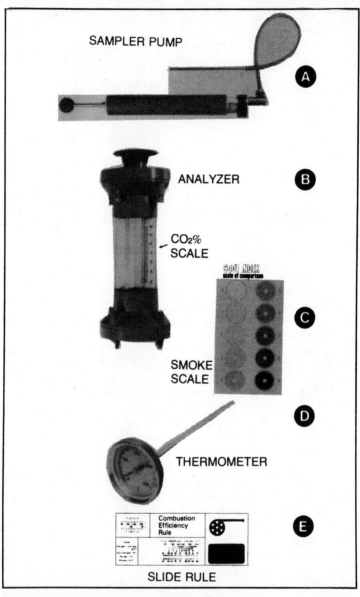

SAMPLER PUMP

A

ANALYZER

B

CO₂%
SCALE

SMOKE
SCALE

C

D

THERMOMETER

Combustion
Efficiency
Rule

E

SLIDE RULE

Fig. 10-20. These are the testing devices used to test the operation of an oil burner. (A) The sampler pump used for the smoke test. (B) The analyzer used to conduct the carbon dioxide analysis. (C) The smoke scale used to read the smoke test results. (D) The thermometer used to test the flue gas temperature. (E) The device used to determine the overall burner efficiency based upon the various test readings (courtesy Goodway Tools Corporation, 404 West Avenue, Stamford, CT).

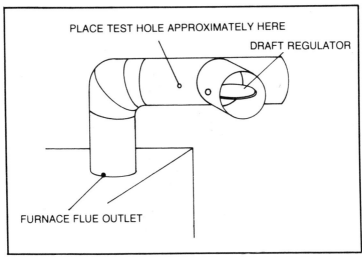

PLACE TEST HOLE APPROXIMATELY HERE

DRAFT REGULATOR

FURNACE FLUE OUTLET

Fig. 10-21. To conduct the oil burner tests, drill a small hole in the flue ahead of the draft regulator (if your furnace has a draft regulator).

To take a smoke test, use a smoke tester that resembles a hand-held pump. The furnace burners must be on. Loosen the nut at the end of the pump and insert a paper filter supplied with the tester. Tighten the nut. Attached to the end of the pump is a tube. Insert this tube into the flue through the hole previously drilled. Pump the pump handle steadily for 10 full strokes. Remove the tube from the flue sampler hole, remove the filter, and compare its shade to those presented in the smoke scale provided with the tester.

For a furnace operating efficiently, the smoke index will be 1, and 2 is acceptable. For older furnaces the readings may be one step higher. Any higher readings mean that excess smoke is being produced, wasting fuel and interfering with heating efficiency.

### Carbon Dioxide Measurement

The next step in the oil burner efficiency analysis is to measure the level of carbon dioxide present in the flue gases. If too much air mixes with the oil during the combustion process, less carbon dioxide is produced, indicating inefficient combustion.

Generally, the higher the carbon dioxide measurement, the less excess air introduced in the combustion process and the more efficient the burning. Turning down the air flow too much causes smoking and also reduces efficiency. The goal is to reach a happy medium between the two inefficient extremes. The furnace should be tuned if possible to a carbon level of at least 9 percent. Levels more than 11 percent are excellent. If you cannot reach a 9 percent reading, you should follow the servicing procedures given later.

To take the carbon dioxide measurement, insert the smoke tube into the test hole in the flue. Pump the analyzer according to the manufacturer's directions. Follow the manufacturer's procedures for conducting the analysis. At some point with most analyzers you will turn the analyzer upside down. The level of fluid in the scale of the analyzer is the percentage of carbon dioxide in the flue gases.

### Stack Temperature Test

A stack temperature thermometer is used for this test. You simply insert the thermometer probe into the flue through the test hole. Wait a few minutes for the thermometer to fully adjust. The temperature indicated is the flue gas temperature.

The proper flue gas temperature is usually between 400 and 600°F, but on older units or conversion units temperatures of up to 700°F may be appropriate. If the flue gas temperature is too high, it means too much heat is passing by the heat exchanger without being transferred to the room air circulating through the exchanger. The furnace is wasting heat up the flue.

### Calculating Overall Efficiency

The testing kit may have a slide rule or something similar that you can use to determine the overall efficiency of the oil furnace. This device uses the temperature measurements and the carbon dioxide measurements to arrive at this overall rating. When using such a device, be sure to follow exactly the manufacturer's procedures for determining the measurements to use. For example, you may have to subtract the room temperature from the stack temperature when reading the scale. Through tune-up and servicing procedures, a new burner should be able to reach 75 to 80 percent efficiency. An older burner should be able to reach at least 65 percent efficiency. When the efficiency levels are lower, or the measurements are inferior to the indicated proper measurements, you should tune up the burner following the procedures outlined earlier. This includes cleaning the burners, adjusting or replacing the nozzles if necessary, and adjusting the air supply. You may also have to vacuum the heat exchanger to remove soot buildup and promote efficient heat transfer, and the flue may have to be cleaned out to remove soot. Table 10-1 shows acceptable oil burner test readings.

### TROUBLESHOOTING WITH TEST INSTRUMENTS

Following are suggestions of things to consider and correct when the test instruments indicate readings that are out of the norm for the furnace. *Excess smoke* means a smoke test reading of more than 1-2 for a burner less than 10 years old and more than 2-3 for a burner more than 10 years old. *Carbon dioxide levels* are as follows: *low* is less than 10 percent; *high* is more than 12 percent. *Stack temperatures* are as follows: *high* is more than 600°F

**Table 10-1. Oil Burner Test Analysis.**

| | | |
|---|---|---|
| $CO_2$ | 11 | Excellent |
| | 9 | Average |
| | 6 | Poor |
| Smoke Index | 0 | Excellent |
| Number | 1 | Excellent |
| | 2 | Good |
| | 3 | Average when burner untuned |
| | 4 | Poor |
| | 5 | Unacceptable |
| Stack temperature | 400-600 | Average for original oil burner |
| (Net) | 600-700 | Average for conversion burner |
| Higher temperatures require adjustment | | |
| Overall Efficiency | 80 percent and up | Excellent |
| | 70 percent - 80 percent | Acceptable |
| | Below 70 percent | Adjustment required |
| For conversion burners and burners more than 10 years old, subtract 10 percent from each figure. | | |

above room temperature for original oil burners and more than 700°F above room temperature for a conversion oil burner.

## Stack Temperature too High

● Burner nozzle too large. Replace with a smaller nozzle.

● Heat exchanger surfaces are thickly covered with soot. Clean and vacuum heat exchanger surfaces and flue.

## Carbon Dioxide Level too Low

When a carbon dioxide level of at least 9 percent cannot be obtained without the furnace smoking, suspect:

● Complete tune-up needed. Tune and clean the burners.

● Firing assembly misadjusted. Reset the igniters for proper spacing from the nozzle.

● Nozzle damaged. Replace the nozzle.

## Low Carbon Dioxide with Low Smoke

● Air adjustment on the burner set too high. Readjust to lower air adjustment.

● Air leaking into combustion chamber. Check for cracks and air leaks; seal them.

## Excess Smoke

● Tune-up needed. Tune up and clean burners.

● Air adjustment set too low. Readjust to increase air flow.

● Restricted air intake. Inspect and clean, if required.

## TROUBLESHOOTING AN OIL-BURNING FURNACE

The first step—as always in troubleshooting—is to make sure that there is not some minor problem preventing the proper functioning of the unit. Make sure there is electricity coming to the unit. Check the fuses and inspect the furnace for unplugged or loose wires. Test the stack overload switch, or reset this switch by pushing it to one side and releasing it.

### Checking and Servicing Igniters

If the pump runs but the igniters don't spark, remove the igniter assembly and check to see if the igniters are clean and properly set. Check for breaks or cracks in the assembly. Clean and reset the igniter gap and check the terminal for loose connections. Replace the igniters if they are damaged.

If the igniter assembly is in good shape and the problem persists, disconnect the transformer from the power supply and check the secondary winding with an ohmmeter. When an ohmmeter is connected to the secondary terminals, it will indicate a definite resistance (not infinity) if the secondary circuit is okay. To check the secondary for a short, attach one ohmmeter lead to the one secondary lead and connect the other ohmmeter lead to the case housing. If the ohmmeter lead to the case housing. If the ohmmeter gives a reading (other than infinity), the transformer is shorted and will have to be replaced.

Test the primary winding in the same way. Always be sure to disconnect the power supply when making these checks.

### Flame not Burning Cleanly

Locate the air adjustment valve and readjust the air mixture on the burner. Remove the igniter assembly and clean the nozzle and screen. The nozzle may have to be replaced if the hole is too large. Remove the plate on the end of the pump and clean the screen. Readjust the pump pressure by installing a gage on the pump and setting the pressure. Clean the flue and flue pipe. Check the automatic damper to make sure it is working properly.

### Checking the Stack Control

If the burner lights but the stack control shuts the unit off, inspect and clean the flue. If the flue is clean a bad igniter relay is probably the cause of the trouble. In this case, the stack control will have to be changed. Sometimes the stack control is too far from the furnace, requiring too much time before the heat reaches it. Try moving the stack control closer before you resort to replacing it.

If the thermostat doesn't turn the unit on, check at the transformer for correct voltage. The transformer is usually in the stack control.

### Checking the Limit Control

If the limit control is functioning improperly, current will not reach the stack control. To check the limit control, short across its two terminals. If the unit starts, the limit control could be bad or the furnace could be too hot.

## Checking the Fan

If the fan won't shut off, check the setting on the fan control. If the switch is stuck closed, it will have to be replaced.

If the fan won't run, check the fan control by shorting across its terminals. The fan motor could be burned out. If this is suspected, remove the motor and check its windings, starter switch, and bearings. If the motor cannot be repaired, it will have to be replaced.

## Further Troubleshooting

If the burner motor won't run, check the stack control burner relay and the limit switch. Remove the motor and check the windings, starter switch, and bearings. Check all wiring connections. Clean any dirt and dust out of the motor.

If the pump motor runs but the pump doesn't, check the coupler between the motor and pump shaft to see if the woodruff key is broken. Check the pressure control on the pump—it could be stuck open. The pump could be out of oil, or the strainer on the tank might be full of water. In the latter case, drain and clean the tank.

Air in the line will cause the pump to pump oil and then shut off. If the tank is above the pump, the air can be bled at the intake line or at the plug on the intake side of the pump. If the tank is on the same level as the pump, remove the line and fill it and the pump with oil. Pump air into the tank through the air vent to force the oil into the line. The air vent must be kept open to prevent the formation of a vacuum above the oil that will cause the pump to run dry.

If the furnace won't light:

● Check for ignition at the igniter. Clean and reset the gap.

● Check the nozzle to see if the orifice is plugged or the screen is clogged. Clean the nozzle and screen.

● Check the filter in the line. Drain and clean.

● Check the high voltage transformer with a voltohmmeter.

● Check the limit switch to be sure the points are open.

# Chapter 11

# Servicing the Electric Furnace

When servicing the furnace, turn off the electrical power except when it must be on for testing.

The electric furnace can be made into an upflow, downflow, or horizontal furnace by simply switching the positions of the components, which is not true of gas and oil furnaces. The electric furnace doesn't have a flue or heat exchanger, because there isn't any burning fuel. Instead, the air to be warmed comes in contact with the resistance coils.

The fan is at one end of the furnace. Next to the fan are the heating elements and the coil case. If a downflow furnace is needed, the fan will be placed on the top. If an upflow furnace is required, the furnace can be turned over so the fan is at the bottom. The fan is connected to the cold air return duct to keep the fan motor cool.

### ELECTRIC FURNACE WIRING

Usually an electric furnace will operate on a 240V circuit. The current drawn by the furnace depends on the number of burners or elements.

There are two different ways that electric furnaces are wired. The first, shown in Figs. 11-1 and 11-2, uses one main circuit breaker and one power circuit for the entire furnace. The wire and circuit breaker size on this type of furnace will have to be large enough to carry the full current load. For a 125A furnace, for example, wire size 00 would be used.

The second type of electric furnace has each heating element of the furnace connected separately in its own circuit to the building's breaker box (Fig. 11-3). Since each element is the only load on each circuit, a smaller breaker and wire size are used. If, for example, each element pulled 20A, a 30A breaker should be used for each element, and the elements would be wired with No. 10 wire. The instruction manual for a given furnace should give the wire and the breaker size for that particular furnace.

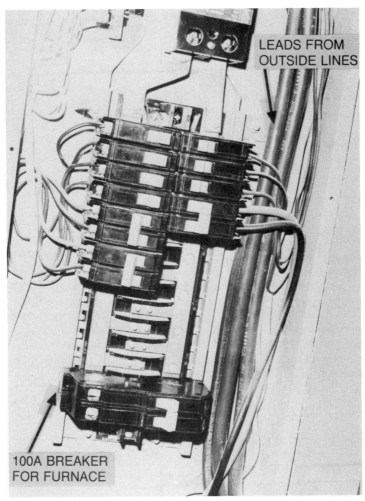

Fig. 11-1. Main breaker box to which all house circuits are run.

In some furnaces two elements are connected to one circuit (Fig. 11-4). This will save running a large number of circuits to the furnace. Heavier wire and a larger breaker must be used.

### OVERLOAD PROTECTORS

There are several types of overload protectors used on electric furnaces. Figure 11-5 shows a terminal board holding the fuses that protect the elements. The wiring shown connects the power mains to each element through a 30A fuse. The main power circuit to the furnace is protected by a circuit breaker. What each 30A fuse does is to protect one element on the

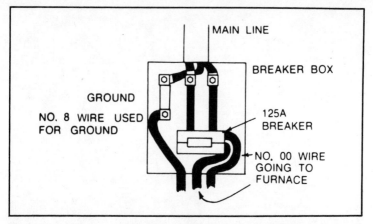

Fig. 11-2. Details of a main breaker box with a breaker for the furnace.

furnace. Since there are four fuses shown in the terminal box in the illustration, the furnace has four elements.

The reason for fusing each element is that if something happens to overload one of the elements, its 30A fuse will blow, whereas the 100A or 125A breaker protecting the main circuit would not blow in time to prevent damage. This type of wiring system is used only if all the elements are connected to the breaker box with one circuit. If each element is wired to the breaker box with its own circuit and breaker as previously discussed, the terminal box and fuses shown in Fig. 11-5 are not needed.

Figure 11-6 shows another type of protector that can be used in the element circuit. This is a bimetal disc that opens the circuit when the element overheats.

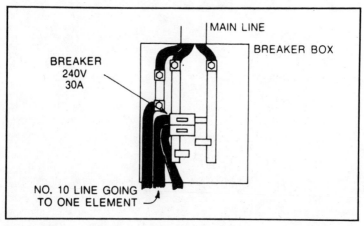

Fig. 11-3. Breaker box with each element of the furnace connected separately to a breaker.

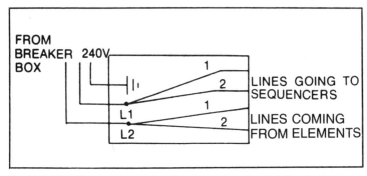

Fig. 11-4. With this arrangement two lines come from the main breaker box, and two furnace elements are wired on each line.

Fig. 11-5. Terminal board on an electric furnace. The main lines connect at the terminals at the top. Fuses protect each element in the furnace. The heater circuit runs from one main terminal, through the fuses to the various elements, through the elements and control devices, and back to the other main terminal.

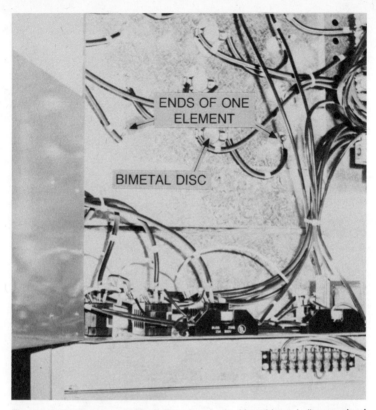

Fig. 11-6. Each element circuit here is wired with a bimetal disc overload protector. The bimetal disc will open the circuit if the element gets too hot.

Figure 11-7 is a complete wiring diagram for one element of an electric furnace. Notice that there is a second fuse connected to the "hot" line coming in from the other power supply terminal, just before this line connects to the element.

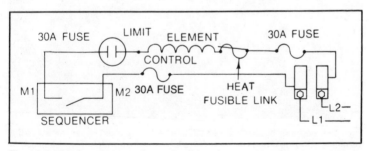

Fig. 11-7. This is a diagram of one circuit in a furnace. Notice the fuse on each end of the circuit.

Fig. 11-8. Four sequencers in an electric furnace circuit.

## SEQUENCERS

The sequencers are time delay relays that are triggered by the control circuit to turn on the furnace elements (Fig. 11-8). The control circuit is at a low voltage and connects to the thermostat. If the furnace has a terminal board, the control circuit will connect to it at a marked terminal (usually W1). For furnaces without terminal boards the control circuit will connect to a terminal or wire elsewhere on the furnace. You may have to check the wiring diagram to determine just where.

The control circuit will run to H1 on the No. 1 sequencer (Fig. 11-9). The thermostat will control the No. 1 sequencer. When the thermostat calls

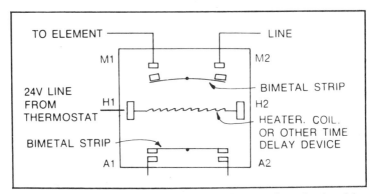

Fig. 11-9. Diagram of the No. 1 sequencer. As the heater, coil, or other time delay device is energized, it will close the points between M1 and M2, completing the circuit to the element. The points between A1 and A2 will close to set up the next sequencer.

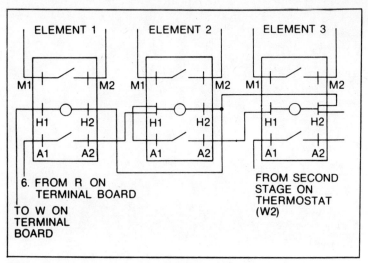

Fig. 11-10. Wiring diagram for electric furnace.

for heat, it will energize terminal H1 on the first sequencer. From H1 to H2 is connected a device such as a resistor, heater, or coil that will close the points between M1 and M2, and A1 and A2. The points between M1 and M2 will complete the circuit to the element and it will heat up.

The circuit wire numbered 6 in Fig. 11-10 runs from the R terminal on the terminal board to the A1 switch on the No. 1 sequencer. When the switch closes between A1 and A2, the power goes through the circuit to H1 on the No. 2 sequencer, then down to A1 on the No. 2 sequencer. This will complete the circuit between H1 and H2 on the second sequencer, closing the switches between M1 and M2 for the second sequencer and turning on the second element. When this happens, the switch between A1 and A2 on the second sequencer will close and set up the No. 3 sequencer.

### TROUBLESHOOTING

When checking relays, sequencers, and transformers, the manufacturer's schematic diagram will have to be obtained and followed. Disconnect the power supply and remove one of the low voltage leads from the terminals of the relay as shown in Fig. 11-11. Place the ohmmeter probes on the H (power) terminals. The meter should give a reading. The purpose of removing the terminal connection from one terminal is to prevent a reading through some other relay in the circuit. All the sequencers and fan relays can be checked in this manner.

If there is continuity through the coil, check the voltage across the points of the relay by turning the meter to "volts" and reconnecting the power to the relay. Check the voltages between A1 and H2, and between A2 and H2. If a reading of 24V is not obtained, the relay is bad and will have to be replaced. To run this check, the No. 1 element must be on.

If there is no voltage reading through the relay in the check above, it may be that there is no power coming to the relay from the transformer. If the circuit into the relay does not have 24V, the sequencers will not work. To check the voltage coming into the relay, disconnect one of the power terminals (H1 or H2) and check for voltage between the wires connected to the terminals. If there is not 24V between those wires with the power on, the relay is not at fault—there is no power coming to the relay. In this case, check the transformer circuit.

## FAN

The fan shown in Fig. 11-12 is a squirrel-cage type. The blades are connected directly to the motor, and the motor is mounted inside the blades.

A shaded-pole motor is used. The speed of a shaded-pole motor can be varied by changing motor leads.

The motor has a running capacitor to help it start and run more efficiently. In the event of suspected motor malfunctioning, you should first check this capacitor because it can go bad and shut off the motor entirely. (See Chapter 12.)

The fan switch is a separate device on an electric furnace. It is a nonadjustable clip-on switch that senses the heat from the No. 1 element. When the No. 1 sequencer activates on the No. 1 element, it will heat and close the fan switch, starting the fan. The fan will run as long as the heat in the elements is above a predetermined temperature.

## TRANSFORMERS

The transformer reduces the 240V or 208V from the power mains to 24V. Figures 11-13 and 11-14 show furnace transformers. If the incoming

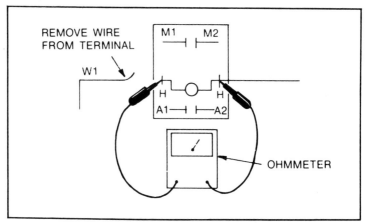

Fig. 11-11. If the ohmmeter doesn't give a reading, the coil is bad and the relay will have to be changed.

Fig. 11-12. Here the motor is shown mounted inside the squirrel-cage fan. The blades of the fan are connected directly to the motor shaft. Screws mount the motor to the frame of the fan. When removing the motor, loosen the holding screw on the fan blades to the motor shaft so the shaft will slip out. The capacitor should be checked before removing a motor that is suspected of being defective. A bad capacitor might mislead the repairman into thinking the motor is defective.

voltage is 208V instead of 240V, the incoming leads will have to be attached to the 208V terminals on the transformer primary winding. If the primary circuit is connected to the 240V lead and the line voltage is 208V, the secondary voltage will be too low, and this voltage could keep the sequencer from working properly.

The primary circuit to the transformer is protected by its own 15A fuse since the main fuses are 30A, too large for the transformer. When checking the circuit, be sure to check this fuse.

Fig. 11-13. The transformer supplies the low voltage for the furnace. The fan relay is used with the air conditioning system.

## Voltage Checks

With the power turned on, place one lead from the voltmeter on terminal R of the terminal board and place the other lead on terminal C or wire C. The meter should give a voltage reading. If it doesn't, you are not getting power to the furnace.

## Ohmmeter Checks

To check the secondary circuit of the transformer with an ohmmeter, disconnect the power supply and remove either the R or C lead from the

Fig. 11-14. (A) Transformer for the furnace. (B) Fuse protecting the transformer. (C) Terminal board connected to the thermostat.

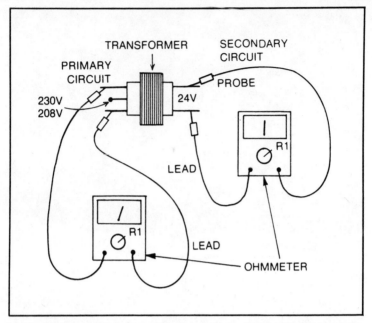

Fig. 11-15. This drawing shows how the ohmmeter is connected to check the primary and secondary coils of the transformer. The transformer must be disconnected from the power line for these tests.

terminal board. If the R-lead is removed, place one ohmmeter probe on the wire going to the transformer and place the other probe on terminal C. The meter will give a continuity reading if the secondary circuit is good. (See Fig. 11-15.)

To check the primary circuit on a transformer; disconnect the power supply and remove the two leads going to the transformer. Place the two probes from the ohmmeters on the two wires going to the transformer primary circuit. The ohmmeter should give a reading (other than infinity). Should any of these checks not result in the meter reading properly, the transformer is bad and will have to be replaced.

## LIMIT SWITCH

The bimetal limit control is shown in Fig. 11-16. If the element gets too hot, it will heat this bimetal switch in the element breaking the circuit. When the element and switch cool below a predetermined heat, the element will come back on. Some elements have a fusible link that cuts off the circuit by melting if the element gets too hot. The link must be replaced should the element ever overheat.

When the limit control has to be replaced (either bimetal or fuse type), you must use the exact replacement. Otherwise, the fan and element will not work properly.

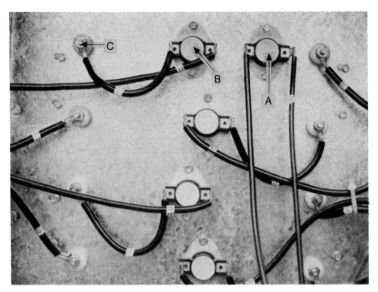

Fig. 11-16. (A) A bimetal fan temperature control that turns the fan off and on as the temperature varies in the heat chamber. (B) Bimetal limit control that keeps the element from overheating. (C) Element terminals connected to the wires.

## ELEMENT CIRCUIT

To check the element circuit, disconnect the power supply and remove the lead wire at the fuse (wire 23 in Fig. 11-17). Place ohmmeter lead on the terminal where the wire was removed; place the second lead on wire 28 where it connects to the fuse or main power supply. If the ohmmeter does not give a reading as shown at ohmmeter A in the figure, move the lead to the other side of the fuse (Fig. 11-17B) at 13. If there is still no reading, move the lead to terminal 12 or where the number 12 wire connects to the element (Fig. 11-17C). If the meter gives a reading, place the ohmmeter leads across the limit control (Fig. 11-17D). If the meter does not give a reading, the limit switch is bad. If the meter gives a reading, check the fuse.

If the meter doesn't give a reading through the element, place the lead on the other end of the element. Keep checking to find where the circuit is open.

## CHECKING ELEMENTS

If the element is bad, it will not register a continuity reading on the ohmmeter, and it will have to be replaced. Usually these elements are held in place with screws on each side. Sometimes all the elements will have to be removed to replace the bad one.

Figure 11-18 shows the element terminals that can be disconnected and checked for continuity. An ammeter clamp-on probe can be placed around each wire going to the elements to see which element isn't working.

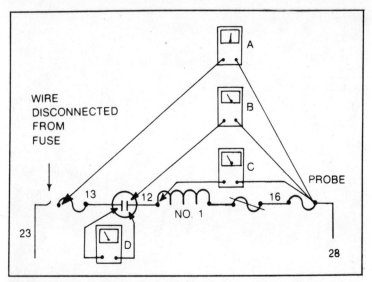

Fig. 11-17. Place the ohmmeter leads as indicated to check overcurrent fuses heat fuses, and elements. An ohmmeter reading as shown at B, C, and D indicates there is no continuity; that is, an open circuit is present. If continuity is present, the meter will read as shown at A.

The element may be broken or burned. Or the sequencer may be bad, in which case the points are not making contact to turn on the element.

Basically there are two types of elements. One type of resistance heater element has a metal case around the element. Another type, resistance wire, is shown in Fig. 11-19.

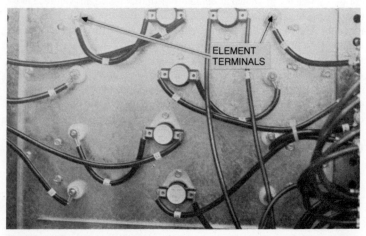

Fig. 11-18. You must remove the nuts from the ends of an element and remove the wires to check for continuity.

Fig. 11-19. Furnace elements.

To check the element for a short, place one lead of the ohmmeter on the element terminal and the other lead on the metal case of the furnace. If the meter gives a reading, the element is shorted and will have to be replaced. Usually when the element is shorted, a fuse will be burned out and will have to be replaced.

## INTERNAL FURNACE WIRING

There are wiring and connections in a furnace that the average homeowner or repairman may never see, simply because these connections are made inside the furnace. What the homeowner or repairman will see, however, is the terminal board of the furnace (Fig. 11-14). All of the connections from the terminal board must be connected to the thermostat for the unit (Fig. 11-20).

The transformer will be located inside the furnace and will reduce the 240V or 208V power supply to 24V to power the low voltage relays, switches, and thermostat. All of these low voltage circuits are connected to the terminal board, where they obtain their power (from the transformer) and their control (from the thermostat).

The two leads from the secondary winding on the transformer may connect internally to the back of the terminal board. The terminal board for the furnaces illustrated by Figs. 11-20 and 11-21 have only four terminals—only one for the transformer. The second transformer wire (C) is not run through the terminal board. In this system the terminals are lettered R, W, G, and Y. Some furnaces have more terminals and different lettering, but they must be connected to the thermostat in proper order. In this case

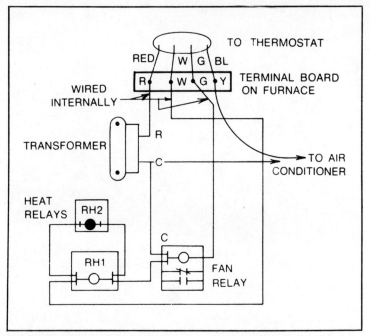

Fig. 11-20. This diagram shows how the wires from the terminal board are connected to the furnace internally for one circuit. The connections from the terminal board are wired to the corresponding terminals on the thermostat.

terminal R is the "hot" line from the transformer, and it supplies the power to the thermostat. Connecting wire G from the terminal board to terminal G on the thermostat hooks up the fan relay. Hooking up the W-terminals on the thermostat and terminal board connects the heating relays and elements into the circuit. Terminal W is wired internally to the No. 1 sequencer. When the thermostat calls for heat, it energizes terminal W to start the sequencers and elements.

Terminal Y is connected to the thermostat and runs from the thermostat to the condensing unit and back to the furnace, where it is connected to wire C, the other "hot" wire from the transformer. This gives the condensing-unit wire Y a complete circuit, so that when air conditioning is called for, the thermostat energizes terminal Y and the condenser kicks on. In most systems the return wire from the condensing unit connects to the terminal board.

## THERMOSTATS

There are two types of thermostats used in heating and cooling units. These are the high voltage (line voltage) and low voltage thermostats. The high voltage thermostat is usually used with baseboard heaters, portable heaters, and ceiling cable. Thermostats are discussed in detail in Chapter 7.

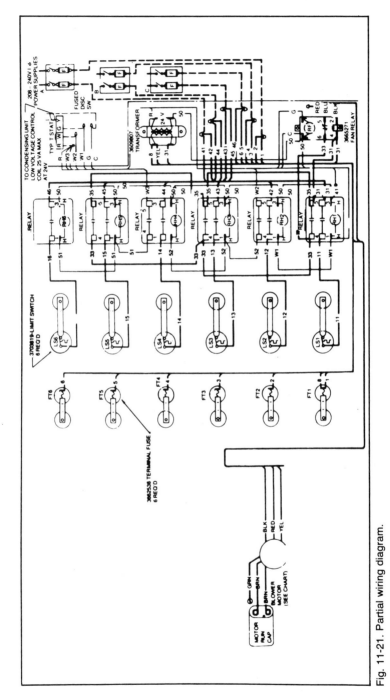

Fig. 11-21. Partial wiring diagram.

Fig. 11-22. A two-stage thermostat used on electric heating and air conditioning units. The terminals labeled RH and RC are the same as the R-terminals on other thermostats. The W1 and W2 terminals are for the heating elements. Terminal Y is connected to the air conditioner, and G goes to the fan.

There are several different types of low voltage thermostats used on heating and air conditioning systems, but basically they are the same. The low voltage transformer feeds one terminal of the thermostat, and a switch opens and closes the circuit as the temperature varies. In this way the thermostat controls the low voltage circuit which feeds power to all the relays to turn the power on to the elements. These points can be installed on a bimetal strip, or there can be a capsule of mercury mounted on a spring that coils and uncoils with temperature variations.

Most thermostats are in the following three functional categories: heating thermostats, the heating-cooling thermostats, and two-stage heating-cooling thermostats. The difference between the heating-cooling thermostat and the heating thermostat is that the heating-cooling thermostat has two sets of contact points whereas the heating thermostat has only one set. The cooling thermostat is used in a system with central air conditioning as well as heat. It has one set of points that closes on the temperature drop, connected to the heating system, and one set of points that closes on the temperature rise, connected to the cooling system.

A two-stage thermostat is shown in Fig. 11-22. This thermostat is usually used on electric furnaces. It has an extra set of points that must close before all the heating elements come on. The first two heating elements will come on when the temperature drops below a certain temperature. These elements are connected to the W1 terminals of the thermostat. The third and fourth elements will not come on unless the temperature

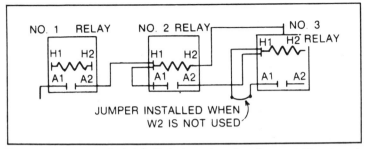

Fig. 11-23. A jumper wire is installed when a two-stage thermostat is not used. Sometimes the factory has already installed this jumper or has taken the wires back to the terminal board. An outside thermostat, if used, is installed between the two points instead of the jumper shown here.

fails to warm up soon enough. These elements are connected to the W2 terminal, and they are more or less auxiliary heating elements.

With the two-stage thermostat the W1 terminal on the thermostat is connected to the H1 terminal on the first-sequencer, and the W2 terminal on the thermostat is connected to the H1 terminal on the third sequencer. See Fig. 11-10. The purpose of the two-stage thermostat is to save energy by not having the third and fourth elements come on unless they are needed. Sometimes an outside thermostat is used to make sure these elements actually need to be turned on. The outside thermostat senses the outside temperature and won't let the third and fourth elements come on unless the temperature outside is below 35°F or so. This prevents the third and fourth element from coming on if the thermostat is suddenly turned from 60°F to 70°F.

When a single-stage thermostat is used with an electric furnace, a jumper wire must be placed between H1 and A1 on the third relay (Fig. 11-23). This connects the third relay so that it will be set up when the second relay goes into operation.

Figures 11-24 and 11-25 show how the thermostat and sequencers are connected to the terminal board. If a two-stage thermostat were used, there

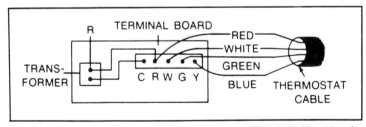

Fig. 11-24. In this drawing note that the red wire leaves the terminal board on the furnace and connects to the R terminal on the thermostat. The white wire leaves the thermostat and connects to the terminal board at W, then goes to the gas valve. There is also a wire leaving the gas valve connected to the terminal board at C as it comes from the other terminal of the transformer.

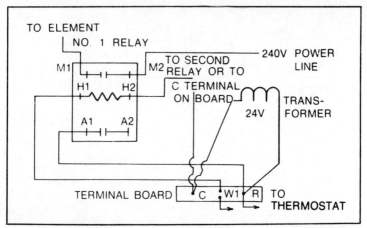

Fig. 11-25. This shows the W1 wire leaving the terminal board and going to the H1 terminal on relay No. 1. This circuit will connect to each relay used. It then goes to terminal C on the board. When terminal H1 is energized, the element circuit will be completed.

would be a terminal W2 as well as a terminal W, and terminal W2 would be connected to the auxiliary elements.

The common terminal C is not connected to the thermostat. It is connected to the transformer line and to all the sequencers (see Fig. 11-24). This line completes the circuit of the sequencers to turn the elements on.

Terminal R is the other transformer connection. It goes to the terminal on the thermostat lettered, R, RC, or RH. The W1 thermostat terminal connects to W1 on the terminal board and goes to the gas valve on a gas furnace. On an electric furnace it goes to the No. 1 sequencer. If used, the W2 terminal will connect to the W2 terminal on the terminal board.

Terminals G on the thermostat and terminal board connect. Terminal G is the fan terminal, and the fan can be operated at any time without running any other unit. Terminal Y goes to the air conditioning unit.

## TROUBLESHOOTING ELECTRIC FURNACES

When troubles occur, check the items listed here, as appropriate:

### Furnace Won't Heat

- Check power supply at breaker box.
- Check all breakers.
- Check fuses in furnace.
- Check transformer primary circuit.
- Check secondary circuit.
- Check No. 1 heating relay.
- Check for loose connections.
- Check thermostat to see if all switches are in the correct position.

## Element Comes On but Goes Off

- Check fan limit switch.
- Check fan relay.
- Check capacitor on fan.
- Check for loose connections.
- Check for worn fan motor bearing.
- Check for burned-out fan motor.
- Check for loose fan blade.
- Check for foreign object in fan.

## Fan Runs but Does not Blow Heat Through the System

- Dirty filter.
- Restriction in air duct.
- Loose belt or broken belt on fan motor.
- Loose fan blade or pulley.
- Return air duct too small.
- Restriction in return air duct.

## Element Nos. 2 or 3 Won't Heat

- No. 2 heating relay is bad.
- Element burned in half.
- Bad fuse.
- Defective heat overload.
- Air over the elements restricted.
- Loose connection.

## Element No. 1 Won't Come On

- Element burned out.
- Blown heat fuse.
- Bad limit switch.
- Fan won't run.
- Bad sequencer.
- Blown fuse.
- Thermostat on "cooling" setting.
- Loose element wires.
- Loose thermostat wires.

# Chapter 12

# Wood Heat and
# Central Wood Furnaces

Wood heat has received considerable attention lately as a way to reduce
rapidly rising heating bills. The addition of wood heat to a home should be
undertaken only after careful thought and planning.

### WOOD HEAT FUEL COSTS

Cost is the primary reason people are adding wood heat to their homes.
For many people wood is a much cheaper source of energy than electricity,
gas, or oil. Homeowners that save plenty by switching to wood heat
generally have a free wood source or one at very low cost. It is difficult to
save significant amounts of money with wood heat if you must pay the
"going rate" for wood. This depends on what the "going rate" for wood is in
your area. The discussion on fuel costs comparisons in Chapter 3 will help
you determine whether wood heat will save you money over your present
fuel.

Wood does not have a standard purchase unit, and this makes it very
difficult for the homeowner to determine the heating value he is getting for
his money. As shown in Chapter 3, wood varies greatly by type in its heating
value per cord. Some hardwoods have almost twice the Btu heating value as
softwoods. This makes it difficult to tell just how much heat you are buying.
People also tend to forget about the heat loss from moisture evaporation
that occurs in burning wood. In green wood this can be a loss of 50 percent
or more of the wood's heating value. Even seasoned wood has a moisture
evaporation loss of 15 to 20 percent. This loss must be accounted for when
calculating the heating value per dollar of wood.

### PLANNING CONSIDERATIONS

Wood heat requires careful planning. You must decide what type of
wood heating system to install and where it will be located. You must plan
for fuel handling.

You will need some place to store the wood, preferably a covered location to shield the wood from moisture. Most wood heating systems must be stoked (have fuel added) at least twice a day. If your schedule does not permit taking time daily to build a fire and stoke a stove, wood heat may not be for you.

## Types of Wood Heating Systems

The fireplace is the best-known wood heating system. It is a very inefficient heating system. The standard fireplace with an open face and without any air circulation around the firebox generally is only about 10 percent efficient at a maximum. It often has a *negative efficiency*—wasting more heat than it produces to heat the home. This is because the standard fireplace loses much of the wood's heat up the flue and also draws heated room air up the flue.

A more efficient fireplace has glass doors that prevent it from drawing room air up the flue. It also has a specially constructed steel firebox that circulates air around the firebox above and behind the fire, so less of the wood's heat output escapes up the flue. Heatilator and other manufacturers make these circulating fireboxes, which must be installed when the fireplace is constructed. They generally have a small fan system that draws room air into the steel jacket and blows it out into the living area.

Fireplace inserts have become very popular in recent years. These are steel fireboxes that are inserted into the fireplace opening and connected to the fireplace flue (Fig. 12-1). They resemble wood stoves in their opera-

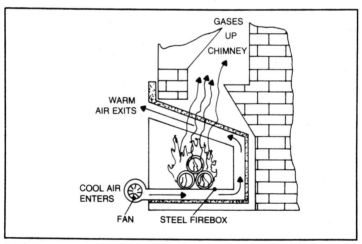

Fig. 12-1. A fireplace insert is constructed from heavy steel and fits inside the fireplace opening. The insert forms a circulating wood heater that seals the fireplace opening and uses the chimney for the exhaust of smoke and gases. Cool air enters at the bottom of the insert and circulates around the back and side of the firebox where the wood burns. Warm air exits at the top of the unit. A small fan generally is used to speed air flow and increase efficiency.

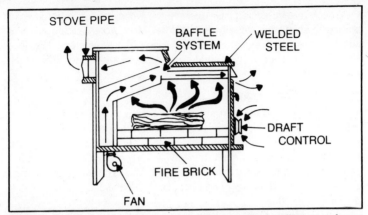

Fig. 12-2. Be sure the stove construction is tight and solid. A baffle system forces the exhaust gases to burn and avoids some of the heat loss up the flue. A fan that circulates room air through the stove and into the room will increase heat transfer and improve efficiency.

tion, and they increase a fireplace's heat output tremendously. This improved efficiency is the result of two factors. First, the insert closes off the large fireplace opening. The air draft into the firebox is tightly controlled, unlike an ordinary fireplace, so room air is not sucked up the chimney. Second, the insert circulates air around all sides of the firebox, and the fire itself is more tightly controlled so that much less heat is wasted.

Another type of wood heating system is the room wood stove. Some stoves will heat several rooms. A room wood stove that has the following features generally is more efficient than others: airtight construction, temperature-activated draft control, baffle system to force secondary burning of the exhaust gases, and a fan system to circulate room air around the firebox for improved heat transfer (Fig. 12-2).

### Planning the Location

Adding a wood stove or furnace to your home involves thought about the location and the traffic flow to the unit that will be required for fire tending and stoking. The chimney location may affect placement of the wood unit.

A fireplace or fireplace insert will not require much space for the unit itself. A wood room-size stove will take up several square feet of a room, because the stove must have adequate clearance on all sides to walls and combustible materials.

A wood furnace will require plenty of space. If your house has a basement and the furnace is located there, you probably should place the wood furnace near the existing furnace. If your house does not have a basement, it will be difficult to install a wood furnace without making special provisions. You might be able to place a wood furnace in one portion of an attached garage and run ducts to it. A special attached room might have to be constructed to house the wood furnace.

## CHIMNEYS AND FLUES

When you install a wood stove or furnace, you will have to install a chimney. There are mainly masonry and metal chimneys. Masonry chimneys are constructed of brick and lined with clay fire tile. They are probably the best and the safest chimneys when properly constructed, as well as the most expensive.

A metal chimney is double-walled—constructed with two walls of steel and a nonflammable substance such as asbestos sandwiched between them (Fig. 12-3). There has been discussion recently concerning the ability of metal chimneys to withstand the extreme temperatures resulting from creosote chimney fires. *Creosote* is a substance produced as wood burns. Creosote collects in the flue and chimney. It can ignite and send flames through the entire chimney.

You should check the recommendations of the stove or furnace manufacturer as to the type of flue. Also, check with the local fire department and building inspector to be sure the installation will meet local fire and building codes. Talk with your homeowner's insurance company representative about your planned wood stove installation.

Never install a wood stove onto a chimney that is being used for another unit. You cannot connect a wood stove to a fireplace chimney. Doing so can result in harmful gases drifting into the living space. Each wood heating unit must have a separate chimney.

If the flue running from the stove to the chimney passes through combustible materials, you must install a thimble (Fig. 12-4). The thimble provides an insulated air space between the flue pipe and nearby combustible wall materials.

## WOOD FURNACES

While wood stoves and fireplaces do not offer the advantages of central heating, wood-burning furnaces are available. These furnaces are in remote

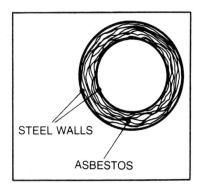

Fig. 12-3. Metal chimneys are made of double-wall steel construction. Asbestos is sandwiched between the two steel walls.

STEEL WALLS

ASBESTOS

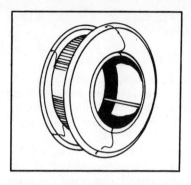

Fig. 12-4. When flue pipe passes through combustible materials such as a wood frame wall, a wall thimble should be used.

locations in the house and distribute warmed air to all the home's rooms by use of a duct system.

From the early models that were little more than large wood stoves, manufacturers have developed efficient wood furnaces that utilize electric controls to tend the fire and ensure efficient combustion. See Fig. 12-5.

Wood furnaces can be installed as a home's only heat source. Many people who use wood want a second fuel available. This backup fuel might be used if the wood supply is low, if the wood fire goes untended too long, or if the weather is especially cold and the wood furnace lacks sufficient capacity to heat the home.

For these reasons, "add-on" wood furnace installations have become very popular for wood furnaces. In an add-on furnace installation, the wood

Fig. 12-5. Valley Forge Model 401 coal/wood furnace manufactured by Valley Forge Stove Company, Spring City, PA. Warmed air exits through the opening at the top of the furnace. If the wood furnace is the only furnace for the home, you can install a plenum chamber at the top of the furnace. The furnace is shown with a duct adapter installed for application as an add-on furnace. Round duct connects the furnace with the existing furnace. This furnace has an automatic electric damper control that opens the damper to increase the fire when the home needs more heat. This damper control can be connected to a thermostat in the home's living area (courtesy Valley Forge Stove Company).

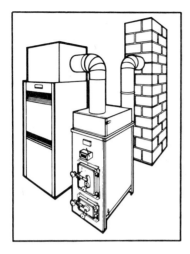

Fig. 12-6. This is an add-on wood furnace installation. The wood furnace is installed next to the existing gas, oil, or electric furnace. The wood furnace is connected by ducts to the plenum chamber of the existing furnace, and from there the wood heat is distributed through the existing duct system. The wood furnace is connected by a flue to a chimney, where gases are exhausted. The add-on furnace may have its own fan, but it also may utilize the fan on the existing furnace (courtesy Russell Furnaces, Decton Iron Works).

furnace is connected into the existing duct system. The present gas, oil, or electric furnace remains in place. The two furnaces are hooked up in such a way that the wood furnace supplies the primary heat to the home. The other furnace serves as a secondary heating source that turns on when wood is unable to meet all the home's heating demands. One add-on furnace installation is shown in Fig. 12-6.

## Selecting a Wood Furnace

You want a wood furnace that is well-constructed, solid, and heavy (to a point). Check the welds and seams for tightness. You should not be able to see light from the inside. The furnace should have a baffle system that slows the escape of exhaust gases up the flue and encourages more complete burning. See Fig. 12-7. Creosote and ashes will build up inside the furnace, so cleanout should be easy—both above and below the firebox. The furnace should circulate air around the firebox, and the heat transfer surface should be large for efficient heat transfer.

The furnace should have the capability for the addition of automatic damper and fan controls. Electric controls can be connected to a thermostat and fan switch to make the furnace's operation coincide with the home's heating needs. These controls cost extra with many wood furnaces, but it is wise to purchase and install them for efficient wood burning.

If Btu figures are provided for the furnaces you are considering, examine them. Sometimes the rating provided is based on a two-hour or a four-hour burn. You would have to refill the firebox every two to four hours to get that Btu capacity. The size of the firebox is generally a good indicator of the furnace's Btu capacity.

If you are going to install a wood furnace as an "add-on" furnace, you will not need enough capacity to heat your entire home all the time. The secondary fuel will take care of whatever the wood furnace can't provide. A

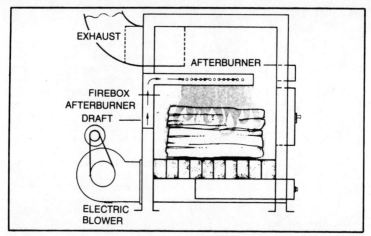

Fig. 12-7. A diagram of a wood furnace. The firebox is constructed of brick-lined steel. The most efficient models have some type of baffle system that impedes the escape of exhaust gases for more complete combustion. Many models come with an electric fan (optional in some cases) that makes the wood furnace a self-contained central furnace system (courtesy Russell Furnaces, Decton Iron Works).

wood furnace with a smaller Btu rating than the present furnace may well meet the home's wood heating needs.

### Dual-Fuel Furnaces

Dual-fuel furnaces are a recent development. Figure 12-8 shows one dual-fuel furnace model.

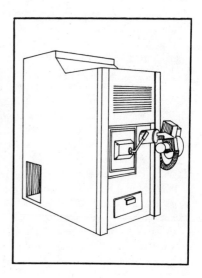

Fig. 12-8. A dual-fuel furnace. This furnace uses oil as its secondary heating fuel, and the oil burner is easily identified on the front of the furnace. Wood is inserted into the firebox through the door next to the oil burner. Dual-fuel furnaces are also available that use gas and electricity as secondary fuels.

These wood-burning furnaces also burn a secondary fuel such as oil, gas, or electricity. Wood is the primary heating fuel. When wood is unable to supply the home's complete heating needs, the secondary fuel burners come on. The secondary fuel makes up the difference.

A dual-fuel furnace is about the same size as a large wood furnace. This furnace takes up less space than a wood furnace "add-on" installation, but it has many of the same operating features. The furnace is considerably more expensive than a plain wood furnace, but not necessarily more expensive than a wood furnace and a secondary furnace. Because of their expense, those furnaces are most economical in new home installations or in older homes where a new furnace installation is planned. In homes where the present furnace is adequate, add-on wood furnace installations are generally more economical.

Dual-fuel furnaces are installed in much the same manner as conventional furnaces. There must be a flue and a chimney for the wood fuel. Air conditioning can be installed with most dual-fuel furnaces.

## ADDING A WOOD FURNACE TO YOUR CENTRAL HEATING SYSTEM

When you add a wood furnace to your central heating system, consider how the system will work. Attaching an add-on wood furnace and making it work properly takes some ingenuity, an understanding of the furnace system, and a knowledge of the furnace components discussed throughout this book. The elements deserving special thought are the duct system and the manner in which the two furnaces will be connected, the fan and fan controls, and the thermostat and wood furnace damper controls.

### Duct System

There are two ways you can connect a wood furnace into a central heating system. The two furnaces can be connected in series, or they can be in parallel (Fig. 12-9).

The installation in series is preferable. Installing an add-on furnace in parallel with the existing furnace can lead to considerable "short circuiting" of the duct system. Air flow becomes circular between the two furnaces, and does not properly become distributed into the duct system (Fig. 12-10).

Short circuits in parallel installations can be avoided if you install a damper to close off one furnace at a time (Fig. 12-11). You then cannot use both furnaces at once, and you must manually switch the system from one furnace to the other. In addition, you must turn off your gas, oil, or electric furnace any time you have its damper closed. Otherwise, the thermostat may call for heat and turn the furnace on.

You also must set up return air ducts going to both furnaces. A damper can be used to switch the return air duct over to the furnace in use.

When the furnaces are connected in series, both furnaces can operate at the same time, so long as they are wired to do so. The wood furnace can be set up as the primary furnace and the gas furnace as the secondary furnace—to come on only when needed.

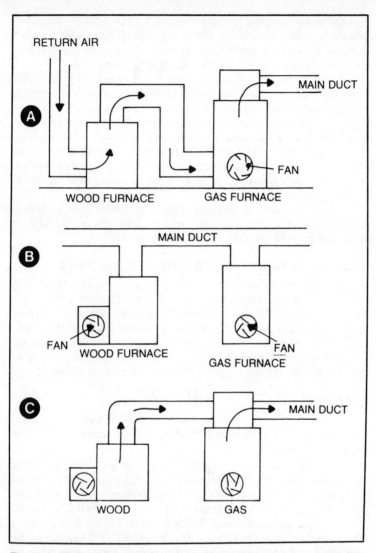

Fig. 12-9. (A) Here the wood furnace and the gas furnace are connected in series. In this type of installation all air flow is through both furnaces. Thus, only one fan is required. (B) Here the wood furnace and the gas furnace are connected in parallel. Both furnaces have their own duct connection to the main duct. Two fans are required. A variation on this same theme is where the wood furnace is connected to the plenum chamber of the secondary fuel furnace, as in (C). This is also a parallel installation.

Figures 12-12 and 12-13 illustrate two different ways to connect the furnaces in series. These diagrams will give you some ideas that you can adapt to your situation.

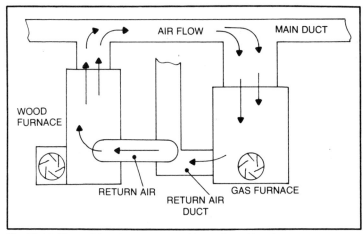

Fig. 12-10. The problem that can occur with parallel add-on furnace installations is illustrated in this diagram. The arrows represent the air flow. If the wood furnace fan turns on, it blows air out into the duct system. When that air reaches the gas furnace's plenum chamber, it will follow the path of least resistance and will downdraft into the secondary furnace. The air will flow backward through the return air duct and back into the wood furnace. This creates a duct system "short circuit." Warm air does not reach the living space. It flows in circles within the furnaces. To prevent this problem you can install dampers made of sheet metal plates to block the air flow through one furnace at a time.

## Fan Controls

When the add-on furnace is connected so it has its own fan, each furnace will have a separate fan controlled by its own fan control or fan limit switch. Fan limit switches are discussed in Chapter 9, and their application in wood furnaces is the same. Essentially, the fan control turns the fan on

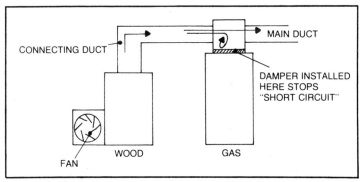

Fig. 12-11. Parallel installation of add-on furnaces work best if you install a system of dampers to block off one furnace at a time not in use. This prevents unwanted backdrafts into the furnace not being used. You also must install similar "switching dampers" in the return air system to direct return air into the furnace being used.

229

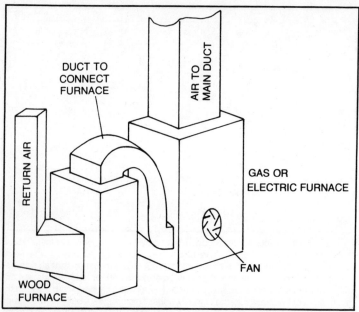

Fig. 12-12. This shows one way you can connect a wood add-on furnace to a secondary fuel furnace. This connection has the furnaces in series. The air enters the wood furnace first, exits the top, and goes through the secondary fuel furnace. The fan on the secondary fuel furnace is the only fan required. When installing furnaces in series, be sure the connecting duct between the two furnaces is large enough to handle the air flow for the furnace system.

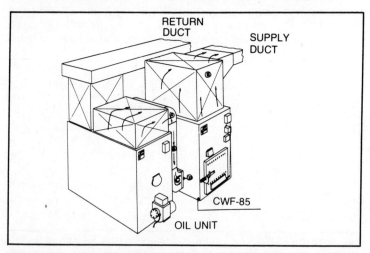

Fig. 12-13. This is another series add-on furnace installation. Here the air enters the secondary fuel furnaces first. The arrows show the air flow through the system (courtesy Fawcett Division, Enheat Inc., Sackville, New Brunswick).

230

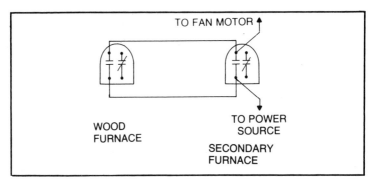

Fig. 12-14. When the fan limit switches for the wood furnace and the secondary furnace are wired in this manner, each will turn on the single fan.

when the temperature in the heat exchanger (the firebox, in a wood furnace) reaches a high enough point. When the heat exchanger or firebox cools, the fan switch turns the fan off.

The fan limit switch is wired into the fan motor circuit. It can be adjusted to turn the fan on at various temperatures.

When add-on furnaces are connected in series, there will only be one fan. This is normally the fan to the secondary fuel (gas, oil, or electric) furnace. To install the wood furnace, you will have to connect the existing fan to an additional limit switch. You need the fan circuit to be wired so that the fan will be turned on by either the wood furnace or the secondary fuel furnace. A fan limit switch in each furnace is connected to the same fan motor (Fig. 12-14). The fan will operate when either furnace is in use.

### Thermostats

An add-on furnace makes your central heating system a two-stage system. Wood is the primary fuel. If the wood furnace does not keep the house temperature high enough, the secondary furnace will come on. To accomplish this, you can use two thermostats. One thermostat is connected to the wood furnace and operates the damper. The second is set several degrees lower and is connected to the secondary heating system. For thermostatic control of a wood furnace, the furnace must have a motorized damper connected to a thermostat.

You also can install a two-stage thermostat, following the general discussion in Chapter 11. The wood heating system is the primary system and is connected to the W1 terminal on the two-stage thermostat. The gas or oil furnace is the second stage and is connected to the W2 thermostat terminal. A two-stage thermostat installation requires five-wire thermostat cable.

When an electric furnace is the backup system, you probably should use two separate thermostats. By connecting the wood furnace and the electric furnace through the same thermostat, you will lose some of the two-stage features of the electric furnace.

# Chapter 13

# Servicing the Air Conditioner

Figure 13-1 shows the two sides of a refrigeration system. The high side is where the heat is removed from the refrigerant, and the low side is where the refrigerant picks up heat. The high side and low side can also be thought of as the different sides of the compressor; the high side is where the compressor exerts its force.

## REFRIGERATION CYCLE

The compressor serves two purposes in the system. First, it keeps the refrigerant moving through the system. Second, it compresses the refrigerant vapor, forcing it into a pressurized state so the excess heat can be liberated at the condenser. The refrigerant vapor moves out of the compressor through the high-side line to the condenser (Fig. 13-2).

The high-side lines connect the compressor to the condenser and are often quite long. The pressure will be built up in these lines.

The condenser is part of the high-pressure side of the system. The high-side lines enter the condenser at the top. The main purpose of the condenser is to change the refrigerant from a vapor to a liquid and remove the heat from the refrigerant vapor. The cooling process is accomplished with a fan working behind the condenser to move air over it. The heat from the refrigerant within the condenser is carried away by the moving air. This cools the refrigerant vapor, and the cooling process along with the pressurization from the compressor transforms the vapor into a liquid (Fig. 13-3). This liquid is then reused in the refrigeration cycle. As the refrigerant condenses back to a liquid, it moves to the bottom of the condenser and into either the high-side line leaving the condenser or a receiver. The refrigerant liquid will travel from here to the expansion valve or capillary tube.

## Expansion Valve

The expansion valve (sometimes called a restrictor) does two things:

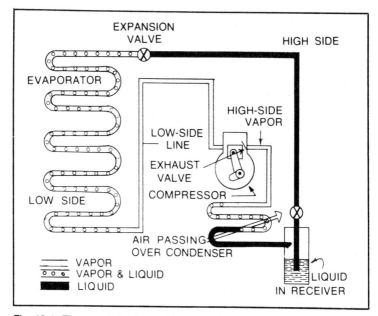

Fig. 13-1. The complete air conditioning system. The high side starts at the compressor exhaust valve and ends at the expansion valve. The low side starts at the expansion valve and ends at the compressor piston.

It meters the liquid refrigerant into the evaporator, and it restricts the flow of the refrigerant so the compressor can build up pressure and raise the temperature of the refrigerant in the high side. As the refrigerant passes through the restrictor, the pressure is lowered, and this is the start of the low-pressure side. When the vapor enters the compressor, it has ended its stay in the low side and is starting on the high side.

Figure 13-4 shows a thermostatic expansion valve. Pressure $P_1$ is the vapor pressure from $P_3$. As the evaporator temperature drops, pressures $P_1$

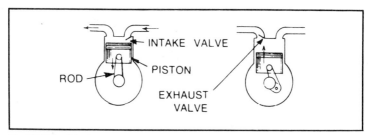

Fig. 13-2. As the piston moves down in the compressor, the intake valve will open and let the vapor from the low side in. As the piston starts upward the intake valve closes, and only when the pressure inside the cylinder reaches the high-side pressure will the exhaust valves open and allow the vapor to move into the high side.

233

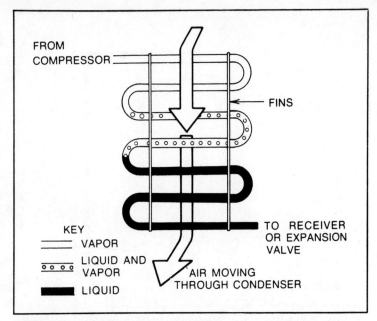

Fig. 13-3. As air moves through the finned condenser, it removes heat from the vapor within the condenser. The vapor will condense back to a liquid and flow into the receiver or restrictor.

and $P_3$ also drop to close the valve needle and seat. $F_2$ is the pressure from the evaporator, and as it decreases it tends to pull the diaphragm down, opening the needle valve. Force $F_1$ is the spring tension that is trying to close the needle valve. Pressure $P_2$ is exerted by the liquid refrigerant on the high side. This expansion valve can be adjusted by changing the spring tension $F_1$.

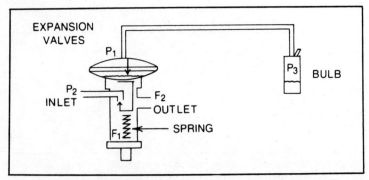

Fig. 13-4. Thermostatic expansion valve. $P_1$ is vapor pressure from bulb ($P_3$). $F_1$ is the spring pressure, and $F_2$ is the pressure from the evaporator. $P_2$ is pressure from the liquid refrigerant on the high side.

The bulb to the expansion valve is usually strapped to the end line of the evaporator. As the evaporator begins to cool, this reduces the pressure on the diaphragm and begins to control the flow or refrigerant through the system. When the compressor is running, it tends to open the needle valve. The pressure will then equalize.

### Checking the Expansion Valve

A good way to tell if the expansion valve is working is to remove the bulb from the evaporator and hold it in your hand. The heat from your hand will cause an increase in pressure in the bulb, and the needle should open. The suction pressure, indicated on the low-side pressure gage, should rise. This will not happen if the valve is open, but the suction pressure should be high to start with unless there is a restriction before it reaches the expansion valve. There is a screen in the inlet side to keep dirt and other foreign material from entering the valve. This could be clogged, producing a restriction. This screen can be removed and cleaned.

### Capillary Tube

A capillary tube may also be used as a restrictor. A capillary tube is a piece of tubing that has a very small hole in it. The restriction through the tube depends on the size hole in the tubing and the length of the tubing. The pressure on the high side as well as the pressure on the low side will have some effect on the amount of refrigerant that flows through the tube.

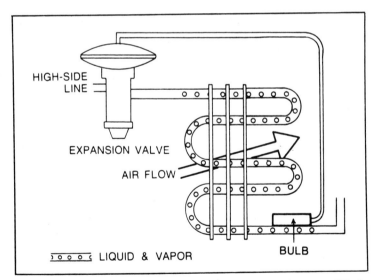

Fig. 13-5. As liquid refrigerant flows through the expansion valve, part of it boils off into a vapor and picks up heat. The boiling occurs because the pressure is reduced at the expansion valve. Under this lowered pressure the refrigerant will boil at lower temperature.

The refrigerant goes from the restrictor into the evaporator. When the refrigerant enters the evaporator, it is no longer under high pressure, and at the lower pressure the liquid refrigerant will boil (Fig. 13-5). In making the change from the liquid state to the gaseous state, it must absorb a great deal of heat. This heat is taken from the air surrounding the coils in the evaporator, and this is how cooling takes place in the system. After the liquid again becomes a vapor, it is carried through the low-side line back to the compressor, where the refrigeration process starts over.

## CHECKING THE COMPRESSOR

Compressors can be divided into three types: open, semihermetic, and hermetic. The open-type compressor may be belt-driven or directly-driven. The semihermetic compressor is usually driven directly by an electric motor. The motor is on one end of the unit, the compressor is on the other end, and both the motor and compressor are sealed in a dome or casting. This type of unit can be taken apart.

The hermetic unit has the motor and compressor sealed in a dome and welded together. It cannot be taken apart unless the weld is broken.

### Compressor Motors

Electric motors are discussed in Chapter 14; their application to refrigeration systems is covered here. You may find it helpful to refer to Chapter 14 from time to time.

A split-phase induction motor is usually used in all three kinds of compressors. The motors used on an open-type compressor may have a centrifugal switch. With the semihermetic and hermetic motors the switch must be located on the outside of the dome, because any spark or arcing of the points would burn the oil moving through the system, contaminate the system, and cause trouble. The switch is a relay located outside of the compressor. (See Figs. 13-6 through 13-8.)

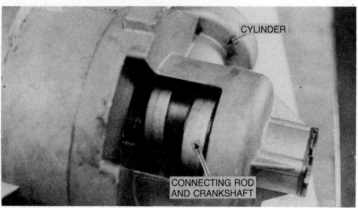

Fig. 13-6. View of compressor inside the dome.

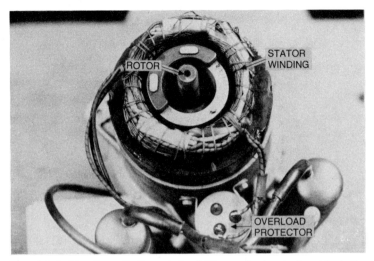

Fig. 13-7. Inside a hermetically sealed unit. The overlead protector protects the motor if the unit pulls too many amps. The rotor is connected to the compressor.

The motor leads (Fig. 13-9) run through the steel dome and connect to terminals on the inside of the dome. The leads are insulated from the metal dome. Sometimes this is done with glass fused around the terminals to make the terminal electrically safe, and sometimes the terminal bolts are insulated with rubber sleeves.

The windings of the motor can be checked with a resistance meter (ohmmeter) to tell if the windings are shorted or open (Fig. 13-10). It is also

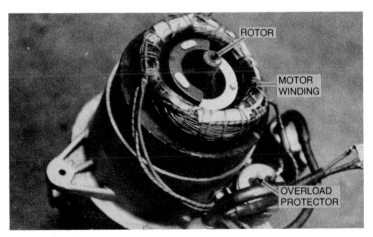

Fig. 13-8. This photo shows the compressor motor which is mounted inside the dome. The start windings are next to the rotor. The run windings are on the outside of the start windings. The internal overload protector will break the circuit if the compressor gets too hot or pulls too many amps due to overload.

Fig. 13-9. The stator after it has been disconnected and removed. The stator is the part of the motor containing the start and run windings. The motor leads connect to terminals through the dome of the sealed unit.

possible to find the starting, running, and common terminals by using an ohmmeter.

## Distinguishing the Winding Terminals

The start and run windings have more resistance than the other windings. When the two terminals having the most resistance are found—

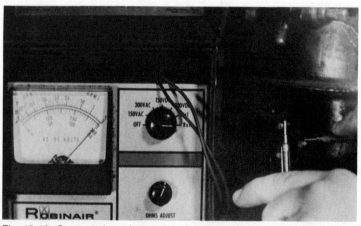

Fig. 13-10. Connected as shown, the ohmmeter will indicate continuity if the winding between the two compressor terminals is complete. The other terminals will also have to be checked. There should be continuity between all three terminals.

238

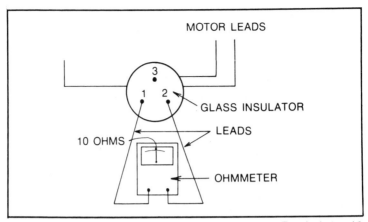

Fig. 13-11. Finding the common terminal with the ohmmeter. Terminals 1 and 2 have more resistance between them, so they go to the run and start windings. The third terminal is the common terminal.

terminals 1 and 2 in Figs. 13-11 and 13-12—this leaves the third terminal as the common terminal.

To distinguish the start winding from the run winding, place one of the leads from the ohmmeter on the common terminal. The start winding will

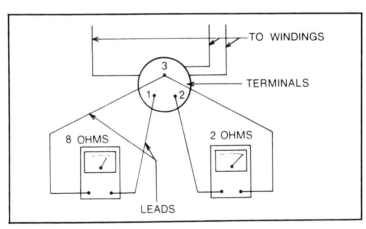

Fig. 13-12. After the common terminal is located and the ohmmeter is connected to terminals 1 and 3, there will be a reading of 8 ohms. This is the next highest reading, so terminal 1 will be for the start winding (higher resistance). When terminals 2 and 3 are connected to the ohmmeter, there is a reading of 2 ohms. Terminal 2 will be the run terminal because it has the lowest reading (lowest resistance). The reading between the start (1) and run (2) terminals in our illustration is 10 ohms. The readings between the start terminal (1) and common (3) is 8 ohms, and between the run terminal (2) and common (3) is 2 ohms. The reading between the start and run windings should be the total of the other two readings. Each compressor will have different readings.

Fig. 13-13. When checking a compressor for a short, touch one lead of the ohmmeter to a terminal on the compressor and the other lead to the bare metal of the case of the compressor. If the meter needle moves, the compressor motor is shorted to the case, and electricity from the ohmmeter is flowing through the case. In service the compressor will draw a large amount of amperage if there is a short, and this can be detected with an ammeter. It will also get hot.

have a higher resistance reading than the run winding. The start winding is wound with a number of turns of small wire. The run winding is wound with fewer turns of larger wire. Thus, the start winding has the higher resistance.

For example, using the examples of Figs. 13-11 and 13-12 again, with one lead on the common terminal, put the other lead from the resistance meter to the No. 1 terminal, and you see a reading of 8 ohms. When terminals 2 and 3 are connected, there is a reading of 2 ohms. Since the start winding has more resistance than the run winding, the No. 1 terminal will be the start terminal, and the No. 2 terminal will be the run terminal.

To check for a short in the winding, one of the leads from the ohmmeter should touch one terminal, and the other should touch the dome of the motor (Fig. 13-13). If there is a reading between these terminals and the dome, there is a short. If the needles do not move, there is not a path for the electricity to flow, so the motor should be all right. Make certain the paint on the dome is removed, as well as the dirt, because this may insulate the checking equipment from the current. Care should also be taken to remove all terminal wires from the terminals because they may be shorted out or touching the case, which would cause you to conclude the motor was shorted.

### Checking for an Open Circuit

If you touch any two of the terminals with the ohmmeter leads and the needle doesn't move or give a reading, the winding is open. There is not a path for the current to flow through. The winding could have burned apart, or a wire may have slipped off the terminal on the inside. Again, be sure to remove all the wires from the terminals, so a false reading will not be taken. If it is necessary to replace a compressor, it may be necessary to use an ohmmeter to find the correct terminal to attach the relay to.

Sometimes compressor malfunctioning is due to a faulty capacitor. Figure 13-14 shows a compressor with two starting capacitors. An extra

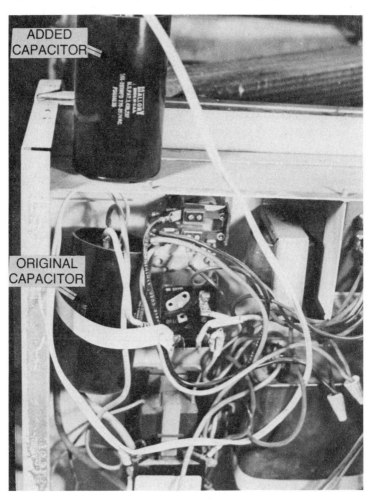

Fig. 13-14. Replacing a capacitor is often necessary. When in doubt, substitute a new capacitor. If the unit runs, the old capacitor is bad and will have to be replaced. It may be desirable to add a starting capacitor to the one already on the unit. When the compressor is "stuck," adding more starting capacitance will often help to start the compressor.

Fig. 13-15. Relays such as this are rated in horsepower. If a relay has to be replaced, the model number and horsepower of the compressor should be known.

capacitor can be used temporarily to check for a shorted original capacitor, or permanently to provide additional capacitance.

## RELAYS

Relays (Figs. 13-15 and 13-16) are used to disconnect the start windings of a compressor when the compressor reaches three-fourths of its running speed. They are usually classified as "hot" wire, current (amperage), and potential (voltage) relays. Usually the "hot" wire and current relays are used on smaller units. The two most common are the potential and the current relays. (See the relays discussed in Chapter 14.)

The potential relay points are normally closed when the unit is not in operation. When the motor starts and reaches three-fourths of its operating speed, the points separate, disconnecting the start windings of the motor (Fig. 13-17). The points close when the power is off, so there is no arcing across them. This makes the points of the relay last longer.

The numbers on the potential relay are shown in Fig. 13-17. The No. 1 terminal is connected to the line or run terminal on the compressor. The current goes through the points at 2 on the relay and on to the start windings. Number 5 on the relay is for the other power line wire, and it feeds the relay coil to complete the circuit to the coil. Another way to tell what the numbers do is to remember that the points are between the 1 and 2 terminal connections, and the relay coil is between the 5 and 2 terminals on the relay.

The current relay points are normally open on the off cycle. When the power is supplied to the circuit by the contactor, the points close. This is brought about by a magnetic buildup in the relay coil that pulls the points together and allows the current to flow to the start windings (Fig. 13-18). Arcs are produced when the points close and open. As the motor starts, there is a high amperage drawn through the current relay, causing a strong magnetic field in the coil. This holds the points together. When the compressor speed increases, the amperage drops, allowing the magnetic field in the coil. This holds the points together. When the compressor speed increases, the amperage drops, allowing the magnetic field in the relay to weaken. The weighted armature then drops, and this opens the points of the relay.

The markings on a current relay are usually L for the line wire, M or R for the run winding, and S for the start windings.

Relays are of great importance because they control the time the start winding stays in the circuit. Usually if you have checked everything else to no avail, it is wise to replace the relay with a new one.

The capacitor has an effect on the relay. If the capacitance ($\mu$F or md) microfarad rating is changed by replacing the capacitor, it can cause the relay to disconnect the start winding too soon or too late.

Fig. 13-16. This type of relay is used on several types of units. The arrows indicate the terminals.

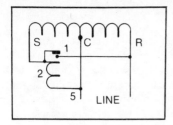

Fig. 13-17. The potential relay coil is connected in parallel with the start windings. As the compressor starts, the current flow through the relay coil produces a magnetic effect that causes the points to open when the motor reaches about three-fourths running speed.

Some units do not use a relay on the compressor, but use a running capacitor instead. This type of unit will usually have a capillary tube restrictor or a special expansion valve. Some units have a relay kit that can be installed if needed. These kits include a relay and starting capacitor along with instructions on connecting the kit. If the compressor is having trouble starting and it doesn't have a relay or starting capacitor, purchasing a kit from a dealer may solve some problems.

## OVERLOADS

There are several types of overloads. The internal overloads are usually found embedded in the motor windings. These are used to protect the compressor or motor. When the motor is just starting, it draws more current than when running at normal speed. The fuse must be sized to take care of the starting load. When the unit is running, the fuse is too large to protect the motor. To solve this problem, a bimetal strip or disc is used (Fig. 13-19) that will carry a heavy load for a few seconds (usually time enough for the compressor to start). When the amperage is lower, the bimetal strip will carry the lower amperage and stay connected. When the amperage increases a few amps, the points will separate and the unit will shut down.

The internal overload can also be a thermistor. These can also be embedded in the motor windings to sense the temperature of the motor winding. If this type of overload is used, it should be checked if you are having compressor trouble to make certain it isn't open.

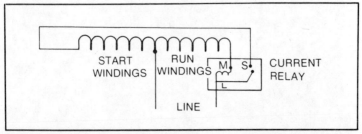

Fig. 13-18. The current relay coil is connected in series with the run windings. As the circuit is completed by the contactors or thermostat, the magnetic field builds up and pulls the points together, completing the circuit to the start windings. These relays will usually have a certain position in which they are to be installed.

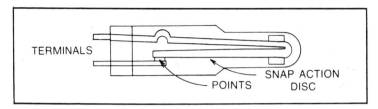

Fig. 13-19. One type of internal overload. As the motor overheats, the bimetal material is heated and bends. This will open the points. Snap action keeps the points from arcing. This device may be used in either voltage or low voltage circuit.

An external overload relay is shown in Figs. 13-20 and 13-21. As the amperage increases the bimetal strip will heat, and at a certain temperature the points will open. Sometimes there is a heater strip under the bimetal strip to help control its temperature. This allows it to operate on a narrower differential.

Often the overload is built into the relay, so when the relay is changed the overload is also changed. The bimetal strip sometimes loses tension due to heat and other causes. This makes it necessary to check the strips to see if they are open or stuck closed. If they are not working properly, it is best to change the relay or overload. This cannot be done with an internal overload. When one of these is not functioning properly, it will be necessary to wire across it to enable the motor to work, but this eliminates the protection of the overload. It would be advisable, in this case, to add an external overload to protect the compressor.

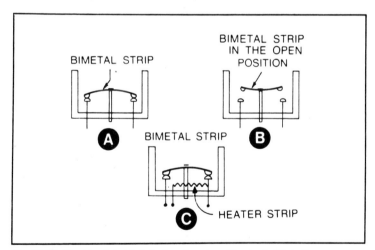

Fig. 13-20. The bimetal strip is in the closed position in A. When the amperage increases, the bimetal strip will open as in B. This opens the circuit, causing the compressor to stop. As the strip cools it will snap back into the closed position, and the unit will start again. There may be a heater strip under the bimetal strip to help control the temperature of the strip as in C.

Fig. 13-21. The connections lead to the motor on the inside of the dome. The 24V overload relay controls a 240V circuit completed through the relay. If the compressor pulls too many amps, the overload relay will open the circuit and stop the compressor.

## CAPACITORS

Capacitors are used to store electricity. There are two types used on air conditioning units: running capacitors and starting capacitors. The running capacitor is connected in the circuit all the time, while the starting capacitor is only connected in the starting circuit. As a result, when the relay disconnects the start winding of the compressor, the starting capacitor will also be disconnected.

The running capacitor is usually made of a sheet of lead foil and a layer of some type of insulation material such as heavy paper. The lead foil and paper are placed together in layers, rolled, and placed in a metal case (Fig. 13-22). Some type of cooling agent (often oil) is put in the case. The two capacitor leads are connected to the foil sheets and brought to the outside of the case. Figure 13-23 shows the safety plug found in the top of the capacitors. This plug will melt when the capacitor gets too hot, and the capacitor will have to be replaced.

The starting capacitor is constructed in a somewhat similar way. The capacitor is usually housed in a plastic case, and it has a higher capacitance rating than a running capacitor. Figures 13-24 and 13-25 show starting capacitors. The relay disconnects the starting capacitor along with the start windings of the compressor.

Another type of capacitor has the running and starting capacitors together in the same case (Fig. 13-26). This type can be recognized by the three leads coming out of the top of the case. One outside terminal is for the running capacitor, and the other is for the starting capacitor. The center terminal is common to both capacitors.

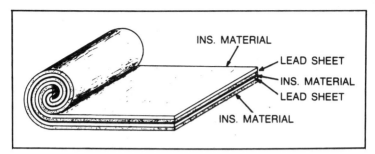

Fig. 13-22. This depiction of a running capacitor shows the layers of lead sheets and insulation (dielectric) material. Running capacitors are usually of the electrolytic type. The plates are sealed in a container filled with a high-dielectric fluid such as a high-resistance oil. This gives the running capacitor the cooling necessary because it is in the circuit all the time.

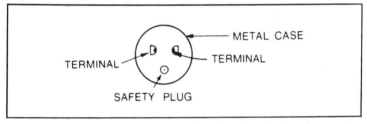

Fig. 13-23. The capacitors have a safety plug that will melt when the capacitor gets too hot. This releases the pressure inside and prevents the capacitor from exploding.

Fig. 13-24. Starting capacitor. Note the capacitance and the voltage ratings.

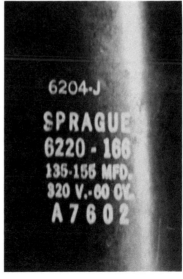

Fig. 13-25. Some starting capacitors have a resistor soldered between the two terminals. This bleeds the capacitor down during the off cycle.

### Capacitor Ratings and Connections

Capacitors are rated in two ways: capacitance (microfarads) and voltage. When changing a capacitor, you should stay within about 25 percent of the microfarad rating, and the voltage should be the same or higher. The running capacitor usually has a smaller microfarad rating and is used to help the compressor or motor to operate more quietly and more efficiently.

Capacitors can be connected in a circuit in series or parallel. Figure 13-27 shows a parallel connection. When capacitors are connected in parallel, the microfarad rating will be the sum of the individual microfarad ratings, and the voltage will be equal to the smallest voltage rating in the group. In Fig. 13-27 the two capacitors connected in parallel are 150 $\mu$F and 100$\mu$F, which adds up to 250 $\mu$F. The voltage is 125V since this is the lower of the two voltage ratings.

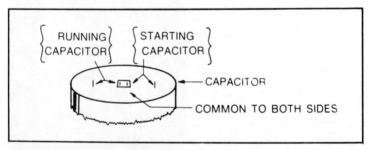

Fig. 13-26. This is a combination running and starting capacitor. The center lead is common to both sides of the capacitor. When one side goes bad, both capacitors have to be changed.

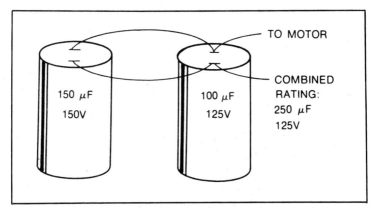

Fig. 13-27. The capacitors connected in parallel will give a combined capacitance, which is the sum of their individual capacitances. The combined voltage rating is equal to the smaller individual rating.

Figure 13-28 shows two capacitors connected in series. When two capacitors are connected in series, the calculation is more complex. The formula for total capacitance of capacitors in series is:

$$C_t = \frac{C1 \times C2}{C1 \times C2}$$

Using this formula to figure the microfarad rating,

$$C_t = \frac{150 \times 150}{150 + 150} = \frac{22,500}{300} = 75 \ \mu F$$

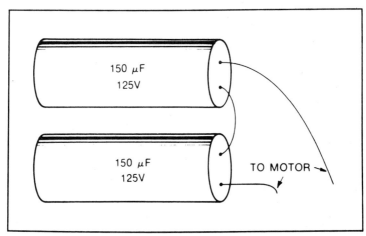

Fig. 13-28. Two capacitors of the same value connected in series would give a capacitance rating one-half that of each capacitor. In this illustration it would be 75 $\mu$F.

249

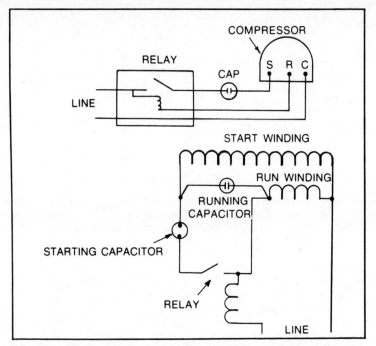

Fig. 13-29. Shown here is a schematic of the starting capacitor connected in series with the start windings. The running capacitor is connected from terminal R to terminal S on the compressor.

If the capacitors above were of different microfarad ratings, the combined microfarad rating would be different. For example, if C1 were 125 $\mu$F instead of 150 $\mu$F, the microfarad rating of the two capacitors would be:

$$C_t = \frac{125 \times 150}{125 + 150} = \frac{18,750}{275} = 68 \ \mu F$$

In series the voltage rating is the sum of the two, or 125 + 125 = 250V.

The starting capacitor is usually connected in series with the start winding. When the motor reaches three-fourths of its running speed, the relay disconnects the start winding of the motor as well as the starting capacitor (Fig. 13-29).

Capacitors are used to produce an electrical difference (phase shift) between the starting and running windings. This results in a rotating component of the magnetic field that adds extra starting torque.

### Servicing Capacitors

There are three main things that go wrong with capacitors. They can be burned up, shorted, or opened.

If a capacitor is shorted, it will make the whole system draw too many amps. Sometimes when a motor is checked it will give all of the appearances of a unit that is shorted out, but often the capacitor is shorted instead of the motor.

To check for a short, the capacitor should be removed from the circuit, or at least one lead should be removed from the circuit. Connect an ohmmeter to the capacitor as shown in Fig. 13-30. If the meter gives a reading (not infinity) and continues to do so, the capacitor is shorted and will have to be replaced.

If the capacitor leads are not removed from the motor circuit, an erroneous reading could result. The circuit could be completed through a motor or some other device, and this could give all the indications of a shorted capacitor.

The insulation may be burned through so that the two foil sheets are in electrical contact. This defect may result from aging or excessive voltage. If the relay has been holding the starting circuit on too long, it will cause the starting capacitor to overheat. Again, the insulation between the plates will break down.

Sometimes when the relay has the starting capacitor in the circuit, a surge voltage due to lightning may break down the insulation. Using a capacitor with an insufficient voltage rating can also cause a breakdown in insulation.

An open capacitor will result in one of the leads from the top of the capacitor comes loose from the plate. This will cause a break in the circuit, and the capacitor will not charge. If the capacitor has an open circuit the compressor will not start. An open capacitor, when checked with an ohmmeter, will give a reading of infinity.

If the capacitor has been hot, usually the safety plug will be open, or the case will be bulged or broken. Any time a capacitor looks as if it has been hot, it should be replaced with a new one.

There are several different types of capacitor checkers on the market that will indicate whether the capacitor is shorted, burned out, or open.

Before working on a capacitor, discharge it by shorting between the two terminals with an insulated-handle screwdriver after each time you charge the capacitor. It may save you from a severe shock.

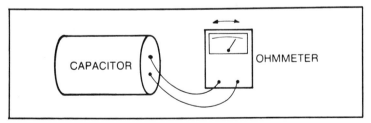

Fig. 13-30. If the ohmmeter gives a continuity reading here, the capacitor is shorted. If the meter reading moves to zero and then drops back to infinity the capacitor should be good.

## EXPANSION VALVES

There are several types of expansion valves used in air conditioning units. Basically the purpose of the expansion valve is to meter the correct amount of refrigerant into the evaporator. The expansion valve is also used to restrict the flow of refrigerant so the compressor can raise the high-side pressure and squeeze the refrigerant vapor into a smaller volume, raising the temperature and compressing the vapor into a liquid in the condenser.

Most expansion valves are of the thermostatic type shown in Fig. 13-31. The thermostatic expansion valve has a control bulb filled with refrigerant attached to it. This bulb, frequently known as the *refrigerant power element*, is attached to the end of the evaporator so that changes in the evaporator temperature cause changes in refrigerant flow through the system. As the evaporator cools, it cools the power element, and there is less pressure applied to the top of the diaphragm. This will close the expansion valve. As the power element warms up, the pressure will build up at the top of the diaphragm. The valve will open to let refrigerant into the evaporator. The compressor will also have to be running so that the low-side pressure will be about normal for the system. If the compressor is not running, the valve will not open. When the compressor starts and lowers the pressure, the valve will open and refrigerant will flow into the system.

### Servicing the Power Element

The bulb of the expansion valve is held in contact with the low-side line at the end of the evaporator as shown in Fig. 13-32. The low-side line should be clean and free of dirt. The clamps should be tight, and the bulb should be on the lower half of the line. The bulb should sense the temperature of the line and not the air temperature around the line. If the bulb senses the air temperature, low-side pressure will be incorrect. The system may not work as it should.

If the low-side and head pressures are low and the unit is not cooling properly, the expansion valve may not be feeding the coil properly. Check the bulb on the low-side line to see if it is making good contact with the line. Remove the bulb and clean the bulb and line. Check the low-side pressure again and check the temperature of the air. If the pressure is still too low, remove the bulb and hold it in your hand; then recheck the low-side pressure. If the pressure comes up, relocate the bulb on the line. If the pressure is still down, remove and clean the expansion valve.

### Servicing High-Side Line Screen

There is a screen in the high side just before the expansion valve inlet that fits in the line (Fig. 13-33). The screen should be removed and cleaned. Care should be taken not to damage the fitting or connection when removing it. The screen should be blown out with air or refrigerant and not cleaned with gasoline or any other solvent that will leave a residue. If the screen is

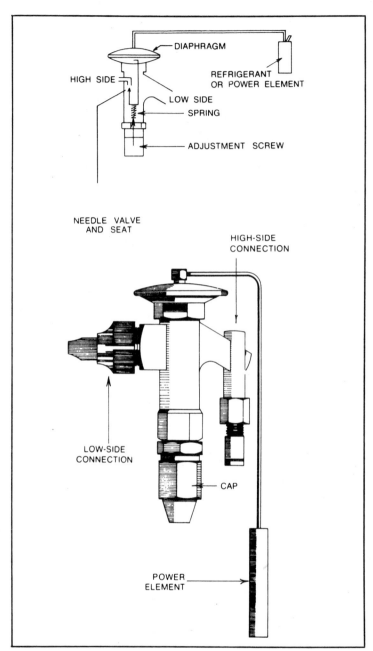

Fig. 13-31. A typical thermostatic expansion valve. The power element controls the refrigerant flow through the valve. A screen is built into the high-side line fitting. The cap can be removed to adjust the valve.

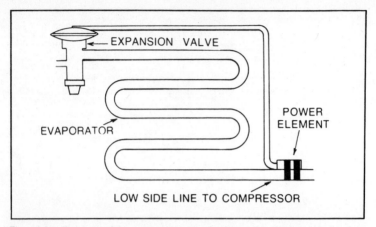

Fig. 13-32. The bulb of the expansion valve is clamped to the low-side line just before it leaves the evaporator cabinet. Sometimes it will be necessary to move the bulb along the line to get the proper location for the bulb to sense the true temperature of the line.

clean and the expansion valve still doesn't work, it will have to be replaced. There are several numbers on top of the valve that specify the refrigerant charge and type of valve to order.

### Expansion Valve Removal

To remove the expansion valve, you will first have to remove the refrigerant. If there is a receiver on the system, pump the refrigerant into the receiver. (The receiver is a canister located where the liquid refrigerant leaves the condenser. The receiver stores surplus refrigerant, but not all units have receivers.) Next close the service valve on the receiver and start the compressor so the refrigerant can be removed from the low-side and

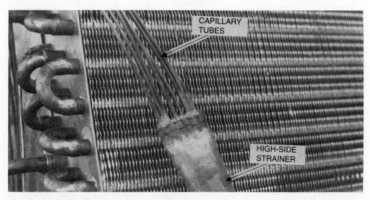

Fig. 13-33. The evaporator coil with capillary tube feeders connecting to the coils. The high-side strainer and screen are inserted where the capillary tubes connect into the high-side line.

placed in the high-side line. Be sure to keep the gages installed so the low-side and high-side pressures are known. If the high-side pressure goes above 400 psi, the unit must be shut down and the rest of the refrigerant bled out of the low side. After the low side goes into a vacuum condition, the unit should be disconnected and enough gas let in the low side to bring it out of the vacuum condition. The expansion valve can then be removed and cleaned.

If a system doesn't have a receiver, take an empty refrigerant cylinder and connect the center charging hose to the service valve on the cylinder, open the valve, and bleed the air at the manifold hose. Place the cylinder in a large container and pour chipped or cracked ice over the cylinder. As the cylinder is cooled, the pressure will go down. The high-side valve on the manifold can be opened, and the refrigerant will flow into the service drum. The cylinder should be pulled on a vacuum before being placed in the ice. The compressor should not be in operation when removing refrigerant unless there is a receiver on the system. When more refrigerant is in the system than the cylinder will hold, use two cylinders. The valves on the manifold should be closed after the refrigerant has been removed. The expansion valve can then be removed and cleaned.

Yet another way to remove the refrigerant is to shut the compressor off and bleed the system out into the air. This can be done by loosening the low-side hose at the manifold. The expansion valve can then be removed, cleaned, and replaced. After replacing the valve, pull the system on a vacuum to remove the air, then recharge the system. Always check systems for leaks after parts have been removed and replaced.

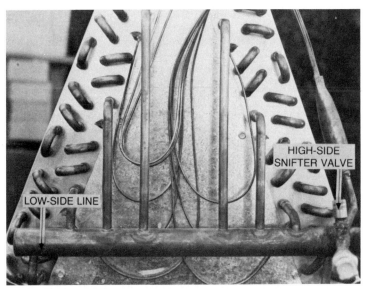

Fig. 13-34. Multiple capillary tubes connecting into the evaporator coil.

## CAPILLARY TUBES

The capillary tube system is used as a metering device in place of the expansion valve on some systems. As noted earlier in this chapter, the capillary tube is a tube with a narrow channel. The smaller the hole and the longer the tube, the more restriction there is. When changing the capillary tube, obtain one with the same size hole and the same length.

There can be several tubes on the evaporator (Fig. 13-34). The high-side line will carry the refrigerant to the capillary tubes, and the capillary tubes will meter the refrigerant into the evaporator. These are sometimes referred to as *feeder tubes* because each tube will feed a certain number of lines in the evaporator and then return to the low-side line manifold at the end of the coil.

Sometimes one of these tubes will clog or get broken and have to be changed. If a tube should clog, part of the coil or evaporator will not be sweating or getting cool. It will be necessary to remove the refrigerant to replace the tube. After the tube has been replaced, pull the system on a vacuum and recharge.

## MOISTURE PROBLEMS

Moisture in a refrigeration system is a very destructive force. In conjunction with the refrigerant and heat from the compressor it forms an acid which affects the motor windings of the compressor, causes rust to form on steel lines, and destroys compressor parts.

Moisture also can cause a sludge that affects the operation of the metering device (capillary tube or expansion valve). When the metering device freezes up, it will cause a vacuum in the low-side line. This may lead a repairman to think that the system is low on refrigerant.

Moisture can get into the system in several ways. Usually it enters because the tubing wasn't protected properly, the system was not charged properly, or the system was left open for a period of time. When installing a new system, the high- and low-side lines should be kept sealed (if there is a factory seal) or plugged. If the unit is a precharged type, the lines have been cleaned, charged, and sealed by the factory. You won't have to do anything to them except keep them sealed.

If the unit is not factory precharged, however, you will have to close up the ends of the lines to prevent dirt from entering. When the system is installed, the moisture and air in the line will have to be removed. The proper way to remove the moisture and air is with a two-stage vacuum pump. The vacuum pump will not only remove the air from the lines, but in doing so, it creates a vacuum that causes the moisture to boil out of the system.

Another way to remove the moisture is to install a drier in the system. The drier will remove the moisture from the refrigerant, and it will have to be changed occasionally. To install or change the drier, the refrigerant will have to be removed. If the system is pumped out and there is a vacuum in the lines, add enough refrigerant to bring the lines up to a slight pressure. With most of the refrigerant out of the system and slight pressure in the lines, the drier can be changed.

So far we have discussed ways that moisture can enter the refrigerant system when the lines are being installed. Once the refrigerant lines are installed, cleaned, and charged, the job is only half over. You must still be very careful that no moisture enters the system.

If the refrigerant is removed from the system to change the expansion valve or drier and is placed in a service cylinder, it is very important that the service cylinder be free of moisture. If the service cylinder has air or moisture in it, putting new refrigerant in the cylinder will contaminate the entire charge of refrigerant. To prevent this, it is advisable to always pull a discarded service cylinder on a vacuum before you use it to store new refrigerant.

When a system that has a leak in it is pulled on a vacuum, air and moisture will be sucked into the system. A new or old system should be pressure-checked for a leak before the system is pulled down (evacuated).

Any time you connect the service gages to the system for charging the system, you must be careful not to allow the air in the hoses to enter the system. The hoses will be full of air and moisture, and they will have to be bled before the system is charged. If they are not bled, the service cylinder will force the air and moisture in the hoses into the system along with the new refrigerant. To bleed the hoses, connect the gages to the service cylinder and service valves. With the service valves on the system closed, open the service valve on the cylinder. Now loosen the connections on the hoses. You will have to loosen the connections where the service hose connects to the gage manifold and the charging hose connects to the service valves on the system. Just crack these connections a bit for a few seconds to remove the air in them.

## EVACUATING A SYSTEM

The refrigerant system should be evacuated any time the lines are opened. This is because air and moisture will enter the system when the lines are opened, and this contamination must be removed before refrigerant is added.

### Vacuum Pump Method

Several types of vacuum pumps are available, but the best type to use is a two-stage pump. The two-stage pump pulls a deeper vacuum than the other pumps. The deeper the vacuum in the system, the better it will be cleaned. In other words, a system that is pulled on a vacuum to 29 inches Hg is better than one that is only pulled to 20 inches Hg. The stronger vacuum pump will also speed the job.

The size of the line between the vacuum pump and system plays a part in the amount of vacuum that can be pulled and the time it will take to do the job. A longer hose will give more restriction than a shorter one, so use as short a hose as possible. Also, a ⅜-inch line with no restrictions will do the job faster and better than a ¼-inch line with restrictions.

## Purging

Another way to remove the air from the refrigerant lines is to purge the system. This method is only a second best to the vacuum pump, and not a very close second at that. To purge the system, connect the gage manifold to the system and run refrigerant into the lines. Bleed the refrigerant out and recharge the system. Charge and bleed the system with refrigerant at least three times before giving the unit the final charge. The refrigerant is heavier than the air, so most of the air will be removed when the refrigerant is bled out. The refrigerant is also dry, so it will carry most of the moisture out of the system.

## TYPES OF REFRIGERANT

There are several refrigerants used, but most units use R-12, R-22, or R-502 refrigerant. The name of the refrigerant required, either its common name or its chemical name, will be stamped on the nameplate on the unit. Before charging any system, the type of refrigerant required must be known so the correct replacement can be put back in. If the wrong refrigerant is put in the system, the unit will not cool to the proper temperature or may develop compressor problems.

### Refrigerant-12

Refrigerant-12 (also known as Freon-12, F-12, dichlorodifluoromethane, or $CCl_2F_2$) operates at lower head and low-side pressure than the two other refrigerants. Refrigerant-12, or R-12, boils at about $-20°F$ at atmospheric pressure. In a condenser with a low-side pressure of 37.0 psi, Refrigerant-12 will boil at 40°F. At this temperature the coil will sweat, but it will not ice over.

The head pressure for R-12 will be around 125 to 150 psi, but this will depend on the outside temperature and the amount of air moving over condenser coil. High outside temperature and reduced air flow over the condenser will cause the head pressure to increase.

Canisters for R-12 are color-coded white, and you can purchase R-12 in 15, 30, 50 and 145-pound cylinders. Some of the cylinders are disposable. R-12 can also be purchased in 1-pound cans. Refrigerant-12 is used on some small air conditioners.

### Refrigerant-22

R-22 (Freon-22 or monochlorodifluoromethane, or $CCIF_2$) boils at $-41.4°F$ at atmospheric pressure. The color code is green. R-22 is purchased in 15, 20, 25, 50, and 125-pound cylinders.

The head pressure for R-22 will be from 225 to 275 psi, according to the outside temperature. This refrigerant will boil in the evaporator at 40°F

**Table 13-1. Pressure for Refrigerants R-12, R-22, and R-502 at Various Temperatures.**

| Temperature | Low-Side Pressure (psi) | | |
|---|---|---|---|
| | R12 | R22 | R502 |
| 35° | 32.6 | 61.5 | 72.8 |
| 38° | 35.2 | 65.6 | 77.4 |
| 40° | 37.0 | 68.5 | 80.5 |
| 46° | 42.6 | 77.6 | 90.4 |

with 69 psi low-side pressure. These pressure-temperature figures are available from either the pressure gages or a chart. Generally the ideal evaporator temperature is considered to be around 40°F, but if your unit has been running properly at 35°F, take note. When you open the system and recharge it, recharge only to the pressure required to reach a 35°F evaporator temperature. This is where the scales and tables come in handy. They can tell you just how much refrigerant pressure should be charged into the system to make the evaporator reach the desired operating temperature. Table 13-1 gives some of the temperatures for the different refrigerants.

### Refrigerant-502

Refrigerant-502 boils at −50°F at atmospheric pressure. It has a boiling point of 40°F evaporator temperature when the low-side pressure is 80.5 psi.

# Chapter 14

# Electric Motors

The electric motors used in heating and cooling systems operate the compressors (sealed or open type), fans, and pumps that circulate refrigerant, air, or water.

## BASIC ELECTRIC MOTOR PRINCIPLES

Two of the most basic principles behind the operation of the electric motor are the principles of alternating current and electromagnetism. Figure 14-1 shows the variations in power line alternating current. The variations shown are repeated 60 times a second, and the direction of the current reverses 120 times per second.

Magnetism is created any time current flows through a wire. The magnetic effect around a wire is illustrated in Fig. 14-2. If several turns of wire are wrapped around a soft iron core and a current is made to flow through the wire (Fig. 14-3), the iron core will become a magnet, or more precisely, an *electromagnet*. The electromagnet's strength will be determined by the number of turns of wire surrounding the core. The individual magnetic fields around each single turn of wire will combine to produce a strong magnetic field around the core.

When the south poles of two magnets are placed in proximity, they will repel each other. The same is true of two north poles when they are brought close together. When a north pole and a south pole come close together, they will be attracted or pulled together. *Likes* repel and *unlikes* attract. This is shown by Fig. 14-4. In this illustration, if we had some way to reverse the stationary bar's magnetic fields at the proper time, the pivoted bar axis would continue to turn. This is similar to what happens in an electric motor and is how its turning can be explained.

In an electric motor the permanent magnets of Fig. 14-4 are replaced by electromagnets (Fig. 14-5). The windings on the stationary part, or

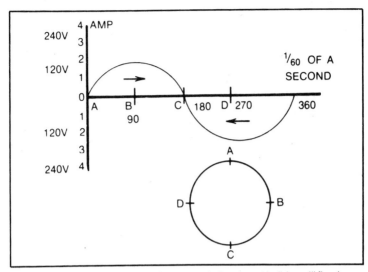

Fig. 14-1. One cycle of sinewave. Starting at A, the current buildup will flow in one direction and peak at B. It then drops off and is at zero at C. Then the current builds up in the opposite direction and peaks at D. It will drop back to zero at A.

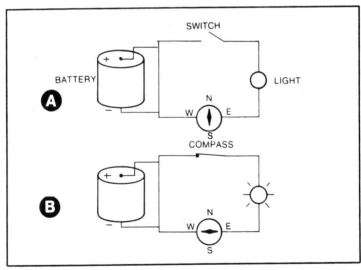

Fig. 14-2. Diagrams showing how current through a wire produces magnetism. With a battery, switch, light, and compass this can be demonstrated. (A) When the circuit is open, with no current flowing through the wire, the compass hand will point north. (B) When the switch is closed and the current is flowing, the compass hand will turn parallel to the wire, showing the pull of the magnetism created by the current in the wire. After the circuit is opened, the hand of the compass will return to north.

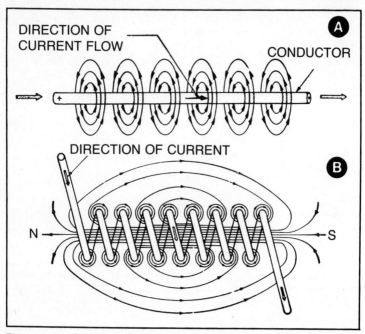

Fig. 14-3. (A) Magnetic field about a conductor (B) Magnetic field about a coil.

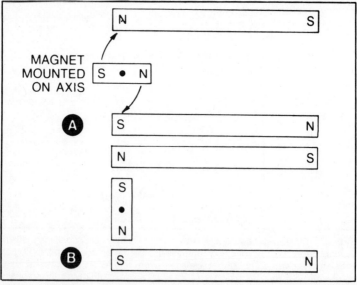

Fig. 14-4. When one magnet is placed in the field of another magnet and one of the magnets is mounted on pivot, the movable magnet will align with the field of the stationary magnet.

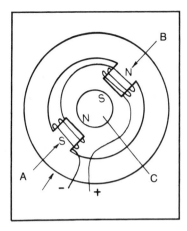

Fig. 14-5. If pole A is a south pole when the current is flowing in the direction shown, then pole B will be a north pole. The attraction and repulsion of the magnetic fields is the force which turns the rotor. This two-pole motor will run at 3450 rpm.

stator, produce magnetism in it which, in turn, induces a current in the rotatable central part or rotor. The induced current in the rotor makes it an electromagnet as well. The motor circuitry is designed so that the alternating current applied to the stator windings gives the effect of a rotating magnetic field around it. The rotor, by virtue of its magnetic nature, follows the magnetic field. The torque, or turning force, of the motor is taken off by means of a shaft attached to the rotor. Although only two separate stator coils are shown, an actual motor would have many such coils. Although only two magnetic poles are present in the stator shown, other even numbers of poles are often used.

## STARTING AND RUNNING WINDINGS

The running winding of an electric motor is wound with fewer turns of larger wire than the starting winding. The greater number of turns of smaller wire in the starting winding results in greater resistance. Because of this large amount of resistance, heat will also increase. This makes it necessary to remove the starting winding from the circuit after the motor has picked up speed, which can be done with a centrifugal switch or a relay (Fig. 14-6). In some motors the starting windings are on the same poles as the running windings.

## MOTOR SPEED

The more poles there are in a motor (excluding separate starting poles), the more slowly it will run. The formula which is used to calculate the speed of a motor is

$$\text{rpm} = \frac{120\,\text{F}}{\text{P}}$$

where

F = frequency (hertz, or cycles per second)
P = number of poles

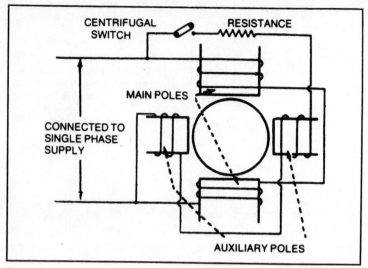

Fig. 14-6. In this motor auxiliary windings are used to start the motor and are then removed from the circuit by a centrifugal switch.

Example: If a motor has four poles (Fig. 14-7) and runs on 60 Hz current, how fast does it run?

$$\text{rpm} = \frac{120 \times 60}{4} = \frac{7200}{4} = 1800$$

A practical motor does not quite live up to the theoretical ideal. *Slippage* occurs, and the rotor does not quite keep up with the action in the stator field. The actual speed of the motor in the above calculation would be approximately 1750 rpm instead of 1800 rpm.

## TYPES OF MOTORS

Most small air conditioners are wired into single-phase—that is, two-wire—power systems. In a single-phase ac machine, the field, instead

Fig. 14-7. This four-pole motor runs at 1750 rpm. The south poles are wound differently than the north poles. As the current in the stator alternates, the stator's north poles become south poles and vice versa. This creates a rotating magnetic field which the rotor follows.

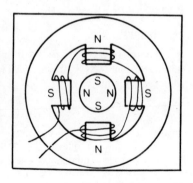

of rotating as in two- and three-phase, merely pulsates. No rotation of the rotor takes place. A single-phase pulsating field may be visualized as two rotating fields revolving at the same speed, but in opposite directions. It follows that the rotor will revolve in either direction, provided it is given an initial impetus in either one direction or the other. The exact value of this initial rotational velocity varies widely with different machines, but a velocity higher than 15 percent of the rated speed is usually sufficient. A single-phase motor can be made self-starting if means can be provided to give the effect of a rotating field.

**Shaded-Pole Motor.** The first development of a self-starting, single-phase motor was the shaded-pole induction motor (Fig. 14-8). This machine has unusual stator poles, a portion of each pole being encircled by a heavy copper ring. The presence of the copper ring causes the magnetic field through the ringed portion of the pole face to lag appreciably behind the field through the other part of the pole face. This produces a slight component of rotation of the field, enough to cause the rotor to revolve. As the rotor accelerates, the torque increases until the rated speed is obtained. Such motors have low starting torque and find their greatest application in small fan motors, where the initial torque required is low.

**Split-Phase Motor.** Various types of self-starting, single-phase ac motors, known as split-phase motors, are manufactured. They are usually of fractional horsepower and are used to operate such devices as washing machines, small pumps, and blowers. The motor has four main parts: the rotor, the stator, the mounting frame, and the centrifugal switch (Fig. 14-6). The winding of the rotor is usually of the squirrel-cage type, consisting of copper bars placed in slots in the laminated iron core and connected to each other by copper rings.

The stator has two windings—the main or running winding and the starting winding—that are wound into slots in the iron core. The main

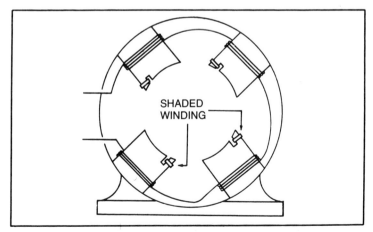

Fig. 14-8. Shaded-pole induction motor.

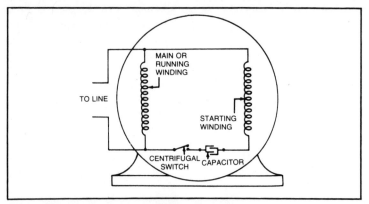

Fig. 14-9. Typical capacitor-start motor connections.

winding is connected across the line in the usual manner and produces the magnetic field for the main poles. The auxiliary windings have a resistance greater than that of the main winding. Sometimes additional resistance is put in series with the auxiliary winding. As the resistance in the auxiliary winding is greater than that in the main winding, the voltages in the auxiliary and main windings differ by about 90°. These two sets of poles produce a sort of rotating field that starts the motor. When the motor reaches a predetermined speed, the starting winding is automatically disconnected by a centrifugal switch inside the motor.

**Capacitor-Start Motors.** With the development of high-capacity electrolytic capacitors, a variation of the split-phase motor, known as capacitor-start motor, was made (Fig. 14-9). Nearly all fractional-horsepower motors in use today on refrigerators, oil burners, and other similar appliances are of this type. In this adaptation, the phase shift of 90° electrical between currents of two windings is obtained by means of the capacitor connected in series with the starting winding.

Capacitor-start motors have a starting torque comparable to their torque at rated speed and can be used in applications where the initial load is heavy. Again, a centrifugal switch is necessary for disconnecting the starting winding when the rotor is at approximately 75 percent of rated speed.

**Capacitor-Start and -Run Motor.** A variation of the capacitor-start motor is the capacitor-start and -run motor. This is similar to the capacitor-start motor except that the capacitor is connected in the circuit all the time. This type of motor is quiet and smooth in operation, but can be used only where medium starting torque is required. Such applications include blowers, fans, and oil burners. The capacitor is usually a paper-insulated, oil-filled type.

## MOTOR RELAYS

Split-phase induction motors can be used in a sealed dome because they do not use brushes or slip rings, which would burn the oil and cause

266

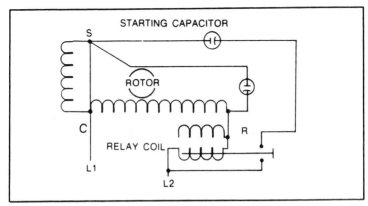

Fig. 14-10. Wiring diagram for a current relay used on a split-phase induction motor. The coil in the relay is connected in series with run windings of the motor. The relay points are normally open on the off cycle. The starting capacitor is connected in series with the start windings when used. The running capacitor will be connected from the start terminal to the run terminal.

trouble inside the sealed unit. A relay is used outside the sealed dome to control the power to the start windings and disconnect them at the proper time. Three types of relays are used on sealed units: the "hot" wire relay, current relay (Fig. 14-10), and potential relay (Fig. 14-11). The latter two are more commonly used. Split-phase and capacitor-start motors use centrifugal switches when used outside of a sealed unit, for example, to run a condenser fan.

## CHECKING MOTOR PARTS

Many times the starter switch of an electric motor and the parts related to the switch are responsible for an electric motor failure. It is necessary to take the motor apart to get to the switch.

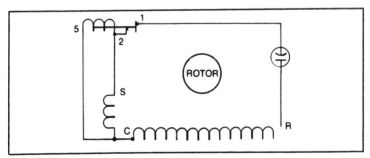

Fig. 14-11. Schematic diagram for a potential relay used on a split-phase induction motor. The coil to the relay is between terminals 2 and 5. The points are between terminals 1 and 2. The starting capacitor is between terminal 1 and the run terminal. The points are closed on the off cycle, but open after the compressor starts.

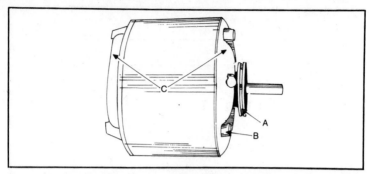

Fig. 14-12. The fan motor has been removed from the mounting base. At A is the rubber mount for base clips or screws to connect the motor to the base. Sometimes it is easier to remove these clips than to remove the mounting base. At B is one of the through bolts which hold the two end bells (C) together. These bolts (there are usually four) have to be removed so the end bell can be taken off.

**Disassembling the Motor.** An electric motor is usually held together with four bolts that have nuts on one or both ends (Fig. 14-12). Before the end bells are removed, they should be marked so they can be replaced in the same position. This can be done with a screwdriver by scratching from the bell housing to the stator housing. Both bells should be marked in this manner. Figure 14-13 shows the bell housing removed. Sometimes the rotor will slip out as the bell housing is removed. The disassembled motor is seen in Fig. 14-14, revealing the stator with the starting and running windings.

**Checking the Starter Switch.** The starter switch is usually located in the rear of the bell housing as shown in Fig. 14-15. Care should be taken not to bend the starter switch or break the wires that leave the starter switch going to the stator.

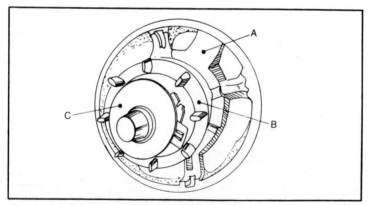

Fig. 14-13. (A) Bell housing after it has been removed. (B) Rotor that has been pressed onto the shaft. (C) Surface of the centrifugal switch that operates the lever to disconnect the start windings of the motor.

RUN
WINDINGS

LEVER ACTUATED BY
CENTRIFUGAL SWITCH

Fig. 14-14. This shows the stator with its start and run windings. As the motor picks up speed, the weights in back of the flat surface of the centrifugal switch move the surface back. The lever, in turn, disconnects the points, and this removes the start windings from the circuit.

There are a number of parts to an electric motor which affect the operation of the starter switch. These include parts such as the counterweights, wear valves, springs, bearings, and bushings.

The points on the starter switch that disconnect the start windings are sometimes burned from arcing. This will prevent the switch from working

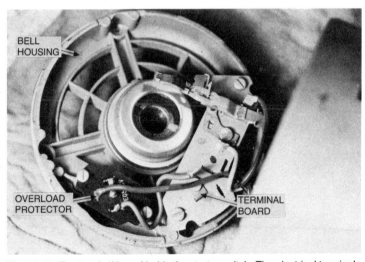

BELL
HOUSING

OVERLOAD
PROTECTOR

TERMINAL
BOARD

Fig. 14-15. The terminal board holds the starter switch. The electrical terminals are on the back of the terminal board. Two screws hold the terminal board to the bell housing. The overload protector is necessary in case the motor gets overloaded and begins to pull too many amps. This overload will disconnect the power to the motor to keep the motor from burning up.

269

properly. A second problem with the starter switch could be the lever that opens the points. Sometimes this lever is broken or bent. In either case the starter switch should be replaced with a new one. The points and lever are shown in Fig. 14-16.

If it appears necessary to replace the starter switch, there are two screws on each end of the switch that can be removed to take the switch out. When replacing it, care must be taken to connect the wires on the proper terminals. Marking the wires is one way to make certain they are replaced properly. Another way is to connect the wires one at a time on the new switch as the old one is removed.

The counterweights on the rotor shaft control the switch. A switch may fail to work because the counterweights are sticking. These parts should be cleaned. All of the parts of the starting device should move freely and should be free from dust and dirt. The springs that hold the weights may be another trouble spot. They may be broken or loose and may need to be replaced. These are special springs and must be working properly.

**Checking Other Motor Parts**. The wear washers at each end of the rotor may be the cause of electric motor failure. These may be completely gone or may be broken. To check them, take hold of the end of the shaft and see if the rotor shaft can be moved back and forth. If there is any play here, new wear washers may have to be added to the front end of the motor shaft.

The bearings in each bell housing should also be checked for wear and must be replaced if they are worn. This checking is done by seeing if the shaft can be moved up and down in the bearing. If ball bearings are used, it is necessary to check after the bell housings have been removed.

When changing bushings in the bell housing, the housing is first removed. The bell housing is then put on the stator, without the rotor, and a line reamer is used to ream and realign the bushings in the bell housing.

Fig. 14-16. The points are separated as the lever moves back. The wires run from the switch to the motor windings in the stator. If the points are burned or covered with carbon, the switch should be replaced. Sometimes the points can be cleaned and made to work until a new switch can be ordered.

This should realign each bearing and let the rotor turn freely. After this is done, replace all parts and tighten the bell housings equally on all four bolts so the rotor will turn freely.

## TROUBLESHOOTING ELECTRIC MOTORS

There are several ways for an electric motor to malfunction. When trouble occurs, find the appropriate symptom from the following list and check out the numbered list of possible causes.

### Motor Won't Start

- Bad starter switch.
- Bad starting capacitor.
- Starting winding burned out.
- Starter switch points not making contact.
- Bad bearings.
- Rotor frozen.
- Bad relay.

### Motor "Tries" to Start, but Won't

- Any of troubles listed above.
- Bearing frozen or worn.
- Compressor stuck.
- Bad running capacitor.

### Motor Pulls too Many Amps

- Motor winding shorted.
- Starter switch points welded together.
- Centrifugal switch stuck.
- Broken spring on switch.
- Worn bearings.
- Wear washer broken.
- Dry bearings.
- Incorrect voltage.

### Motor Hums but Won't Run

- Starter switch not engaged.
- Shorted capacitor.
- Worn bearings.
- Incorrect voltage.
- Rotor stuck.
- Dry bearings.
- Broken starter switch.

### Motor Starts but Doesn't Reach Running Speed

- Capacitor burned out.
- Bad starter switch.
- Motor overloaded.
- Worn bearings.

# Chapter 15

# Resistance Heating

There are several types of electric resistance heating. We will discuss two types in this chapter: ceiling cable and baseboard heaters. These heating systems have features similar to many other resistance heating systems.

All electric resistance heaters rely on the heating effect of current passing through a resistance. In this sense, this type of heating is like the electric furnace. The difference lies in the fact that baseboard heaters and ceiling cable use individual heating elements in each room. They have no fan or other source of air circulation, so they rely solely on the natural air currents of the room to circulate the heat. Since they have no duct system, they are not considered to be members of the family of central heating units.

Ceiling cable and baseboard heaters are used in homes as primary and secondary sources of heat. If the furnace (primary source) in a house is not heating it well enough, the installation of one of these forms of heating will provide a cheap and effective secondary source. Resistance heating is especially useful in providing supplemental heat to a single room in a house that is constantly cold. In this way the room is made warmer without making complicated furnace modifications.

Resistance heating has the advantage of providing in each room an individual thermostat to adjust the heat in that room as needed, without changing the temperatures of other rooms. This is not possible with central heating by itself, but the addition of resistance heating as a secondary heat source will give this versatility.

A disadvantage of resistance heating as the primary heat source is the lack of a central duct system. Central air conditioning cannot be added without a duct system. With ceiling installations, the big advantage is the uniform distribution of heat in a room, without hot spots or any other apparent heat source.

## CEILING CABLE

Ceiling cable is a resistance wire or cable that is placed in the ceiling to heat a room. Each room has its own thermostat. After the cable is placed in the ceiling, the ceiling is finished with texturing material to cover the cable.

To install ceiling cable, you must first figure the heat load for the room. Then you must determine the wattage required to handle the heat load and buy the cable for this wattage. The cable is precut at the factory and should not be cut in installation. At the ends of the cable there are lengths of nonheating wire to be run to the thermostat.

### Thermostat

The thermostat for ceiling cable will be either a double-pole, single-throw type or a single-pole, single-throw type. The thermostat will be a line voltage thermostat, which means that it will be connected directly to the power mains. If the ceiling cable is connected to a 120V line, the thermostat will operate at 120V.

An ordinary electrical receptacle is installed in the wall, and a circuit is run from the breaker box. If the ceiling cable is a 4000W cable on a 240V circuit, the circuit can be installed on a 20A breaker with No. 12, three-conductor wire. A 120V heater with 2000W would be run with the same size wire.

Figure 15-1 shows how the circuit is connected at the thermostat. The wires from the breaker are installed in the receptacle box, and the line from the cable is connected. After the wires have been connected, the thermostat will mount on the receptacle. The thermostat should be installed about 60 inches from the floor on an inside wall where there will be good air movement over it.

### Heating Panels

Heating panels are ceiling panels with heating cable embedded in them. These panels come in a variety of styles just as regular panels do.

The panels are wired through a line voltage thermostat. They are ideal for large windows areas, entry hallways, and any small area where supple-

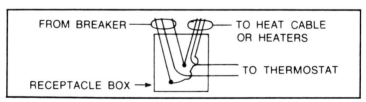

Fig. 15-1. The lines from the breaker and ceiling cable are brought to the receptacle. One line from the heater is connected to the thermostat, and the second line from the heater is connected to the line from the breaker. The second breaker "hot" line connects to the thermostat, and the ground wire is grounded to the receptacle and heater.

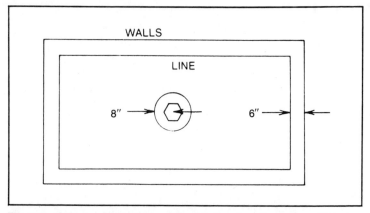

Fig. 15-2. Lines are drawn on the ceiling 6 inches from the walls and 8 inches from any fixtures. If cabinets were installed or planned for installation, the line would be 6 inches from the cabinet face.

mental heat is desired. One important note about these panels is that the house must have an attic above the area where the panels will be installed. This is to allow access to the panels so they can be wired and repaired.

### Installation

The most important part of installing ceiling cable is planning out the ceiling so that all the cable can be installed. This is because the cable comes in a given number of feet according to the wattage desired, and it can't be cut. In planning the route for the cable on the ceiling, remember to take light fixtures and cabinets into account. The cable will have to be run around any items that come in contact with the ceiling. If cabinets or fixtures are to be installed later, be sure to put the cable around the area these items will occupy. The cable should not be installed above or behind any objects. When installing light fixtures or any object that comes in contact with a ceiling equipped with ceiling cable, make sure you know where the cable is so you don't break it or short it out.

### Ceiling Layout

The cable should be no closer than 6 inches to a wall and no closer than 8 inches to a fixture or receptacle box. Begin the layout by drawing a line on the ceiling 6 inches from the walls all around the room, as shown in Fig. 15-2.

After the heat load for the room has been figured and converted to watts, the proper size cable is purchased. Let's assume the heat load for a room is such that we require 1475W. Cable can be purchased in 1400W and 1500W lengths. The 1500W cable should be used in this instance since it is closer to the desired rating. The cable length will be 545 feet. The following formula is used to determine the proper spacing for the cable on the ceiling:

$$s_c = \frac{12 \, (1_c - 1) \, ( w - 1)}{1_c - (2w + 1_r)}$$

where

$s_c$ = cable spacing in inches
$1_r$ = length of room (in feet)
$w$ = width of room (in feet)
$1_c$ = length of cable (in feet)

Assuming the room was 10 × 10,

$$sc = \frac{12 \, (10 - 1) \, (10 - 1)}{545 - [ \, (2 \times 10) + 10]} = \frac{12 \times 9 \times 9}{545 - 30} = 1.88 \text{ inches}$$

The spacing of the cable should be measured to the nearest ⅛ inch. In this example the spacing would be 1⅞ inch.

Figure 15-3 shows how the cable is laid out. Starting at the 6-inch mark on the outside wall, the lines are marked off 1⅞ inches apart. This should be done by measuring at both ends of the room and snapping a chalk line to make the marks the length of the room. Be sure to make the turns for the cable before the cable crosses the 6-inch line at the wall.

Two holes will have to be bored through the ceiling so the ends of the cable can be run to the thermostat. These wires will be 6 inches away from the wall and will run into the attic and down to the thermostat (Fig. 15-4).

Be careful when installing the cable not to break or kink it. Unroll the cable carefully and staple it to the ceiling along the mark you have made. Begin by stapling the first three staples 3 inches apart, then change to 6 inches apart. For turns, the staples should be placed in the center of the turn, 3 inches before the turn and 3 inches after the turn. Figure 15-5 shows

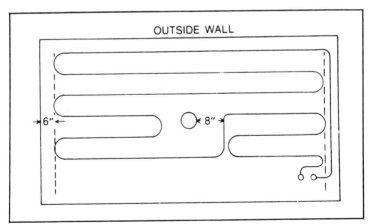

Fig. 15-3. The ceiling should be marked with chalk lines to determine the proper placing for the cable. Be sure to keep the turns at least 6 inches from the walls and 8 inches from any fixtures.

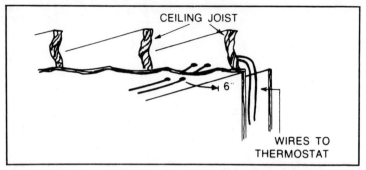

Fig. 15-4. This shows how the wires are run from the cable up through the ceiling and joists. The wires then go down a partition wall to connect to the thermostat.

the proper stapling procedure. Above all, follow factory instructions when installing the cable.

### Continuity Check

After the cable has been installed, a continuity check should be run to make sure there are no breaks in the cable. Be sure to make this check before the cable is plastered over. To run the check, place the two ohmmeter leads on the cable terminals at the thermostat. The meter should give a continuity reading. It will not show zero resistance, since the purpose of the cable is to provide resistance to the flow of electricity so as to produce heat.

While the ohmmeter is connected to the two ends of the cable, take a broom and sweep the cable. Note whether the meter needle moves. If the needle moves to show no continuity, there is a break in the cable, and it will have to be spliced before the ceiling is plastered. If the needle doesn't move, the cable is ready to be covered.

Connect the line voltage to the thermostat and check the cable for heat. The cable should heat within 5 minutes.

The ends of the cable are color-coded. If the loom leads are red, the cable must be connected to 240V or 208V. If the ends are yellow, the proper voltage is 120V. Be sure to connect the cable to the correct voltage.

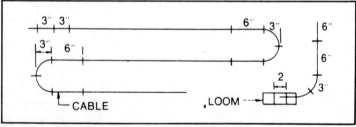

Fig. 15-5. Place staples in the centers of the turns and 3 inches on each side. The loom (the wires running from the cable to the thermostat) should be stapled about 2 inches apart. All tags and labels from the factory should be left on the ends.

Do not cut off any of the loom (nonheating lead) or cable. Any extra loom wire can be pulled up into the attic and stapled. All identification tags should be left on the cable and loom.

## Locating the Break

A stepup transformer is used to locate a break in the cable. The primary circuit is connected to the power supply, and the secondary winding is connected to the cable leads after they are removed from the thermostat. When the power is turned on, the high voltage will cause a buzzing sound at the break. The buzzing can be traced by ear or with a microphone and amplifier.

## Splicing the Cable

After locating the break, the cable can be repaired from the bottom. If the ceiling has been finished, the wire will have to be dug out from the top side. Care must be taken not to crack the finish of the ceiling. After the break is spliced, a continuity check should be run to make sure the cable is working.

The cable can be spliced with a compression connection. The ends of the cable must be stripped of insulation before the compression connection is installed. The ends of the cable are placed in the compression fitting and crimped together. The joint is taped with a special *thermosetting* tape. This tape is available from dealers and small appliance repair shops. The cable is taped about an inch on each side of the joint.

## BASEBOARD HEATERS

The sizes of these heaters range from 500W to 2500W. Since each room in the house will have its own heating unit (or combination of units), the heat loads must be figured for each room separately. A unit of the proper size must be installed in each room.

Sometimes a room will require more than one heater, or it may be more convenient and efficient to install more than one heater in a room. When baseboard heaters are installed in this manner they may be placed end to end on the same wall, or they may be separated and placed on different walls. When more than one heater is used, both heaters may be controlled by the same thermostat.

Most baseboard heaters are for 240V, but a 120V heater may be installed if the proper wattage can be obtained. When only one heater is installed in a room, the current draw will likely be less than 20A, so No. 12 wire will be used. When two or three heaters are used for one room, larger wire will have to be installed if the amperage draw is more than 20A. Three-wire cable can be used on most installations. The ground wire is used to ground the heaters to the fuse box, and a four-wire cable isn't necessary. Figures 15-6 and 15-7 show the wiring for single-heater installations.

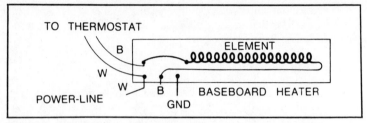

Fig. 15-6. A single heater connected to the circuit from the fuse box.

When two or more heaters are connected to one thermostat, they may be connected to either a single- or a double-pole thermostat. Figures 15-8 through 15-10 show wiring diagrams for two heaters.

When two or more heaters are connected to one thermostat and the current is more than 20A, two different circuits may be connected through a double-pole thermostat as in Fig. 15-11. Care should be taken to make all connections tight, because a loose connection can cause the heater to malfunction.

### Electric Baseboard Heater Installation

Electric baseboard heaters are normally installed on separate circuits, but when installing more than one heater on the same circuit, make sure the sum of the currents of the units is less than the size of the breaker. The wire size will also have to be the right size to handle the current.

A No. 12 wire will carry 20A without overloading. If more amperage is needed, go to a No. 10 wire and a 30A breaker.

To find the amperage rating of a heater, use the formula $I = P/E$, where P is power in watts, I is amps, and V is voltage. If a baseboard heater uses 1000W and the voltage is 240V, the amp rating is $1000/120 = 8.33A$.

When connecting two heaters together, connect the units in parallel, not in series (Figs. 15-9, 15-10, and 15-12). Connected in series, heaters get warm but will not supply the proper amount of heat.

Figure 15-13 shows how two heaters can be connected together with a third wire (ground) in the circuit to protect a person from a shock if the

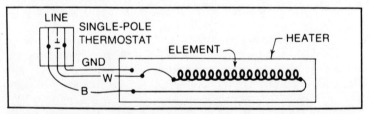

Fig. 15-7. The heater is connected to the single-pole thermostat in the circuit with the power supply. Notice that the thermostat operates on the same circuit as the heater. There is no secondary circuit to supply low voltage power to the thermostat.

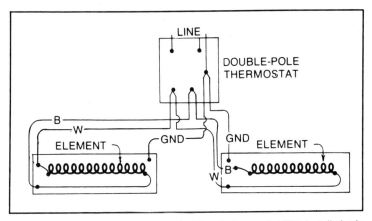

Fig. 15-8. Two heaters connected to a double-pole thermostat. This installation is used in a room where two or more heaters are needed. The heaters are on different walls.

heater develops a short. (The ground wire is used with single-heater installations as well as double-heater installations.) The ground wire runs from the thermostat box to each heater, where it is grounded to the metal case.

There are several styles and sizes of baseboard heaters currently being sold. Some of these heaters can be installed in the wall with fans to circulate the air. Some are installed in the ceiling with the exhaust fan. All of these units should be properly grounded. Some heaters have a built-in thermostat on the heating unit, which saves having to install a thermostat.

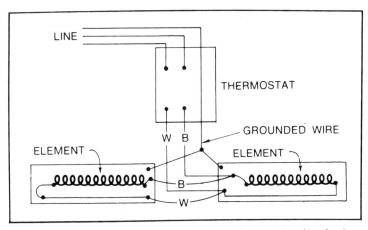

Fig. 15-9. Shown here is another connection of one thermostat and two heaters. The ground wire should be connected to both heaters and connected to the ground wire in the thermostat. The heaters could be on the same wall or butted together.

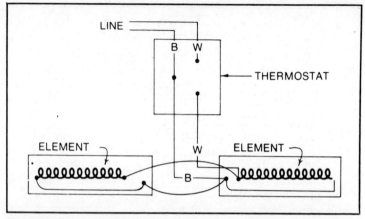

Fig. 15-10. Two heating elements connected to a single-pole thermostat.

The baseboard heaters are usually placed on an outside wall under the windows, where most of the heat loss in a room occurs. This helps warm the cooler air in these places. The thermostat, on the other hand, should be installed on an *inside* wall, where there is good air movement.

### Troubleshooting Baseboard Heaters

There aren't many types of heater failure. Ordinarily, a baseboard heater will either work properly or not at all. Occasionally, however, a unit will fail to deliver heat consistently, which indicates an intermittent connection. The following trouble list will serve as a guide in servicing units that are not heating satisfactorily.

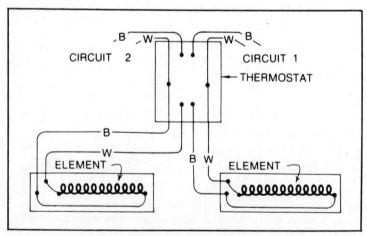

Fig. 15-11. This is a double-pole thermostat with two separate circuits. The ground wire should be connected to the receptacle box and heaters.

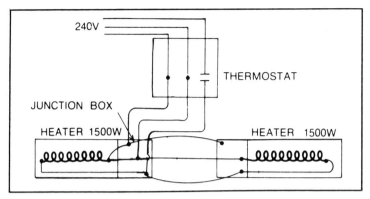

Fig. 15-12. This shows the proper connections to connect two heaters together in the same 240V circuit. The units must be wired in parallel.

### Heating Will not Heat Adequately

- Two 240V heaters connected in series instead of parallel.
- 120V applied to 240V heater.
- Loose connection.

### Heater Will not Heat

- Blown fuse.
- Loose connection.
- Element burned out.
- Bad thermostat.
- A wire is connected to the wrong fuse or same legs at the breaker box.

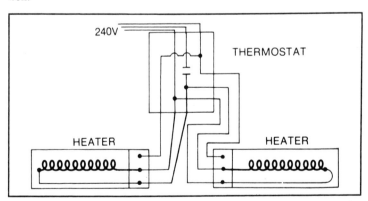

Fig. 15-13. The heaters are connected together at the thermostat instead of at the heaters as some of the previous diagrams have shown. Whether the units are connected at the thermostat or at the heater terminals depends on which is easier. The third wire is the bare ground wire connected to the heater case and the receptacle box. The ground wire protects against a short in the heater.

### Blowing Fuses

- Loose connection.
- Fuse too small for circuit.
- Shorted element.
- "Hot" wire touching ground wire.
- Shorted thermostat.

## THERMOSTATS

There are two types of thermostats used on ceiling cable and baseboards: the single-pole, single-throw (SPST) type and the double-pole, single-throw (DPST) type. The only difference between these is that the SPST thermostat opens and closes only one conductor, while the DPST opens and closes two conductors.

Usually SPST thermostats are used with one heater and one circuit, but they may be used with two heaters in parallel within the same circuit if the sum of the amp ratings for the two heaters is less than the amp rating for the thermostat. Figure 15-14 shows wiring for the SPST thermostat.

The DPST thermostat is typically used as shown in Figs. 15-15 and 15-16, with two heaters connected in two circuits. The thermostat will control both circuits and both heaters simultaneously.

Figure 15-17 shows two heaters connected in one circuit controlled by a DPST thermostat. The DPST thermostat is also sometimes used on a single heater (Fig. 15-18). In this case, both lines to the heater are broken.

Ceiling cable and baseboard heater thermostats are line voltage thermostats: They are connected in the same circuit that powers the heating unit. If the heater is operated by a 120V circuit, the themostat will be connected in the same circuit, and it will be a 120V thermostat (and similarly for 240V). In contrast, in furnace systems, the furnace is on a 120V or a 240V circuit, and the thermostat is powered by a 24V low voltage circuit.

### Thermostat Ratings

Thermostats carry an amperage rating that tells the maximum heater current the thermostat can switch. Each heater or ceiling cable unit will

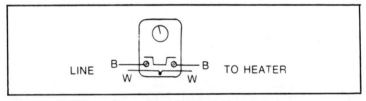

Fig. 15-14. The single-pole, single-throw thermostat has only two terminals, and the switch breaks and closes the circuit by opening and closing one line. The black wire from the fuse box is cut, and the two ends are placed on the terminals of the thermostat. The white line goes straight through to the heater.

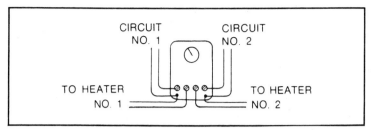

Fig. 15-15. Two separate circuits for two heaters are wired through one DPST thermostat.

have a current rating that tells how much current the unit will draw when in operation, and the amp rating of the thermostat must be larger than the amperage draw of the heater. If two or more heaters are connected through the same thermostat, their total amperage draw will be the sum of the amp ratings of the units. The thermostat must have an amp rating greater than the sum of the heater amp ratings. For most single-heater installations, 20A for the thermostat will be adequate. If you use two heaters on the same thermostat, a 30A or larger thermostat may be needed. For most ceiling cable installations a 30A thermostat will be adequate. When more current-carrying ability is required of the thermostat, a second thermostat should be installed as in Fig. 15-19.

The thermostat should be placed on the inside wall where the room air is free to move around it. The thermostat will not sense the correct temperature if the control is placed in a corner or an area where the air can't move freely. This will result in a room that is too hot or too cold.

### Installing Thermostats

This type of thermostat is easiest installed in the same way you would put in an electrical outlet. On unfinished walls (where the walls are not yet covered with wallboard or paneling), simply nail an electrical receptacle box to a stud. Bring in the wires from the fuse box and run them through the receptacle box (Fig. 15-20). Connect the incoming wires to the proper terminals on the thermostat plate. Run the wires going to the heater from the thermostat terminals, through the box, and to the heater. Place the

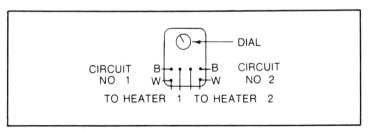

Fig. 15-16. When a DPST thermostat is connected to two heaters in two circuits, the black wires are connected as shown. The white wires go straight through.

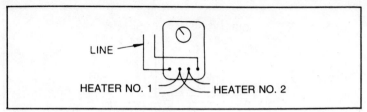

Fig. 15-17. Here two heaters are wired in the same circuit through a DPST thermostat.

thermostat plate on the receptacle box just like you would an electrical switch, and the job is finished.

If the walls have already been covered with wallboard, the installation will be more difficult because a hole will have to be cut in the wall. Once this is done, the installation is exactly like the installation of an electrical switch or outlet. It might be easier and cheaper to purchase a baseboard heater with a built-in thermostat.

## HEAT LOADS FOR RESISTANCE HEAT

Heat loads for electric heat are figured somewhat differently than burning-fuel heaters. With burning-fuel heaters, at least 25 percent of the heat produced is lost up the flue.

Electric heat is measured in kilowatts. As a general rule, for baseboard and ceiling cable, use about 1500W (1.5 kilowatts) per 100 square feet of floor area. This figure applies to the middle and southern states, where the temperature range is about 0° to 70°. In the northern states, where colder temperatures occur during winter, a larger factor will have to be used.

With baseboard heat or ceiling cable each room has its own heating unit and thermostat, so heat loads are calculated individually for each room. The method for figuring heat loads has already been presented.

The 1500W/100 square feet of floor area presented earlier assumes not only a temperature range above 0°, but also that the standard insulation has been installed: 6-10 inches of insulation in the ceiling, 3⅝ inches in the walls, and 2 inches in the floor. If less insulation is used or the location is in a

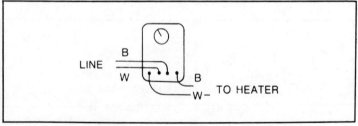

Fig. 15-18. When the DPST thermostat is connected with a single heater, both lines are opened and closed instead of just the one line as with a single-pole thermostat.

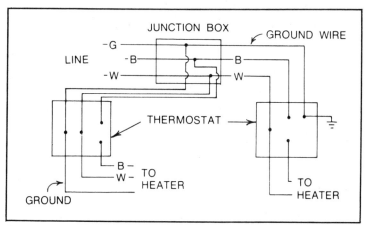

Fig. 15-19. Two heaters are connected to a single main circuit through a junction box and two single-pole thermostats.

colder part of the country, a higher factor, such as 3000W/100 square feet must be used.

As an example, assume we have a house in a part of the country with a temperature usually above 0°. A room in the house is 12 feet by 8 feet. To heat this room with ceiling cable or baseboard heat, we can calculate the heater size as follows if the insulation is adequate.

$$12 \text{ feet} \times 8 \text{ feet} = 96 \text{ square feet}$$

At 1500W/100 square feet, the power required is:

$$96/100 \times 1550 = 1440W$$

Therefore, we will need a heater rated at 1440W to heat this room. This would probably require a 1500W heater. The amperage draw of the 1500W heater at 240V would be 6.5A.

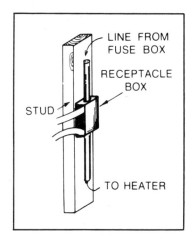

Fig. 15-20. Before the wall is finished, a receptacle box is installed for the thermostat.

An alternate way of figuring the heater size for the room is to figure the heat load for the room using the heat load charts. After the heat load for the room has been figured in Btu, convert the Btu figure to watts by multiplying by 0.293 or dividing by 3.415 (1W = 3.415 Btu). This method of figuring the heat load will be especially useful when using ceiling cable or baseboard heat as a supplement to a furnace system. In this situation you will take the heat load of the room, subtract the amount of heat supplied by the furnace in Btu, and figure the size of the heater according to the size of the remainder.

In figuring the size of the heater needed by these two methods, it is evident that the factor (1500W/square feet floor space) is faster and easier to use if the house is insulated properly and other conditions are favorable. On the other hand, when variable factors enter the process, the second method is by far the better. With some practice and skill a good serviceman will be able to develop his own conversion ratio for his area to give him quick estimate of the heat load required.

## ELECTRIC POWER SUPPLY

Be sure to check with the power company before installing any type of electric heating system. This check is necessary to ensure that the electrical supplier can supply all the electricity needed. Sometimes it will be necessary for the power company to change the transformer, lines to the house, breaker box, or entrance cable.

# Chapter 16

# Heat Pumps

Any refrigeration system is a heat pump because it removes heat from one area and deposits it in another area. This is the principle behind the refrigerator, freezer, and air conditioner. For understanding heat pumps it will be helpful to review the refrigeration cycle.

## REFRIGERATION CYCLE

The evaporator picks up the heat from the area to be cooled, and the heat is taken to the condenser, where the excess heat is discharged into the air. The absorption of heat is accomplished by the gas (refrigerant) in the refrigeration system. The refrigerant leaves the outside condensing coil in a liquid state and travels through the lines to the evaporator coil.

In the evaporator it picks up the heat to be carried away. The refrigerant enters the coil as a liquid, but in the evaporator the liquid boils to form a vapor. The evaporation process absorbs large amounts of heat from the surrounding air. See Chapter 13.

When the refrigerant vapor returns to the condenser, the compressor puts it under pressure, forcing the vapor back into the liquid state. The transformation from the gas into the liquid state liberates the heat, and the refrigerant goes back to the evaporator. The heat liberated at the condenser is dissipated into the surrounding air.

Why not use the heat from the condenser to heat a house in the winter? If the evaporator coil and the condenser were juxtaposed in the central air conditioning system, the heat dissipated at the condenser would be used to heat the house. In the summer the normal positions for refrigeration could be restored, and the system would cool the house. This would not be a very practical use of a central air conditioning system, but it shows the basic way in which a heat pump works.

## HEATING CYCLE

In a heat pump a special valve (reversing valve) reverses the direction of the refrigerant flow—in effect, changing the position of the coils. What was the condenser becomes the evaporator, and vice versa (Fig. 16-1).

When the reversing valve is in the cooling position, the indoor coil will be the evaporator. It will be cooler than the air moving over it. The refrigerant will vaporize at the indoor coil and absorb heat from the surrounding air. The refrigerant then flows through the reversing valve to the outdoor coil. The outdoor coil will be the condenser and will dissipate the heat into the air as the refrigerant liquefies once again under the force of the compressor.

When the reversing valve changes to the heating position, the refrigerant will flow to the inside coil, which becomes the condenser. The refrigerant will liquefy in the condenser, liberating heat into the air. This excess heat is distributed to the rooms to be heated. The outside coil is now the evaporator, where the refrigerant boils and absorbs heat (Fig. 16-2). As long as the temperature of the outside air is above the boiling point of the refrigerant, the refrigerant will boil and absorb heat from the outdoors to carry into the condensing coil inside. The critical temperature is around 15° because at this point plenty of air has to be moved over the coil to absorb any

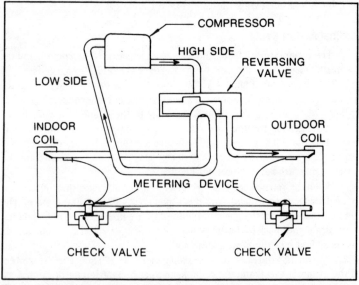

Fig. 16-1. Here the reversing valve is in the cooling position. The check valve on the outside coil is open, letting the refrigerant pass through unrestricted. The check valve on the indoor coil is closed, forcing the refrigerant to pass through the metering device. The metering device or expansion valve is a restriction in the line that holds the pressure in the line between the compressor and the evaporator. After the refrigerant passes through this valve, it goes into the evaporator and expands, boils, and absorbs heat.

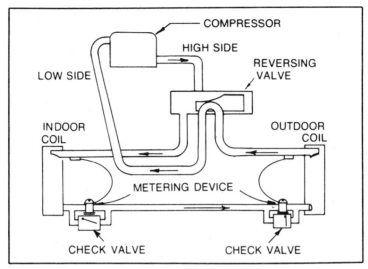

Fig. 16-2. This is the heating cycle of the heat pump. The reversing valve has changed positions from the previous figure, and the refrigerant is traveling in the opposite direction. Now the inside coil is the condenser, and the outside coil is the evaporator. The check valve is open next to the inside coil, but is closed next to the outside coil. Now the refrigerant is forced to pass through the expansion valve before it enters the evaporator.

heat. Heat pumps will operate at temperatures below 15°, but efficiency becomes limited around this point. If you live in an area where temperatures are often much lower than 15°, installation of a heat pump may not be a wise decision.

## INSTALLATION TRADEOFFS

When the temperature occasionally drops below 15°, an auxiliary heating unit will be energized to assist the heat pump. At temperatures above 15° the heat pump should adequately take care of the heat load if the heat pump is sized correctly for the house.

Manufacturers and dealers claim that heat pumps will save a customer up to two-thirds of his heating bill over other types of heating. This is because the only electricity required is for the compressor, and it will use much less energy than other types of electric heating. When the temperature drops, so do your savings, as the resistance heat comes on to assist the heat pump.

Purchase costs of heat pumps are notably higher than for other central heating and conditioning systems. The size of the unit is just slightly larger than the size required for air conditioning.

## INSULATION AND SIZE OF UNIT

The house should be insulated for a heat pump just as it would be for any type of heat—which is to say that it should be insulated very well. The heat pump units will be rated in Btu for both the heating and cooling capacities. If the unit is oversized it will heat better, but on the cooling cycle all sorts of frustrating problems will develop. The humidity will be too high, and the unit will *short cycle*. By short cycling we mean that the air conditioner will have so much cooling power that it will cool the area in a very short time and shut off. This reduces the efficiency of the unit and wastes money in electricity bills, not to mention the higher purchase price of the oversized unit.

## TYPES OF HEAT PUMPS

There are two different types of heat pumps. One is the self-contained unit shown in Fig. 16-3, and the other is the split system shown in Fig. 16-4. The self-contained unit has the evaporator, fan, condenser, and compressor all in one unit installed outside the house. The main duct and return air duct are run out to the unit. Usually these units are set close to the house—less than 2 feet from the foundation in most cases. One advantage of this system is that a room isn't needed to house the heating and cooling equipment.

The split system has the indoor coil placed in the house, and the duct system is connected to it. The refrigerant lines are run from the inside coil

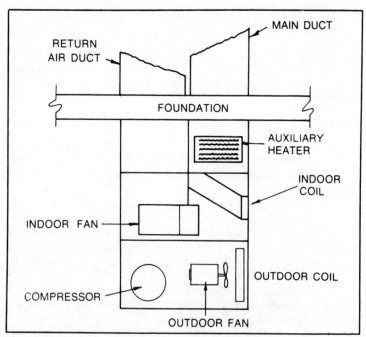

Fig. 16-3. The self-contained heat pump is installed outside the house. The auxiliary heater is installed in the main duct running from the unit through the foundation to the house.

Fig. 16-4. With the split system the two coils are separated; one coil is outside and the other is inside. The refrigerant lines run through the wall to connect them.

to the unit outside. The main difference between the split system and the self-contained system is the location of the components. The parts for both are the same.

## HEAT PUMP VERSUS OTHER SYSTEMS

The heat pump system can only be purchased as one unit. With the other central heating and air conditioning systems, the furnace is installed first. The air conditioner can be installed later.

The heat pump has two metering devices and two check valves. The conventional air conditioner has only one metering device and no check valve. The heat pump has a defrost system on the condensing unit and several types of relays. When the outside temperature is below freezing, frost and ice can form on the outside coil and restrict the air flow over the coil. A system of pressure switches and sensing devices turn on the defrosting system to keep the coil clear.

## THERMOSTATS

As a rule, the thermostat for a heat pump is different than for a normal heating—cooling system. The heat pump has a two-stage thermostat. The first stage turns on the compressor to start the refrigerant flowing and bring heat into the house. The second stae is set 1.5° below the first setting and is connected to an auxiliary heater (see Fig. 16-5). If the heat pump can't produce enough heat to bring the temperature of the house up, and the temperature continues to fall, the second stage will turn the auxiliary heater on when it falls 1.5°.

Sometimes an outside thermostat is used to assist the two-stage thermostat to alleviate some of the problems that can occur with this system. Assume that with the two-stage thermostat you have the heat

Fig. 16-5. A two-stage thermostat is used on heat pumps. The first stage (W1) is connected to the heating circuit. The second stage (W2) is connected to the auxiliary terminals.

turned down to 60° at night. You get up in the morning and turn the heat up to 70°. Since the house temperature is 60°, the second stage will turn the auxiliary heater on before the heat pump has had a chance to raise the house temperature to 70°. The outside thermostat corrects this problem by sensing the outside temperature. If the outside thermostat is set for 35°, it will not let the auxiliary heater come on until the outside temperature drops below 35°.

### CONTACTORS

When the thermostat calls for heat or cooling, the contactor coil will be energized. The contactor points will close. The power supply from the fuse box connects to the L1 and L2 terminals on the contactors (Fig. 16-6). When the contactor points are closed, the compressor will come on.

The transformer primary circuit is connected to the "hot" lines ahead of the contactor (Fig. 16-7). The transformer powers the low voltage circuits in the heat pump with 24V. Some of these transformers have 120V primary circuits, so be sure to get the right replacement if you have to change one.

### DEFROSTING CONTROLS

The defrosting controls sense the temperature of the outside coil. As ice and frost build up, the defrosting controls sense the temperature drop. When the temperature control bulb gets cold enough, it will open one relay and close another to energize the defrosting system on the unit.

When the outdoor coil has reached a certain temperature, the coil will be defrosted. The temperature-sensing device will disconnect the defrosting relay circuit, and the heating relay will return the system to heating.

## AUXILIARY HEATERS

The auxiliary heaters in a heat pump system are like the resistance elements in an electric furnace. The auxiliary elements slip inside the main duct or plenum chamber, and electric wiring is run from the elements to the breaker box. The size of the wire will depend on the number of strips in the heater and the amperage rating. Usually a 60A fuse will carry two strips. The thermostat wiring is connected from the thermostat to the terminal board. The number of thermostat wires will depend on how the system is set up.

The auxiliary heater will work just like an electric furnace, with one element coming on and setting up the second element. The auxiliary heater should be checked in the same way you would check an electric furnace.

## SERVICING

There are several relays used in heat pumps. There is a heating relay, outdoor fan relay, No. 1 cooling relay, No. 2 cooling relay, No. 1 defrost relay, and No. 2 defroster relay. Some systems have all these relays, and others don't.

Figure 16-8 shows defroster and heat relays on one heat pump. The wiring diagram for the unit will have to be followed in checking the relays. The basic operation of the heat pump and the relay sequence follows.

When the thermostat calls for heat, the heating relay is energized and the pump starts (see Fig. 16-9). The reversing valve is switched to heating unless the outside coil is iced over. If this is the case, the sensing device will energize the No. 1 defroster relay. This will switch the reversing valve into cooling. When this happens, the circuit to the outdoor fan relay will

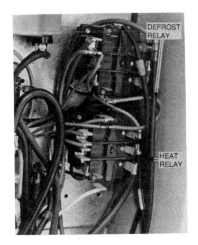

Fig. 16-6. The contactors are energized by the thermostat to start the compressor. The transformer powers the low voltage circuit.

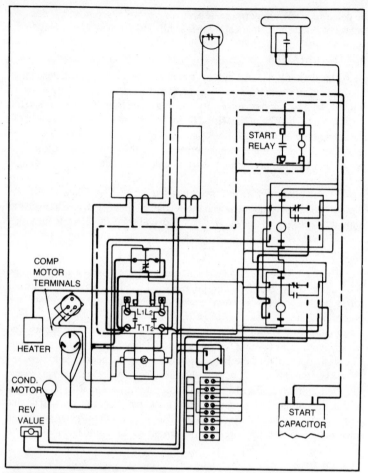

Fig. 16-7. The contactor is connected to the incoming power lines. The wires from the contactor go to the compressor. The transformer powers the thermostat which, in turn, powers the coil for the contactor. When the thermostat calls for heat, it will send power to the contactor coil, closing the contacts and sending 240V to the compressor. Some transformers may have 120V primary circuits.

open. The fan will stop. Another relay will energize, and the auxiliary heater will come on. When the sensing switch warms, the contacts will close and the system will reverse to go into normal heating operation.

One way to find the source of trouble in a heat pump system is to follow the unit through its series of operations and check to make sure all the steps are being made. When something that is supposed to happen doesn't, you have localized the source of trouble. The relays can be checked using a voltohmmeter as described earlier. Once you have localized the trouble, try substituting a good part for the suspected part.

294

Fig. 16-8. Here are shown the heat and defrost relays for a heat pump. The voltages going to the relays are 24V and 240V. Be careful not to cross the 24V line with the 240V line.

## CHECKING REFRIGERANT PRESSURE

Figure 16-10 shows a precharged refrigerant system connected to the outside unit. The caps are removed from the valves, and the charging hoses and pressure gages are connected to the fittings so a pressure reading can be obtained. The cap is replaced after the gages are removed.

To charge the system, the heat pump should be switched to cooling. An amperage check should be run as described in Chapter 13. The owner's manual or service manual for the unit should give some charts relating the pressure and temperature to aid you in charging the system.

## TROUBLESHOOTING HEAT PUMPS

When a heat pump fails or operates improperly, check the possible causes listed here.

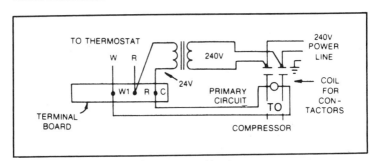

Fig. 16-9. A wiring diagram for one type of heat pump.

Fig. 16-10. Remove cap A to install the low-side service hose and gage. The high-side hose and gage are connected at B.

### Unit Won't Run

- Check fuse box.
- Check power at L1 and L2 contactor terminals.
- Check tranformer on secondary circuit.
- Check contactor coil.
- Check compressor.
- Check starting and running capacitors on the compressor motor.
- Check voltage at the compressor.
- Check internal overload in the compressor.
- Check high and low-pressure switches.

### Unit Runs, but System Doesn't Heat or Cool

- Check system for refrigerant.
- Check for leaks in refrigerant system.
- Check condenser fan.
- Check evaporator.

### Unit Cools, but Won't Heat

- Unit low on refrigerant.
- Reversing valve stuck.

- Bad coil on reversing valve.
- Bad heat relay coil.
- Defrost thermostat stuck.
- Thermostat set too high.
- Thermostat manual control set on cooling cycle.

## Unit Heats but Won't Cool

- Reversing valve stuck.
- Bad coil on reversing valve.
- Heat relay points burned.
- Thermostat set too low.
- Thermostat manual control set for heat.

## Evaporator Fan Won't Run

- Motor burned out.
- Bad capacitor.
- Indoor fan relay stuck or has bad coil.
- Foreign material holding fan blade.
- Loose connection.
- Loose fan blade.

## Condenser Fan Won't Run

- Motor burned out.
- Bad capacitor.
- Fan blade stuck.
- Loose connection.
- Bad motor bearing.
- Bad starter switch on motor.

## Auxiliary Heater Won't Heat

- Loose thermostat wire.
- Breaker thrown at breaker box.
- Heating element burned in half.
- Thermostat set for cooling.
- Bad sequencers.
- Loose high voltage line.
- Outdoor thermostat set too low.
- Blown fuse in element.

## Inadequate Air Flow

- Dirty air filter.
- Restricted return air duct.
- Loose fan blade.
- Dirty fan blade.
- Loose belt.
- Motor running on low speed.
- Loose motor pulley.

# Appendix

## TABLE OF OUTDOOR DESIGN CONDITIONS

| State and City | Winter Dry-Bulb Temp. (F) | Summer Dry-Bulb Temp. (F) | Summer Wet-Bulb Temp. (F) | Latitude | Daily Range |
|---|---|---|---|---|---|
| **ALABAMA** | | | | | |
| Birmingham | 10 | 95 | 78 | 35 | M |
| Gadsden | 10 | 95 | 78 | 35 | M |
| Mobile | 20 | 90 | 80 | 30 | L |
| Montgomery | 20 | 95 | 79 | 30 | M |
| Tuscaloosa | 10 | 95 | 80 | 35 | M |
| **ARIZONA** | | | | | |
| Bisbee | 30 | 100 | 72 | 30 | H |
| Flagstaff | -5 | *85 | 61 | 35 | H |
| Globe | 30 | 105 | 76 | 35 | H |
| Nogales | 30 | 105 | 72 | 30 | H |
| Phoenix | 35 | 105 | 76 | 35 | H |
| Tucson | 30 | 100 | 72 | 30 | H |
| Winslow | -5 | 95 | 65 | 35 | H |
| Yuma | 40 | 110 | 78 | 35 | H |
| **ARKANSAS** | | | | | |
| Bentonville | 0 | 95 | 76 | 35 | M |
| Fort Smith | 5 | 95 | 79 | 35 | M |
| Hot Springs | 10 | 95 | 78 | 35 | M |
| Little Rock | 10 | 95 | 79 | 35 | L |
| Pine Bluff | 10 | 95 | 81 | 35 | M |
| Texarkana | 10 | 100 | 79 | 35 | M |
| **DISTRICT OF COLUMBIA** | | | | | |
| Washington | 10 | 90 | 77 | 40 | M |
| **FLORIDA** | | | | | |
| Apalachicola | 25 | 95 | 80 | 30 | L |
| Fort Myers | 40 | 95 | 80 | 25 | M |
| Gainesville | 30 | 95 | 78 | 30 | M |
| Jacksonville | 30 | 95 | 78 | 30 | M |
| Key West | 55 | 100 | 79 | 25 | L |
| Miami | 45 | 90 | 79 | 25 | L |
| Orlando | 35 | 90 | 79 | 30 | M |
| Pensacola | 25 | 95 | 81 | 30 | L |
| Tallahassee | 25 | 95 | 79 | 30 | M |
| Tampa | 35 | 95 | 79 | 30 | M |
| **GEORGIA** | | | | | |
| Athens | 10 | 95 | 76 | 35 | M |
| Atlanta | 10 | 95 | 77 | 35 | M |
| Augusta | 20 | 100 | 79 | 35 | M |
| Brunswick | 25 | 95 | 78 | 30 | L |
| Columbus | 20 | 100 | 76 | 35 | M |
| Macon | 20 | 95 | 79 | 35 | M |
| Rome | 10 | 95 | 76 | 35 | M |
| Savannah | 25 | 95 | 80 | 30 | M |
| Waycross | 25 | 95 | 78 | 30 | M |

## CALIFORNIA

| City | | | | | |
|---|---|---|---|---|---|
| Bakersfield | 30 | 105 | 71 | 35 | H |
| El Centro | 35 | 110 | 80 | 35 | H |
| Eureka | 30 | 90 | 65 | 40 | M |
| Fresno | 30 | 105 | 72 | 35 | H |
| Los Angeles | 40 | 90 | 71 | 35 | M |
| Montague | 15 | 95 | 66 | 40 | M |
| Needles | 25 | 115 | 75 | 35 | H |
| Oakland | 30 | *80 | 64 | 40 | M |
| Sacramento | 30 | 95 | 71 | 40 | H |
| San Bernardino | 30 | 105 | 72 | 35 | H |
| San Diego | 45 | *80 | 70 | 35 | L |
| San Francisco | 35 | *80 | 63 | 40 | M |
| San Jose | 40 | 90 | 70 | 35 | M |

## COLORADO

| City | | | | | |
|---|---|---|---|---|---|
| Boulder | −15 | 95 | 64 | 40 | M |
| Colorado Springs | −10 | 95 | 62 | 40 | H |
| Denver | −10 | 95 | 64 | 40 | H |
| Durango | −5 | 95 | 65 | 35 | H |
| Fort Collins | −15 | 95 | 65 | 40 | M |
| Grand Junction | 5 | 95 | 64 | 40 | M |
| Leadville | −10 | 95 | 64 | 40 | M |
| Pueblo | −15 | 95 | 65 | 40 | H |

## CONNECTICUT

| City | | | | | |
|---|---|---|---|---|---|
| Bridgeport | 0 | *85 | 75 | 40 | L |
| Hartford | 0 | 90 | 76 | 40 | M |
| New Haven | 0 | *85 | 76 | 40 | M |
| New London | 5 | *85 | 75 | 40 | L |
| Torrington | 0 | 90 | 75 | 40 | M |
| Waterbury | 0 | 90 | 75 | 40 | M |

## DELAWARE

| City | | | | | |
|---|---|---|---|---|---|
| Dover | 10 | 90 | 78 | 40 | M |
| Milford | 10 | 90 | 78 | 40 | M |
| Wilmington | 5 | 90 | 77 | 40 | M |

## IDAHO

| City | | | | | |
|---|---|---|---|---|---|
| Boise | −10 | 95 | 66 | 45 | H |
| Idaho Falls | −15 | 90 | 64 | 45 | *H |
| Lewiston | −10 | 95 | 65 | 45 | H |
| Pocatello | −15 | 90 | 63 | 45 | *H |
| Twin Falls | −15 | 95 | 65 | 40 | H |

## ILLINOIS

| City | | | | | |
|---|---|---|---|---|---|
| Aurora-Joliet | −10 | 95 | 76 | 40 | M |
| Bloomington | −10 | 95 | 76 | 40 | M |
| Cairo | 0 | 100 | 78 | 35 | M |
| Champaign-Urbana | −10 | 95 | 77 | 40 | M |
| Chicago | −10 | 95 | 76 | 40 | M |
| Danville | −10 | 95 | 77 | 40 | M |
| Decatur | −10 | 95 | 77 | 40 | M |
| Elgin | −15 | 95 | 78 | 40 | M |
| Moline-Rock Island | −10 | 95 | 77 | 40 | M |
| Peoria | −15 | 95 | 77 | 40 | M |
| Rockford | −15 | 95 | 78 | 40 | M |
| Springfield | −10 | 95 | 78 | 40 | M |

## INDIANA

| City | | | | | |
|---|---|---|---|---|---|
| Evansville | −5 | 95 | 78 | 40 | M |
| Fort Wayne | −5 | 95 | 76 | 40 | M |
| Indianapolis | −10 | 90 | 77 | 40 | M |
| Lafayette | −10 | 95 | 76 | 40 | M |
| South Bend | −10 | 95 | 76 | 40 | M |
| Terre Haute | −5 | 95 | 78 | 40 | M |

## IOWA

| City | | | | | |
|---|---|---|---|---|---|
| Burlington | −10 | 95 | 78 | 40 | M |
| Cedar Rapids | −15 | 95 | 78 | 40 | M |
| Charles City | −20 | 95 | 75 | 45 | M |
| Clinton | −15 | 95 | 78 | 40 | M |
| Council Bluffs | −15 | 100 | 78 | 40 | M |

# Table of Outdoor Design Conditions (Continued)

| State and City | Winter Dry-Bulb Temp. (F) | Summer Dry-Bulb Temp. (F) | Summer Wet-Bulb Temp. (F) | Latitude | Daily Range |
|---|---|---|---|---|---|
| **IOWA—Continued** | | | | | |
| Davenport | −10 | 95 | 78 | 40 | M |
| Des Moines | −15 | 95 | 77 | 40 | M |
| Dubuque | −15 | 95 | 78 | 40 | M |
| Fort Dodge | −15 | 95 | 78 | 40 | M |
| Keokuk | −15 | 95 | 78 | 40 | M |
| Marshalltown | −15 | 95 | 78 | 40 | M |
| Sioux City | −15 | 95 | 77 | 40 | M |
| Waterloo | −15 | 95 | 78 | 40 | M |
| **KANSAS** | | | | | |
| Atchison-Leavenworth | −10 | 100 | 76 | 40 | M |
| Concordia | −15 | 95 | 78 | 40 | M |
| Dodge City | −10 | 95 | 73 | 40 | H |
| Iola | −5 | 100 | 75 | 40 | M |
| Salina | −10 | 100 | 78 | 40 | M |
| Topeka | −10 | 95 | 78 | 40 | M |
| Wichita | −5 | 100 | 76 | 40 | M |
| **KENTUCKY** | | | | | |
| Bowling Green | 0 | 95 | 78 | 35 | M |
| Frankfort | 0 | 95 | 78 | 40 | M |
| Hopkinsville | 0 | 95 | 78 | 35 | M |
| Lexington | 0 | 95 | 77 | 40 | M |
| Louisville | 0 | 95 | 78 | 40 | M |
| Owensboro | 0 | 95 | 78 | 40 | M |

| State and City | Winter Dry-Bulb Temp. (F) | Summer Dry-Bulb Temp. (F) | Summer Wet-Bulb Temp. (F) | Latitude | Daily Range |
|---|---|---|---|---|---|
| **MASSACHUSETTS—Continued** | | | | | |
| Plymouth | 0 | *85 | 75 | 40 | L |
| Springfield | −5 | 90 | 75 | 40 | M |
| Worcester | −5 | 90 | 73 | 40 | M |
| **MICHIGAN** | | | | | |
| Alpena | −10 | 90 | 75 | 45 | M |
| Ann Arbor | −5 | 90 | 75 | 40 | M |
| Big Rapids | −5 | 90 | 75 | 45 | M |
| Cadillac | −10 | 90 | 75 | 45 | M |
| Calumet-Houghton | −20 | *80 | 73 | 45 | M |
| Detroit | −5 | 90 | 75 | 40 | M |
| Escanaba | −20 | *85 | 74 | 45 | M |
| Flint | −10 | 90 | 75 | 45 | M |
| Grand Rapids | −5 | 90 | 74 | 45 | M |
| Kalamazoo | −5 | 90 | 75 | 40 | M |
| Lansing | −10 | 90 | 75 | 45 | M |
| Ludington | −5 | 90 | 75 | 45 | M |
| Marquette | −15 | *80 | 73 | 45 | M |
| Muskegon | −5 | 90 | 74 | 45 | M |
| Port Huron | −10 | 90 | 75 | 45 | M |
| Saginaw | −10 | 90 | 75 | 45 | M |
| Sault Ste. Marie | −20 | *80 | 71 | 45 | M |
| **MINNESOTA** | | | | | |
| Alexandria | −25 | *85 | 74 | 45 | M |
| Duluth | −25 | *80 | 71 | 45 | M |
| Minneapolis-St. Paul | −25 | 90 | 75 | 45 | M |
| St. Cloud | −25 | 90 | 75 | 45 | M |

## LOUISIANA

| City | | | | | |
|---|---|---|---|---|---|
| Alexandria | 20 | 95 | 80 | 30 | M |
| Baton Rouge | 20 | 95 | 80 | 30 | M |
| New Orleans | 25 | 95 | 80 | 30 | L |
| Shreveport | 15 | 95 | 80 | 30 | M |

## MAINE

| City | | | | | |
|---|---|---|---|---|---|
| Augusta | -15 | *85 | 73 | 45 | L |
| Bangor | -20 | *85 | 73 | 45 | L |
| Bar Harbor | -10 | *85 | 73 | 45 | L |
| Belfast | -10 | *85 | 70 | 45 | L |
| Eastport | -10 | *85 | 73 | 45 | L |
| Lewiston | -10 | *85 | 73 | 45 | L |
| Millinocket | -15 | *85 | 73 | 45 | M |
| Portland | -10 | *85 | 73 | 45 | M |
| Rumford | -15 | *85 | 73 | 45 | L |

## MARYLAND

| City | | | | | |
|---|---|---|---|---|---|
| Annapolis | 10 | 90 | 78 | 40 | M |
| Baltimore | 10 | 90 | 78 | 40 | M |
| Cambridge | 10 | 90 | 78 | 40 | L |
| Cumberland | 0 | 90 | 75 | 40 | M |
| Frederick | 5 | 90 | 78 | 40 | M |
| Salisbury | 10 | 90 | 78 | 40 | M |

## MASSACHUSETTS

| City | | | | | |
|---|---|---|---|---|---|
| Amherst | -5 | 90 | 75 | 40 | M |
| Boston | 0 | *85 | 74 | 40 | M |
| Fall River- New Bedford | 0 | *85 | 75 | 40 | L |
| Fitchburg | -5 | 90 | 75 | 45 | M |
| Lawrence-Lowell | -5 | *85 | 74 | 45 | L |
| Nantucket | 0 | *85 | 72 | 40 | L |
| Pittsfield | -10 | 90 | 75 | 40 | M |

## MISSISSIPPI

| City | | | | | |
|---|---|---|---|---|---|
| Biloxi | 25 | 90 | 80 | 30 | L |
| Columbus | 10 | 95 | 78 | 35 | M |
| Corinth | 5 | 95 | 78 | 35 | M |
| Hattiesburg | 20 | 95 | 80 | 30 | M |
| Jackson | 15 | 95 | 79 | 30 | M |
| Meridian | 15 | 95 | 79 | 30 | M |
| Natchez | 15 | 95 | 78 | 30 | M |
| Vicksburg | 15 | 95 | 78 | 30 | M |

## MISSOURI

| City | | | | | |
|---|---|---|---|---|---|
| Columbia | -10 | 100 | 78 | 40 | M |
| Hannibal | -10 | 95 | 77 | 40 | M |
| Kansas City | -10 | 100 | 77 | 40 | M |
| St. Joseph | -10 | 100 | 78 | 40 | M |
| St. Louis | -5 | 95 | 78 | 40 | M |
| Springfield | -5 | 100 | 77 | 40 | M |

## MONTANA

| City | | | | | |
|---|---|---|---|---|---|
| Billings | -30 | 90 | 66 | 45 | *H |
| Butte | -30 | *85 | 59 | 45 | H |
| Great Falls | -40 | 90 | 63 | 50 | *H |
| Havre | -40 | 95 | 70 | 50 | H |
| Helena | -40 | 90 | 63 | 45 | *H |
| Kalispell | -30 | 90 | 63 | 50 | H |
| Miles City | -35 | 95 | 69 | 45 | *H |
| Missoula | -30 | 90 | 63 | 45 | H |

## NEBRASKA

| City | | | | | |
|---|---|---|---|---|---|
| Grand Island | -15 | 95 | 75 | 40 | H |
| Hastings | -15 | 95 | 75 | 40 | M |

# Table of Outdoor Design Conditions (Continued)

| State and City | Winter Dry-Bulb Temp. (F) | Summer Dry-Bulb Temp. (F) | Summer Wet-Bulb Temp. (F) | Latitude | Daily Range |
|---|---|---|---|---|---|
| **NEBRASKA—Continued** | | | | | |
| Lincoln | -15 | 95 | 77 | 40 | M |
| Norfolk | -15 | 95 | 78 | 40 | M |
| North Platte | -15 | 100 | 73 | 40 | H |
| Omaha | -15 | 100 | 78 | 40 | M |
| Valentine | -20 | 95 | 78 | 45 | M |
| **NEVADA** | | | | | |
| Elko | -10 | 95 | 63 | 40 | H |
| Las Vegas | 10 | 110 | 71 | 35 | H |
| Reno | 5 | 95 | 63 | 40 | H |
| Tonopah | 5 | 90 | 63 | 40 | M |
| Winnemucca | -10 | 95 | 65 | 40 | H |
| **NEW HAMPSHIRE** | | | | | |
| Berlin | -15 | *85 | 73 | 45 | H |
| Claremont | -15 | *85 | 73 | 45 | M |
| Franklin | -15 | *85 | 73 | 45 | M |
| Hanover | -15 | *85 | 73 | 45 | M |
| Keene | -10 | *85 | 73 | 45 | M |
| Manchester | -10 | *85 | 74 | 45 | M |
| Portsmouth | 0 | *85 | 74 | 45 | L |
| **NEW JERSEY** | | | | | |

| State and City | Winter Dry-Bulb Temp. (F) | Summer Dry-Bulb Temp. (F) | Summer Wet-Bulb Temp. (F) | Latitude | Daily Range |
|---|---|---|---|---|---|
| **NORTH CAROLINA** | | | | | |
| Asheville | 5 | 90 | 75 | 35 | M |
| Charlotte | 15 | 95 | 77 | 35 | M |
| Greensboro | 10 | 90 | 76 | 35 | M |
| Hatteras | 20 | 90 | 80 | 35 | L |
| New Bern | 20 | 95 | 81 | 35 | L |
| Raleigh | 15 | 95 | 78 | 35 | M |
| Salisbury | 10 | 90 | 78 | 35 | M |
| Wilmington | 20 | 90 | 81 | 35 | M |
| Winston-Salem | 10 | 90 | 76 | 35 | M |
| **NORTH DAKOTA** | | | | | |
| Bismarck | -30 | 95 | 73 | 45 | H |
| Devils Lake | -30 | 90 | 70 | 50 | M |
| Dickinson | -30 | 95 | 70 | 45 | H |
| Fargo | -30 | 95 | 74 | 45 | H |
| Grand Forks | -30 | 90 | 72 | 50 | M |
| Jamestown | -30 | 95 | 73 | 45 | M |
| Minot | -35 | 90 | 71 | 45 | M |
| Pembina | -35 | 90 | 73 | 50 | M |
| Williston | -35 | 90 | 73 | 50 | M |
| **OHIO** | | | | | |
| Akron | -5 | 90 | 75 | 40 | M |
| Cincinnati | -5 | 95 | 78 | 40 | M |
| Cleveland | -5 | 90 | 75 | 40 | M |

| City | | | | | |
|---|---|---|---|---|---|
| Asbury Park | 5 | 90 | 78 | 40 | L |
| Atlantic City | 10 | 90 | 78 | 40 | L |
| Bridgeton | 5 | 90 | 78 | 40 | L |
| Camden | 5 | 90 | 78 | 40 | L |
| Jersey City | 0 | 90 | 75 | 40 | L |
| Newark | 0 | 90 | 76 | 40 | M |
| New Brunswick | 5 | 90 | 75 | 40 | L |
| Paterson | 0 | 90 | 75 | 40 | L |
| Trenton | 0 | 90 | 78 | 40 | L |

**NEW MEXICO**

| City | | | | | |
|---|---|---|---|---|---|
| Albuquerque | 10 | 95 | 65 | 35 | M |
| El Morro | 0 | *85 | 65 | 35 | H |
| Raton | — | 95 | 65 | 35 | H |
| Roswell | 5 | 100 | 71 | 35 | H |
| Santa Fe | 5 | 90 | 64 | 35 | M |
| Tucumcari | 5 | 95 | 70 | 35 | H |

**NEW YORK**

| City | | | | | |
|---|---|---|---|---|---|
| Albany | -10 | 90 | 74 | 45 | M |
| Auburn | -10 | 90 | 74 | 45 | M |
| Binghamton | -5 | 90 | 72 | 40 | M |
| Buffalo-Niagara Falls | -5 | *85 | 73 | 45 | M |
| Elmira | -5 | 90 | 73 | 45 | M |
| Glens Falls | -15 | 90 | 73 | 45 | M |
| Ithaca | -5 | 90 | 73 | 40 | M |
| Jamestown | -5 | 90 | 74 | 40 | M |
| Lake Placid | -15 | 90 | 73 | 45 | M |
| New York | -5 | 90 | 76 | 40 | M |
| Ogdensburg | -20 | 90 | 73 | 45 | M |
| Oneonta | -10 | *85 | 73 | 45 | M |
| Oswego | -5 | 90 | 74 | 45 | M |
| Port Jervis | 0 | 90 | 75 | 40 | L |
| Rochester | -5 | 90 | 74 | 45 | M |
| Syracuse | -10 | 90 | 74 | 45 | M |
| Watertown | -15 | *85 | 73 | 45 | M |

| City | | | | | |
|---|---|---|---|---|---|
| Columbus | 5 | 90 | 76 | 40 | M |
| Dayton | 5 | 90 | 76 | 40 | M |
| Lima | 5 | 90 | 75 | 40 | M |
| Marion | 5 | 90 | 75 | 40 | M |
| Sandusky | 5 | 90 | 75 | 40 | M |
| Toledo | 5 | 90 | 75 | 40 | M |
| Warren-Youngstown | 5 | 90 | 75 | 40 | M |

**OKLAHOMA**

| City | | | | | |
|---|---|---|---|---|---|
| Ardmore | 5 | 100 | 78 | 35 | M |
| Bartlesville | 5 | 100 | 77 | 35 | M |
| Muskogee | 0 | 95 | 79 | 35 | M |
| Oklahoma City | 0 | 100 | 77 | 35 | M |
| Tulsa | — | 100 | 78 | 35 | M |
| Waynoka | 5 | 105 | 75 | 35 | M |

**OREGON**

| City | | | | | |
|---|---|---|---|---|---|
| Arlington | 5 | 95 | 68 | 45 | M |
| Baker | -15 | 90 | 65 | 45 | H |
| Eugene | 15 | 90 | 67 | 45 | *H |
| Medford | 20 | 95 | 68 | 40 | H |
| Pendleton | -10 | 90 | 65 | 45 | *H |
| Portland | 10 | *85 | 68 | 45 | M |
| Roseburg | 20 | 90 | 66 | 45 | *H |
| Salem | 15 | 90 | 68 | 45 | *H |

**PENNSYLVANIA**

| City | | | | | |
|---|---|---|---|---|---|
| Altoona | 5 | 90 | 74 | 40 | M |
| Bethlehem | 0 | 90 | 75 | 40 | M |
| Erie | 5 | *85 | 74 | 40 | M |
| Harrisburg-York | 5 | 90 | 75 | 40 | M |
| New Castle | 5 | 90 | 75 | 40 | M |
| Oil City | 5 | 90 | 75 | 40 | M |
| Philadelphia | 5 | 90 | 77 | 40 | M |
| Pittsburgh | 5 | 90 | 74 | 40 | M |
| Reading | 5 | 90 | 75 | 40 | M |

**Table of Outdoor Design Conditions (Continued)**

| State and City | Winter Dry-Bulb Temp. (F) | Summer Dry-Bulb Temp. (F) | Summer Wet-Bulb Temp. (F) | Latitude | Daily Range |
|---|---|---|---|---|---|
| PENNSYLVANIA—Continued | | | | | |
| Scranton | 0 | 90 | 75 | 40 | M |
| Warren | −5 | 90 | 75 | 40 | M |
| Williamsport | −5 | 90 | 75 | 40 | M |
| RHODE ISLAND | | | | | |
| Block Island | 5 | *85 | 75 | 40 | L |
| Kingston | 0 | *85 | 75 | 40 | L |
| Providence | 0 | 90 | 75 | 40 | M |
| SOUTH CAROLINA | | | | | |
| Charleston | 20 | 90 | 80 | 35 | L |
| Columbia | 20 | 95 | 78 | 35 | M |
| Florence | 20 | 95 | 79 | 35 | M |
| Greenville | 10 | 95 | 76 | 35 | M |
| Spartanburg | 10 | 95 | 77 | 35 | M |
| SOUTH DAKOTA | | | | | |
| Aberdeen | −25 | 95 | 75 | 45 | M |
| Huron | −20 | 100 | 75 | 45 | H |
| Pierre | −20 | 95 | 74 | 45 | M |
| Rapid City | −20 | 95 | 71 | 45 | H |
| Sioux Falls | −20 | 95 | 75 | 45 | H |
| Watertown | −25 | 95 | 74 | 45 | M |
| VERMONT | | | | | |
| Bennington | −10 | 90 | 73 | 45 | M |
| Burlington | −15 | 90 | 73 | 45 | M |
| Montpelier | −20 | 90 | 73 | 45 | M |
| Newport | −20 | *85 | 73 | 45 | M |
| Rutland | −15 | 90 | 73 | 45 | M |
| VIRGINIA | | | | | |
| Charlottesville | 10 | 90 | 78 | 40 | M |
| Danville | 10 | 90 | 78 | 35 | M |
| Lynchburg | 10 | 90 | 76 | 35 | M |
| Norfolk | 15 | 90 | 78 | 35 | M |
| Petersburg | 10 | 90 | 78 | 35 | M |
| Richmond | 10 | 90 | 78 | 35 | M |
| Roanoke | 5 | 90 | 75 | 40 | M |
| Wytheville | 5 | 90 | 76 | 35 | M |
| WASHINGTON | | | | | |
| Aberdeen | 20 | *85 | 64 | 45 | L |
| Bellingham | 10 | *80 | 65 | 50 | L |
| Everett | 15 | *80 | 65 | 50 | L |
| Olympia | 15 | *80 | 65 | 45 | H |
| Seattle | 15 | *80 | 65 | 50 | M |
| Spokane | −15 | 90 | 64 | 50 | *H |
| Tacoma | 15 | *80 | 64 | 45 | M |
| Walla Walla | −10 | 90 | 67 | 45 | *H |

## TENNESSEE

| | | | | |
|---|---|---|---|---|
| Chattanooga | 10 | 95 | 77 | 35 | M |
| Jackson | 5 | 95 | 80 | 35 | M |
| Johnson City | 5 | 95 | 78 | 35 | M |
| Knoxville | 5 | 95 | 77 | 35 | M |
| Memphis | 5 | 95 | 79 | 35 | M |
| Nashville | 5 | 95 | 78 | 35 | M |

## TEXAS

| | | | | |
|---|---|---|---|---|
| Abilene | 5 | 95 | 75 | 30 | M |
| Amarillo | 5 | 95 | 71 | 35 | H |
| Austin | 15 | 100 | 78 | 30 | M |
| Brownsville | 30 | 95 | 80 | 25 | M |
| Corpus Christi | 25 | 95 | 80 | 30 | M |
| Dallas-Fort Worth | 10 | 100 | 78 | 35 | M |
| Del Rio | 20 | 100 | 79 | 30 | H |
| El Paso | 20 | 100 | 69 | 30 | M |
| Galveston | 25 | 95 | 81 | 30 | L |
| Houston | 20 | 95 | 80 | 30 | M |
| Palestine | 10 | 100 | 78 | 30 | M |
| Port Arthur | 20 | 95 | 80 | 30 | M |
| San Antonio | 20 | 100 | 77 | 30 | M |
| Waco | 10 | 100 | 78 | 30 | M |
| Wink | 10 | 95 | 74 | 30 | H |

## UTAH

| | | | | |
|---|---|---|---|---|
| Logan | −10 | 95 | 65 | 40 | H |
| Milford | −5 | 95 | 66 | 40 | H |
| Ogden | −5 | 90 | 65 | 40 | *H |
| Salt Lake City | 0 | 95 | 66 | 40 | H |

| | | | | |
|---|---|---|---|---|
| Wenatchee | −10 | 90 | 65 | 50 | M |
| Yakima | −5 | 90 | 67 | 45 | *H |

## WEST VIRGINIA

| | | | | |
|---|---|---|---|---|
| Bluefield | 0 | 95 | 75 | 35 | M |
| Charleston | 0 | 90 | 76 | 40 | M |
| Elkins | −5 | 90 | 73 | 40 | M |
| Fairmont | 0 | 90 | 75 | 40 | M |
| Huntington | 0 | 90 | 76 | 40 | M |
| Martinsburg | 0 | 90 | 77 | 40 | M |
| Parkersburg | −5 | 90 | 77 | 40 | M |
| Wheeling | −5 | 90 | 75 | 40 | M |

## WISCONSIN

| | | | | |
|---|---|---|---|---|
| Ashland | −25 | *80 | 71 | 45 | M |
| Beloit | −15 | 95 | 78 | 45 | M |
| Eau Claire | −20 | 90 | 74 | 45 | M |
| Green Bay | −20 | 90 | 73 | 45 | M |
| La Crosse | −20 | 95 | 76 | 45 | M |
| Madison | −15 | 90 | 75 | 45 | M |
| Milwaukee | −20 | 90 | 75 | 45 | M |
| Oshkosh | −20 | 90 | 75 | 45 | M |
| Sheboygan | −20 | 90 | 75 | 45 | M |

## WYOMING

| | | | | |
|---|---|---|---|---|
| Casper | −25 | 90 | 62 | 45 | H |
| Cheyenne | −20 | 90 | 62 | 40 | *H |
| Lander | −30 | 90 | 65 | 45 | *H |
| Sheridan | −30 | 90 | 66 | 45 | *H |
| Yellowstone Park | −35 | *85 | 62 | 45 | H |

*See Paragraph 5.21.

# Glossary

**absolute humidity**—Grains of moisture in the air per cubic foot.

**absolute pressure**—Gage pressure plus 14.7 psi atmospheric pressure.

**absolute temperature**—Temperature measured from absolute zero.

**absolute zero**—Temperature where all molecular motion ceases (−460°F).

**accumulator**—Sometimes called suction accumulator; prevents refrigerant from entering the suction line.

**ACR tubing**—Tubing for refrigeration which has been cleaned, sealed, and charged with dry nitrogen. (ACR) = air conditioning and refrigeration.)

**air cleaner**—Device used to remove dirt, lint, and impurities from the air.

**air coil**—Coil used in refrigeration as condenser or evaporation to remove heat or pick it up.

**air conditioner**—A device used to reduce temperature, humidity, and impurities in the air.

**air-cooled condenser**—A device used to remove heat from the vapor or refrigerant by passing air through the unit.

**air washer**—Unit used to clean the air.

**alternating current**—Current which changes direction every 120th of a second.

**ambient temperature**—Free air temperature surrounding an object.

**ammeter**—An electric meter used to measure electric current.

**ampere**—Current of 1 coulomb of electricity per second past a given point.

**annealing**—Process used to soften metal to form a new shape.

**armature**—Revolving part of an electric motor or relay.

**automatic expansion valve**—Device used to control the flow of a refrigeration system by pressure.

**back pressure**—Pressure in the low side or suction pressure.

**bending spring**—A spring that is placed over or inside tubing to keep the tubing from collapsing while bending.

**bimetal strip**—Two different metals fused together so that, when heated, the strip will bend and open and close points (as on a thermostat).

**British thermal unit**—The amount of heat it takes to raise the temperature of 1 pound of water 1°F.

**burner**—Device in which combustion of fuel takes place.


**capacitor**—Device for electricity storage, used in starting and running circuits of many electric motors.

**capacitor-start motor**—Motor that has a capacitor in the starting circuit.

**capillary tube**—A very small tube to meter refrigerant into the evaporator. Usually this is several feet in length.

**check valve**—Valve which permits flow in only one direction.

**circuit breaker**—Safety device which automatically trips an electrical circuit and cuts off the power in that circuit.

**circuit, parallel**—A circuit in which devices are connected across one another in a ladder-like arrangement.

**circuit, series**—A circuit connected so the electrical current passes through devices in succession.

**comfort chart**—Chart used in air conditioning work to show dry bulb temperature.

**compound gage**—Instrument used to measure pressures above and below atmospheric.

**compression**—Increasing pressure (especially on a gas) by using a mechanical device.

**compression gage**—Gage used to measure pressure above atmospheric.

**compressor**—A mechanical device used to move refrigerant through a system by removing the refrigerant from the low side and raising the pressure on the high side.

**compressor, hermetic**—Unit in which compressor and motor are sealed in a dome.

**compressor, reciprocating**—Compressor that uses a piston and cylinder to provide the pumping action.

**compressor, rotary**—A type of compressor that uses vanes instead of pistons for the pumping action.

**condensate**—Water that forms on the cool evaporator coil.

**condensate pump**—A pump used to remove the moisture from underneath the evaporator coil.

**condensation**—The formation of liquid or droplets when the vapor is cooled below a certain point.

**condense**—To change a gas or vapor back to a liquid.

**condenser**—A part of a refrigeration system that removes the heat from the high pressure vapor, causing the vapor to change back to a liquid.

**condenser, air-cooled**—A heat exchanger that transfers heat from the vapor as the surrounding air is moved through.

**condenser fan**—A motor with a blade that moves the air through the condenser.

**condensing unit**—Unit containing the compressor, condenser, fan motor, service valves, lines, and devices used to start the compressor.

**conductivity**—Ability of a material to transmit or conduct heat or electricity.

**control, motor**—A control used to start and stop a motor at the proper time.

**control, pressure**—A control used to stop a motor at a certain pressure, sometimes used as a safety device.

**control, refrigerant**—A device used to control the amount of refrigerant that flows through the system.

**control, temperature**—A mechanism used to control the temperature that starts and stops the compressor.

**convection**—Transfer of heat from one place to another by virtue of warm air rising.

**coulomb**—Quantity of electricity transferred by electric current of 1 ampere in 1 second.

**current**—Transfer of electrical energy in a conductor by means of electrons changing positions; a flow of electrical charge carriers.

**current relay**—Device used to open or close a circuit based on the change of current flow strength.

**detector, leak**—A device, typically a form of propane torch, used to find a leak in a refrigeration system.

**dew point**—The temperature at which water vapor will condense.

**dichlorodifluoromethane**—A refrigerant commonly known as refrigerant-12 or Freon-12 (R-12).

**direct current**—Flow of electrons in only one direction through a circuit.

**draft gage**—Instrument used to measure air movement.

**draft indicator**—An instrument used to indicate or measure chimney draft and combustion gases.

**drier**—A device used to remove moisture from a refrigeration system.

**dry bulb**—Instrument used to measure air temperature.

**dry bulb temperature**—Temperature taken with an ordinary thermometer.

**electric heat**—Heat produced by a flow of electrons through a resistive element.

**electrostatic filter**—Device in which particles of dust are given an electrical charge and oppositely charged plates collect the particle.

**end bell**—End structure of an electrical motor that usually houses the bearings.

**end play**—Movement of motor shaft along center line.

**evaporator**—A part of the refrigeration system that absorbs heat as the refrigerant boils off into a vapor.

**expansion valve**—A device to meter the refrigerant from the high side to the low side.

**filter**—A device used to remove dust and lint from the air.

**flare fitting**—A device used to conect two lines together.

**fuse**—Electrical safety device that melts and interrupts current flow when the current becomes dangerously large.

**gage, compound**—Instrument used for measuring pressure above and below atmospheric.

**gage, manifold**—A device constructed to hold the low and high pressure gages and two valves and connect them to a refrigeration unit.

**ground, short-circuit**—Fault in an electrical circuit in which current passes to ground instead of through the desired parts.

**halide torch**—A propane torch used to detect refrigerant leaks.

**head pressure**—Pressure that exists on the high side of a refrigeration system.

**head pressure control**—A control that is used to disconnect the circuit if the head pressure becomes excessive.

**heat load**—Amount of heat removed from an area in 24 hours.

**heat pump**—A system used to heat or cool an area that has a compression cycle, and a reverse refrigeration cycle.

**hermetic motor**—A motor compressor and housing sealed in a dome.

**high side**—The part of the refrigeration system that is under pressure. Heat is given up here, and the refrigerant changes back to a liquid.

**high-vacuum pump**—Mechanism that will pull a deep vacuum and is used to remove the moisture and air from a system.

**humidifier**—A device used to add moisture to a confined space.

**humidistat**—A device used to control a humidifier; it senses the humidity in a confined space.

**limit control**—A control used to open or close a set of points on temperature rise or fall.

**liquid indicator**—Device located in liquid line where the liquid flow can be observed.

**liquid line**—A tube that carries the liquid refrigerant from the condensing unit to the refrigerant control.

**liquid receiver**—A cylinder for liquid storage located after the condenser.

**low side**—The parts of a refrigeration system that are under low pressure.

**manifold service**—A device equipped with gages, service hoses, and valves used for servicing refrigeration equipment.

**microfarad**—The practical unit of measure for a capacitor; one-millionth of a farad.

**moisture indicator**—Instrument used to measure the moisture content in a refrigeration system.

**monochlorodifluoromethane**—A common refrigerant known as Refrigerant-22 or Freon-22 (R-22 or F-22).

**off cycle**—When the system is not in operation.

**ohmmeter**—An instrument used to measure resistance.

**oil, refrigeration**—A special oil used in refrigeration systems.

**open circuit**—An interrupted electrical circuit (electricity cannot flow).

**overload**—Load greater than the intended load for system.

**overload protector**—A device used to protect the system from overload by excess pressure, temperature, or current.

**plenum chamber**—The chamber used to connect the furnace and duct together.

**potential relay**—A voltage controlled switch used to disconnect the starting windings of a compressor motor.

**pulling down**—Removing refrigerant from a part or removing all of the refrigerant from a system; literally, creating a vacuum in a closed system.

**pumping down**—Removing the refrigerant from one part of the system to another part; removing the refrigerant from a system.

**purging**—Removing the refrigerant from a system and letting it bleed into the atmosphere. This is followed by recharging the system.

**quick-connect or quick-disconnect coupling**—A device used for fast, easy connection of refrigeration lines.

**R-12 (dichlorodifluoromethane)**—Refrigerant-12 or Freon-12, often used in small air conditioning units.

**R-22 (monochlorodifluoromethane)**—Refrigerant-22 or Freon-22, a common refrigerant.

**radiant heating**—A heating system with warm or hot surfaces used to radiate heat into a cooler area.

**refrigerant**—A substance used in a refrigeration system to absorb heat in the evaporator and release it in the condenser as it changes in physical state; sometimes called gas.

**refrigerant charge**—The amount of refrigerant a system holds, usually in pounds per square inch gage.

**refrigerant control**—A device to meter the correct amount of refrigerant into the evaporator and maintain a certain pressure.

**register**—Combination grille and damper used on the end of a duct system to direct the air flow into a room.

**relay**—An electrically operated switch. It has one or more sets of points and a coil. A small current through the coil will close the points of the relay. In this manner a small amount of voltage or current can control the power in a high voltage circuit of high power circuit.

**remote system**—A refrigeration system that has the condensing unit outside and the evaporator inside the area to be cooled.

**reversing value**—A device used to reverse the flow of refrigerant in a heat pump system.

**running windings**—Electrical windings of a motor that have current flowing through them continuously in normal operation.

**saddle valve (line tap valve)**—A valve that can be installed around the refrigeration lines so a pressure reading can be taken. It can also be used to tap a water line.

**Schraeder valve**—A type of service valve that can be installed in a refrigeration system to read the pressure (has a spring-loaded core).

**sequencer control (heat relays)**—A control for the elements in a electrical heating system.

**service valve**—A device used on a system so a pressure reading can be obtained.

**shaded-pole motor**—A type of motor used for fans that does not have a start winding and can be used at different speeds.

**short cycle**—A system tendency of start and stop more frequently than it should.

**sight glass**—Glass window or tube installed in a refrigeration system to see the refrigerant flow or to check the oil.

**split-phase motor**—A motor with two windings: the start and run windings.

**split system**—Air conditioning system that places the condensing unit outside and the evaporator inside the house.

**starting relay**—An electrical device used to connect and disconnect the starting winding at the proper time.

**start winding**—Auxiliary windings that are used to help the motor get started and are disconnected at about three-fourths running speed.

**suction line**—The line is used to carry the vapor that has boiled off in the evaporator back to the compressor; the low-side line.

**swaging tool**—A tool used to enlarge one end of a piece of tubing so another end of the same size tubing will fit inside.

**thermostat**—A device used to control the temperature in a confined area.

**thermostatic expansion valve**—A control valve that meters refrigerant into the evaporator and is controlled by pressure and temperature.

**ton of refrigeration**—The amount of heat it takes to melt a ton of ice in 24 hours. It takes 12,000 Btu/hour or 288,000 Btu/day to equal a ton of refrigeration.

**vacuum pump**—A pump used to remove the air and moisture from the inside of a refrigeration system.

**voltmeter**—A high-resistance instrument used to check the voltage in a circuit.

# Index

314

Edited by Robert Ostrander